Exploring maths

Class Book

7

Anita Straker, Tony Fisher, Rosalyn Hyde, Sue Jennings and Jonathan Longstaffe

PEARSON
Longman

Published and distributed by Pearson Education Limited, Edinburgh Gate, Harlow, Essex, CM20 2JE, England

www.pearsonschoolsandfecolleges.co.uk

First published 2009

ISBN-13 978-1-405-84406-2

Typeset by Tech-Set, Gateshead

Printed and bound in Great Britain at Scotprint, Haddington

The publisher's policy is to use paper manufactured from sustainable forests.

Picture credits

The publisher would like to thank the following for their kind permission to reproduce their photographs:

(Key: b-bottom; c-centre; l-left; r-right; t-top)

Alamy Images: Paul Broadbent 83t; Ron Buskirk 202; Design Pics Inc 239b; Mary Evans Picture Library 1; Paul Glendell 141; Jeff Greenberg 312; Anthony Hatley 343c; icpix_uk 127; Image Source Pink 379; Peter Jordan 91b; Justin Leighton 249b; Manor Photography 27; MBI 258; Mediacolor's 3; Nicemonkey 239t; North Wind Picture Archives 16, 91t, 180l, 319; David Pearson 129; Armin Puschmann 35; Helene Rogers 220l; Ian Shaw 317; SHOUT 52; David Taylor 30; The London Art Archive 77, 180r; Tony West 343l; Westend61 GmbH 33; **Corbis:** Bettmann 278; Johnathan Smith; Cordaiy Photo Library Ltd 268; **DK Images:** 34, 130b; Demetrio Carrasco 84; Andy Crawford 41; Colin Salmon 119; **Mary Evans Picture Library:** 131, 242, 301, 367; Edwin Wallace 104; **Getty Images:** Doug Armand/Stone 238; Alfred Eisenstaedt/Time & Life Pictures 252; George Karger/Pix Inc./Time Life Pictures 298b; **iStockphoto:** 20, 31, 42b, 44, 49, 112, 121, 130t, 136, 137, 148br, 179b, 198, 215, 226, 227l, 248, 296b, 374; Cornel Stefan Achirei 18, 220r; Xavi Arnau 43b; Simon Askham 298t; Adrian Beesley 249t; Nick Belton 164l; Rob Bouwman 230; Orhan Çam 43t; Tony Campbell 306; David Cannings-Bushell 124; Cathleen Clapper 148tl; Greg Cooper 255; Jim DeLillo 36; Guy Erwood 348; Andy Gehrig 307b; Andrea Gingerich 179t; Joe Gough 304; Paul Gsell 201b; Guenter Guni 349; David Hernandez 337; Karim Hesham 171; Brett Hillyard 271; Alexey Kashin 67; Britta Kasholm-Tengve 289; Aaron Kohr 251; Jim Kolaczko 148bl; Yury Kosourov 315; Robert Lerich 294; David H. Lewis 51; Marcus Lindström 264; Klaas Lingbeek- van Kranen 350; Sean Locke 296t; Michelle Malven 60; Kristoff Meller 307t; Dean Mitchell 313; Kati Neudert 139; David Newton 132; Greg Nicholas 143t; Jane Norton 26t; Maciej Noskowski 351; Skip ODonnell 138; Nikolai Okhitin 71b, 245; Slavoljub Pantelic 140; Alberto Pomares 197; Mario Ragma Jr 336; Rick Rhay 71t; Alexey Romanov 83b; John Solie 299; Lorraine Swanson 143b; Tony Tremblay 148tr; Sergii Tsololo 45; Steve Vanhorn 70; Kelvin Wakefield 371; Stephen Walls 345; Dave White 189; Forest Woodward 201t; Jun Xiao 178; Feng Yu 40; Dušan Zidar 195; Kenneth C. Zirkel 284; Билиба Елена 25; **Jupiter Unlimited:** Comstock Images 213; Stockxpert 164r; Thinkstock Images 218, 295; **No Trace:** 6, 42t, 210, 227r, 292, 362; **Pearson Education Ltd:** International Bureau of Weights and Measures, Sevres, France 39t; NASA 222, 376; NASA/JPL-Caltech/ESA/Harvard-Smithsonia CfA 38; PEARSON SCOTT FORESMAN 39b; **Jenny Penfold:** 343r; **Photolibrary.com:** PureStock 320; **Science Photo Library Ltd:** 61, 341; Max Alexander/Trinity College, Oxford 311; Los Alamos National Laboratory 26b; NASA GSFC 134; RIA NOVOSTI 24; Science Source 208; **Texas Instruments:** Suzie Williams 203, 308, 327, 353; **TopFoto:** The National Archives/HIP 240

All other images © Pearson Education

Picture Research by: Louise Edgeworth

Acknowledgements

We are grateful to the following for permission to reproduce copyright material:

Data from 'Great Langdale Christmas Pudding 10km race 2007'; 'Promenade 5km Portsmouth' and 'SWVAC 5km Yeovilton' granted by kind permission of Athletics Data Ltd, www.thepowerof10.info; Data for 'Foot lengths for 100 secondary pupils'; and 'Saturday morning exercise' reproduced with kind permission of CensusAtSchool, www.censusatschool.org; Data 'Height of girls and boys in Year 5 in New Zealand' sampled, with permission, from CensusAtSchool New Zealand, www.censusatschool.org.nz; Crime Data from www.crimereduction.homeoffice.gov.uk, © Crown copyright 2009. Crown Copyright material is reproduced with permission under the terms of the Click-Use License; Screenshot from http://www.mathscareers.org.uk/14_-_16/maths_in_everyday_life.cfm copyright © Council for Mathematical Sciences; Data from 'Quarterly gas production of Australia between December 1989 and September 1994 in millions of megajoules' and 'moving averages and line of best fit for those averages with some data on car sales in thousands in Quebec in 1960 and 1961' source: Hyndman, R.J. (n.d.) Time Series Data Library, http://www.robhyndman.info/TSDL. Accessed in March 2009; Extract from 'The whole history of the universe' Times Educational Supplement 13 August 1999 copyright © TES 1999; and The tables 'Individual Cycle age 10', and 'Individual Cycle age 13-14 results' www.worldsportstackingassociation.org/results.htm granted by kind permission of World Sport Stacking Association; Edexcel GCSE exam questions granted by kind permission of Edexcel Limited. Edexcel Limited accepts no responsibility whatsoever for the accuracy or method of working in the answers given.

Every effort has been made to trace the copyright holders and we apologise in advance for any unintentional omissions. In some instances we have been unable to trace the owners of copyright material, and we would appreciate any information that would enable us to do so. We would be pleased to insert the appropriate acknowledgement in any subsequent edition of this publication.

Contents

N7.1   Powers and roots   **1**
1   Negative powers   1
2   Fractional indices   3
3   Surds   6
How well are you doing?   10

A7.1   Linear graphs and inequalities   **12**
1   Working with coordinates   12
2   Exploring linear graphs   14
3   Simultaneous linear equation   16
4   Linear inequalities in one variable   19
5   Linear inequalities in two variables   21
6   Optimisation problems   24
How well are you doing?   28

Functional skills 1   30

N7.2   Decimals and accuracy   **32**
1   Significant figures   32
2   Standard form   36
3   Accuracy of measurements   39
4   Upper and lower bounds   42
5   Dimensions   45
How well are you doing?   48

S7.1   Enquiry 1   **51**
1   Sampling   51
2   Planning and collecting data   55
3   Drawing histograms   56
4   Choosing class intervals   59
5   Using histograms   61
6   Moving averages   65
How well are you doing?   68

Functional skills 2   70

G7.1   Measures and mensuration   **72**
1   Arcs and sectors of circles   72
2   Circle problems   75
3   Volume of 3D shapes   77
4   Surface area of 3D shapes   81
5   Problem solving   84
How well are you doing?   93

A7.2   Expressions and formulae   **97**
1   Simplifying expressions   97
2   Expanding brackets   100
3   Factorising expressions   102
4   Working with formulae   104
5   Investigations   106
6   Deriving formulae   110
How well are you doing?   113

G7.2   Trigonometry 1   **115**
1   Pythagoras' theorem in 3D   115
2   Finding an unknown angle   119
3   Finding an unknown side   122
How well are you doing?   125

N7.3   Proportional reasoning   **127**
1   Percentage problems   127
2   Direct proportion 1   131
3   Direct proportion 2   135
4   Inverse proportion   138
5   Proportion and square roots   142
How well are you doing?   145

Functional skills 3   148

G7.3   Geometrical reasoning   **150**
1   Tangents and chords   150
2   Circle theorems   153
3   More circle theorems   156
4   Using the circle theorems   160
5   Congruent triangles   164
6   Proving congruency   168
7   Similar shapes and solids   171
How well are you doing?   176

Functional skills 4   178

S7.2   Probability 1   **180**
1   Using tree diagrams   180
2   The probability of combined events   184
3   Investigating a game of chance   186
4   Conditional probability   189
5   The 'and' and 'or' rules   193
How well are you doing?   197

A7.3 Solving equations — 200

1 Linear equations — 200
2 Solving quadratic equations graphically — 202
3 Solving quadratic equations by factorisation 1 — 204
4 Solving quadratic equations by factorisation 2 — 206
5 Completing the square — 208
6 Using the quadratic formula — 210
7 Simultaneous linear and quadratic equations — 212
8 Simultaneous linear and non-linear equations — 214
How well are you doing? — 216

Functional skills 5 — 218

G7.4 Transformations and vectors — 220

1 Symmetry patterns *(double lesson)* — 220
3 Vectors and vector notation — 222
4 The magnitude of a vector — 225
5 Vector addition — 227
6 Parallel vectors and problem solving — 231
How well are you doing? — 236

Functional skills 6 — 238

S7.3 Enquiry 2 — 240

1 Sampling and statistics — 240
2 Five-figure summaries — 242
3 Cumulative frequency 1 — 245
4 Cumulative frequency 2 — 247
5 Estimating statistics for grouped data — 250
6 Box plots — 252
7 Histograms and frequency density — 254
8 Moving averages — 257
How well are you doing? — 261

G7.5 Trigonometry 2 — 264

1 2D and 3D problems — 264
2 Area of a triangle — 268
3 Angles larger than 90° — 271
4 Graphs of trigonometric functions — 273
5 The sine rule — 275
6 The cosine rule — 278
7 Using the sine and cosine rules — 281
How well are you doing? — 286

S7.4 Probability 2 — 289

1 Capture-recapture — 289
2 The birthday problem — 292
3 Using probability 1 — 296
4 Using probability 2 — 298
5 Quincunx — 300
How well are you doing? — 303

Functional skills 7 — 306

A7.4 Exploring graphs — 308

1 Exploring quadratic and cubic functions — 308
2 Properties of polynomial functions — 311
3 Reciprocal functions — 314
4 Exponential functions — 316
5 Generating trigonometric functions — 319
6 Exploring trigonometric functions — 321
7 Transformations of functions — 324
8 Loci — 328
9 Solving problems — 330
How well are you doing? — 333

Functional skills 8 — 336

N7.4 Using and applying maths — 338

1 The history of convex polyhedra *(double lesson)* — 338
3 Algebraic proof — 341
4 Careers in mathematics — 343
How well are you doing? — 345

R7.1 Revision unit 1 — 348

1 Percentages and ratios — 348
2 Expressions and equations — 353
3 Formulae, functions and graphs — 356
4 Geometrical reasoning — 362
5 Probability — 367

R7.2 Revision unit 2 — 373

1 Indices and standard form — 373
2 Equations and inequalities — 377
3 Functions and graphs — 381
4 Pythagoras' theorem and trigonometry — 385
5 Graphs, charts and statistics — 389

Answers — 399
Index — 406

Powers and roots

This unit will help you to:

- use the index laws for negative and fractional powers;
- understand and use rational and irrational numbers;
- use surds in exact calculations, without a calculator.

1 Negative powers

This lesson will help you to work with zero and negative powers.

 Did you know that...?

The French mathematician **René Descartes**, famous for his invention of coordinates, lived in the first half of the 17th century. He was the first to write positive integer powers as we write them today, apart from a^2 for the square of a number. For this, he wrote aa instead, maybe because aa takes up the same space as a^2, and is just as quick to write.

Negative integer powers were first written as we do by **Sir Isaac Newton** (1642–1727) in a letter he wrote in 1676 describing his discovery of a theorem 12 years earlier.

Isaac Newton

Exercise 1

For any non-zero value of a, $a^0 = 1$.

For any number n, $a^{-n} = \dfrac{1}{a^n}$. For example, $10^{-2} = \dfrac{1}{10^2} = \dfrac{1}{100}$.

To **multiply** two numbers in index form, **add** the indices, so $a^m \times a^n = a^{m+n}$,

e.g. $10^4 \times 10^2 = 10^{4+2} = 10^6$.

To **divide** two numbers in index form, **subtract** the indices, so $a^m \div a^n = a^{m-n}$,

e.g. $10^3 \div 10^2 = 10^{3-2} = 10^1 = 10$.

Example

Simplify $\dfrac{2^3 \times 2^4}{2 \times 2^8}$.

$\dfrac{2^3 \times 2^4}{2 \times 2^8} = \dfrac{2^7}{2^9}$

$= 2^{-2} = \dfrac{1}{2^2} = \dfrac{1}{4}$

You can use a calculator to find the values of powers of numbers.

For example, to find 2.5^{-3} a common key sequence is

$\boxed{2}\boxed{.}\boxed{5}\boxed{x^y}\boxed{3}\boxed{+/-}\boxed{=}$

which produces the answer 0.064.

Make sure that you know how to use your own calculator to find powers of numbers.

Do questions 1 to 6 **without using your calculator**.

(1) Work out each value.

a 2^{-1} b 3^{-2} c 5^{-3} d 10^{-3}

e 12^0 f $\left(\frac{1}{3}\right)^{-1}$ g $\left(\frac{2}{3}\right)^{-2}$ h 2.5^{-1}

(2) Simplify these.

a $2^2 \times 2^{-5}$ b $3^{-2} \times 3^{-3}$ c $10^{-2} \times 10^{-2}$ d $9^5 \times 9^{-3}$

e $5^{-3} \div 5^{-1}$ f $10^{-4} \div 10^{-3}$ g $4^{-2} \div 4^{-1}$ h $3^2 \div 3^{-1}$

i $(2^{-3})^2$ j $(5^2)^{-2}$ k $(3^4)^2$ l $(2^{-1})^{-4}$

(3) Simplify these.

a $\dfrac{2^4 \times 2^2}{2^7}$ b $\dfrac{3^4 \times 3^{-2}}{3^5}$ c $\dfrac{10^{-2} \times 10^2}{10}$ d $\dfrac{2^{-4} \times 2^2}{2^{-7}}$

e $\dfrac{2^4}{2^7 \times 2^{-2}}$ f $\dfrac{3^4 \times 3^2}{3 \times 3^7}$ g $\dfrac{4^4 \times 4^{-2}}{4^{-1}}$ h $\dfrac{2^4 \times 2^2}{2^7 \times 2^{-1}}$

(4) Find the value of n in each of these.

a $2^n = \dfrac{2^2}{2^5}$ b $3 \times 3^n = \dfrac{3^4}{3^6}$ c $\dfrac{10^n}{10} = \dfrac{10^3}{10^5}$ d $4^2 \times 4^n = \dfrac{4}{4^5}$

(5) Work out each value.

a 6×10^{-1} b 8.2×10^2 c 2.9×10^{-3}

d 8.7×10^{-2} e 1.6×10^3 f 4×10^{-4}

(6) Find the value of n in each of these.

a $5000 = 5 \times 10^n$ b $28\,000 = 2.8 \times 10^n$ c $0.3 = 3 \times 10^n$

d $6380 = 6.38 \times 10^n$ e $0.0051 = 5.1 \times 10^n$ f $0.234 = 2.34 \times 10^n$

(7) **Use your calculator** to work these out.
Where appropriate, give your answer correct to two decimal places.

a 1.25^{-1} b 0.16^{-1} c 0.4^{-2} d 2.5^{-3}

e 12.5^{-2} f 0.45^{-1} g 0.96^{-8} h 0.6^{-4}

Extension problems

8 What is the last digit of 5^{-55}?

9 Use each of the digits 2, 3 and 4 once.
What is the biggest number that you can make?

For example:
$2 \times 3^4 = 162$ or $32 \times 4 = 128$

Points to remember

- To **multiply** two numbers in index form, add the indices, so $a^m \times a^n = a^{m+n}$.
- To **divide** two numbers in index form, subtract the indices, so $a^m \div a^n = a^{m-n}$.
- To **raise the power of a number to a power**, multiply the indices, so $(a^m)^n = a^{m \times n}$.
- These rules work with both positive and negative integer powers.

2 Fractional indices

This lesson will help you to work with fractional indices.

Did you know that...?

No-one knows for certain the origin of the square root symbol $\sqrt{\ }$. The Swiss mathematician **Leonhard Euler** (1707–1783) thought it came from the letter r, the first letter of the Latin word *radix*, which means 'root'.

A square root symbol like a capital R with a line across its tail was used in 1220 by **Leonardo of Pisa**.

The symbol $\sqrt{}$ without the vinculum (the top bar over the numbers) was used in 1525 by **Christoff Rudolff**, a German mathematician.

In 1637, **Rene Descartes** used the symbol $\sqrt{\ }$, adding the vinculum, in his book *La Geometrie*.

Leonhard Euler

Since $a^m \times a^n = a^{m+n}$,

$$a^{\frac{1}{2}} \times a^{\frac{1}{2}} = a^1 = a$$

This means that $a^{\frac{1}{2}}$ multiplied by itself gives a, so $a^{\frac{1}{3}}$ is the same as the **square root of** a,

that is, $a^{\frac{1}{2}} = \sqrt{a}$.

In the same way, $a^{\frac{1}{3}} \times a^{\frac{1}{3}} \times a^{\frac{1}{3}} = a^1 = a$, so $a^{\frac{1}{3}}$ is the same as the **cube root of** a.

In general, $a^{\frac{1}{n}} = \sqrt[n]{a}$, where $\sqrt[n]{a}$ means the **nth root of** a.

The index law $(a^m)^n = a^{m \times n}$ holds for fractional powers. So:

$$(a^{\frac{1}{m}})^n = a^{\frac{1}{m} \times n} = a^{\frac{n}{m}} \text{ and } (a^m)^{\frac{1}{n}} = a^{m \times \frac{1}{n}} = a^{\frac{m}{n}}$$

Example

Simplify $(\sqrt[3]{11})^2$.

$$(\sqrt[3]{11})^2 = (11^{\frac{1}{3}})^2 = 11^{\frac{2}{3}}$$

(1) **Without using a calculator**, work out the value of each of these.

a $9^{\frac{1}{2}}$ 　　　 b $121^{\frac{1}{2}}$ 　　　 c $36^{-\frac{1}{2}}$ 　　　 d $10\,000^{\frac{1}{2}}$

e $27^{\frac{1}{3}}$ 　　　 f $1\,000\,000^{\frac{1}{3}}$ 　　　 g $-64^{-\frac{1}{3}}$ 　　　 h $216^{-\frac{1}{3}}$

i $9^{\frac{5}{2}}$ 　　　 j $16^{\frac{3}{4}}$ 　　　 k $(-27)^{\frac{2}{3}}$ 　　　 l $25^{\frac{3}{2}}$

(2) Write each of these as a single fraction.

a $\left(\frac{1}{2}\right)^4$ 　　　 b $\left(\frac{1}{3}\right)^2$ 　　　 c $\left(\frac{2}{5}\right)^4$ 　　　 d $\left(\frac{3}{4}\right)^3$

e $25^{-\frac{1}{2}}$ 　　　 f $27^{-\frac{2}{3}}$ 　　　 g $32^{-\frac{4}{5}}$ 　　　 h $64^{-\frac{4}{3}}$

(3) Simplify and write these in the form a^n.

a $2^{\frac{1}{2}} \times 2^{\frac{1}{2}}$ 　　　 b $3^{\frac{1}{2}} \div 3^{\frac{1}{3}}$ 　　　 c $10^{\frac{1}{5}} \times 10^{\frac{1}{2}}$ 　　　 d $8^{\frac{5}{6}} \div 8^{\frac{5}{6}}$

(4) Find the value of n in each of these.

a $(\sqrt{5})^6 = 5^n$ 　　　 b $(\sqrt[3]{7})^8 = 7^n$ 　　　 c $\sqrt{5^8} = 5^n$ 　　　 d $(\sqrt[3]{2})^{11} = 2^{-2n}$

(5) **Use your calculator** to work these out.
Where appropriate, give your answer correct to two decimal places.

a $\sqrt[3]{1.728}$ **b** $\sqrt{8.41}$ **c** $\sqrt[3]{3.375}$ **d** $\sqrt[4]{33.1776}$

(6) State which of each pair of numbers is larger. **You may use your calculator.**

a $\sqrt{10}, \sqrt[3]{50}$ **b** $\sqrt[3]{60}, \sqrt[4]{235}$ **c** $\sqrt[4]{20}, \sqrt[5]{40}$

d $35^{\frac{1}{2}}, 200^{\frac{1}{3}}$ **e** $55^{\frac{1}{3}}, 210^{\frac{1}{4}}$ **f** $40^{\frac{1}{4}}, 100^{\frac{1}{5}}$

(7) I am an integer less than 10.
Cube me, rearrange my digits, then take my cube root to get another integer less than 10.
What are the two integers?

(8) I am a three-digit cube that is also a square. What am I?

Extension problems

A **rational number** is any number that can be expressed in the form $\frac{a}{b}$, where a and b are integers, and $b \neq 0$. Examples are:

$$2\frac{1}{2} = \frac{5}{2} \qquad 1.3 = \frac{13}{10} \qquad 129 = \frac{129}{1} \qquad \sqrt{0.81} = 0.9 = \frac{9}{10} \qquad 0.\dot{3}\dot{6} = \frac{4}{11}$$

Numbers that cannot be written as a fraction are **irrational numbers**.
Examples are decimals like π that neither terminate nor recur, some roots like $\sqrt{2}$, and expressions like $\frac{3\pi}{4}$ or $4\sqrt{7}$.

Together, all rational and irrational numbers make up the set of **real numbers**.

(9) $\sqrt{5\frac{4}{9}}$, or $\sqrt{\frac{49}{9}}$, is a rational number, since it equals $\frac{7}{3}$, or $2\frac{1}{3}$.

$\sqrt{5\frac{1}{16}}$, or $\sqrt{\frac{81}{16}}$, is a rational number, since it equals $\frac{9}{4}$, or $2\frac{1}{4}$.

$$\sqrt{5\frac{4}{9}} = 2\frac{1}{3} \quad \text{and} \quad \sqrt{5\frac{1}{16}} = 2\frac{1}{4}$$

Find three more numbers between 5 and 6 that have rational square roots.

(10) Can you get TEN by finding the square root of a DOZEN?

$$\sqrt{\text{DOZEN}} = \text{TEN}$$

Each letter stands for a different single-digit number. Find the values of the digits.

Points to remember

- $a^{\frac{1}{2}}$ is the same as the **square root** of a.
- $\sqrt[n]{a}$ or $a^{\frac{1}{n}}$ means the **nth root** of a, e.g. $\sqrt[3]{a}$ or $a^{\frac{1}{3}}$ is the **cube root** of a.
- The **index laws** also hold for fractional powers, so:
$$\left(a^{\frac{1}{m}}\right)^n = a^{\frac{1}{m} \times n} = a^{\frac{n}{m}} \text{ and } (a^m)^{\frac{1}{n}} = a^{m \times \frac{1}{n}} = a^{\frac{m}{n}}$$

3 Surds

This lesson will help you to use surds in exact calculations, and rationalise expressions such as $\frac{5}{\sqrt{3}}$.

Did you know that...?

Al-Khwarizmi was an Arab who wrote about Hindu–Arabic numerals and how to use place value in calculations. The word *algorithm* comes from his name, and the word *algebra* from his book *Hisab al-jabr*.

The translators of the mathematical work of the ancient Greeks wrongly used the Arabic for 'deaf and dumb' for 'irrational'. So when Al-Khwarizmi wrote about irrational numbers he called them 'inaudible'.

The Italian **Gherardo** translated the work of the Arabic mathematicians into Latin in the 12th century. He used the Latin *surdus*, meaning 'deaf', for 'inaudible numbers'.

The term eventually reached Britain. In 1551, **Robert Recorde** described quantities that are 'partly rationall, and partly surde'.

Statue of Al-Khwarizmi, c. 790 to 840, in Tehran, Iran

Exercise 3

A **surd** is a root that does not have an exact value. For example:

$\sqrt{2}$ is a surd but $\sqrt{4}$ (which equals ± 2) is not.

$\sqrt[3]{5}$ is a surd but $\sqrt[3]{1000}$ (which equals 10) is not.

These two identities are often used to simplify expressions involving surds.

$$\sqrt{a} \times \sqrt{b} = \sqrt{ab} \qquad \frac{\sqrt{a}}{\sqrt{b}} = \sqrt{\frac{a}{b}}$$

To simplify surds of the form $\sqrt{n}$, write n as a product that includes a square number.

Example 1

Simplify $\sqrt{75}$.

$\sqrt{75} = \sqrt{25 \times 3} = \sqrt{25} \times \sqrt{3} = 5\sqrt{3}$

Example 2

Simplify $\sqrt{\dfrac{32}{81}}$.

$\sqrt{\dfrac{32}{81}} = \dfrac{\sqrt{16 \times 2}}{\sqrt{81}} = \dfrac{\sqrt{16} \times \sqrt{2}}{\sqrt{81}} = \dfrac{4\sqrt{2}}{9}$

You can simplify an expression such as $(4 + \sqrt{2})(5 - 3\sqrt{2})$ by multiplying out the brackets.

Example 3

Simplify $(4 + \sqrt{2})(5 - 3\sqrt{2})$.

$(4 + \sqrt{2})(5 - 3\sqrt{2}) = 14 - 7\sqrt{2}$

$\times$	4	$+\sqrt{2}$	
5	20	$+5\sqrt{2}$	$20 + 5\sqrt{2}$
$-3\sqrt{2}$	$-12\sqrt{2}$	-6	$-6 - 12\sqrt{2}$
			$14 - 7\sqrt{2}$

To simplify a fraction of the form $\dfrac{a}{\sqrt{b}}$ where a and b are positive integers, multiply both the numerator and the denominator by $\sqrt{b}$. This is called **rationalising** the denominator.

Example 4

Simplify $\dfrac{6}{\sqrt{3}}$.

$\dfrac{6}{\sqrt{3}} = \dfrac{6 \times \sqrt{3}}{\sqrt{3} \times \sqrt{3}} = \dfrac{6\sqrt{3}}{3} = 2\sqrt{3}$

(1) Find the value of n in each of these expressions.

a $\sqrt{8} = n\sqrt{2}$ b $\sqrt{80} = n\sqrt{5}$ c $\sqrt{18} = n\sqrt{3}$ d $\sqrt{50} = n\sqrt{2}$

(2) Expand and simplify these expressions.

a $\sqrt{3}(4 + \sqrt{3})$ b $(\sqrt{3} + 1)(2 + \sqrt{3})$ c $(\sqrt{5} - 1)(2 + \sqrt{5})$

d $(\sqrt{7} + 1)(2 - 2\sqrt{7})$ e $(3 - \sqrt{5})^2$ f $(\sqrt{5} - \sqrt{3})(\sqrt{5} + \sqrt{3})$

(3) Rationalise the denominators in these expressions.

a $\dfrac{1}{\sqrt{2}}$ b $\dfrac{4}{\sqrt{5}}$ c $\dfrac{3}{\sqrt{7}}$ d $\dfrac{3}{\sqrt{2}}$ e $\dfrac{5}{\sqrt{13}}$

(4) Rationalise the denominators and simplify the answers in these expressions.

a $\dfrac{2}{\sqrt{6}}$ b $\dfrac{3}{\sqrt{15}}$ c $\dfrac{15}{\sqrt{20}}$ d $\dfrac{5}{\sqrt{5}}$ e $\dfrac{14}{\sqrt{7}}$

(5) Rationalise the denominators in these expressions.
Give your answers in the form $a + b\sqrt{c}$, where a, b and c are integers.

a $\dfrac{10 + \sqrt{5}}{\sqrt{5}}$ **b** $\dfrac{2 - \sqrt{2}}{\sqrt{2}}$ **c** $\dfrac{22 + \sqrt{11}}{\sqrt{11}}$ **d** $\dfrac{14 - \sqrt{14}}{\sqrt{14}}$

(6) The lengths of the two shorter sides of a right-angled triangle are $\sqrt{11}$ cm and 5 cm.
Find the length of the third side.

(7) A square has an area of 40 cm². Write in surd form:

a the length of each side of the square;

b the perimeter of the square.

(8) **a** The diagram shows a right-angled triangle.
Show that it has an area of 8 m².

b Show that $2\sqrt{8}$ can also be written as $4\sqrt{2}$.

c Calculate the length of the hypotenuse.
Leave your answer in surd form, writing it
as simply as possible.

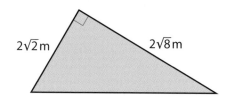

$2\sqrt{2}$ m $\qquad$ $2\sqrt{8}$ m

(9) The length of a rectangle is $(3 + \sqrt{5})$ cm. The width is $(4 - \sqrt{5})$ cm.
Work out the perimeter and area of the rectangle.

(10) Ten concentric circles are drawn.
The smallest circle has a radius of 1 cm.

The area between any two consecutive circles is
equal to the area of the smallest circle.

Show that the radius of the largest circle is $\sqrt{10}$ cm.

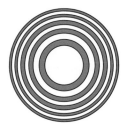

Extension problems

To rationalise a fraction of the form $\dfrac{1}{\sqrt{a} + \sqrt{b}}$, multiply by $\dfrac{\sqrt{a} - \sqrt{b}}{\sqrt{a} - \sqrt{b}}$.

Example

Simplify $\dfrac{1}{\sqrt{3} - 1}$.

Multiply by the fraction $\dfrac{\sqrt{3} + 1}{\sqrt{3} + 1}$.

$$\dfrac{1}{\sqrt{3} - 1} = \dfrac{1}{\sqrt{3} - 1} \times \dfrac{\sqrt{3} + 1}{\sqrt{3} + 1} = \dfrac{\sqrt{3} + 1}{3 - 1} = \dfrac{\sqrt{3} + 1}{2}$$

11 Six circles touch each other as shown.
The radius of each pink circle is 1 cm.

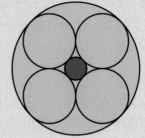

    a Show that the radius of the green
circle is $(\sqrt{2} + 1)$ cm.

    b Show that the radius of the blue
circle is $(\sqrt{2} - 1)$ cm.

 12 A square is of side 10 cm.

It is made into a regular octagon by
cutting off the four corners.

Show that the cuts should be made at a
distance $5(2 - \sqrt{2})$ cm from the vertices of
the square.

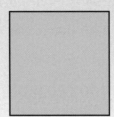 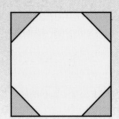

 Points to remember

- ◉ A **surd** is a root that does not have an exact value.
- ◉ $\sqrt{a} \times \sqrt{b} = \sqrt{ab}$ and $\dfrac{\sqrt{a}}{\sqrt{b}} = \sqrt{\dfrac{a}{b}}$.
- ◉ $(\sqrt{a} + \sqrt{b})(\sqrt{a} - \sqrt{b}) = a - b$
- ◉ To **rationalise** $\dfrac{a}{\sqrt{b}}$, multiply the numerator and denominator by $\sqrt{b}$.

How well are you doing?

Powers and roots (no calculator)

1 *2004 level 8*

    a Look at these equations.

       $48 = 3 \times 2^a$

       $56 = 7 \times 2^b$

       What are the values of a and b?

    b $48 \times 56 = 3 \times 7 \times 2^c$

       What is the value of c?

2 *2007 level 8*

Look at this information.

$$y^2 = 10$$

Use this information to copy and complete the equations below.

    a $y^4 = \square$
                         b $y^{\square} = 1000$

3 *1997 level 8*

For each of these cards n can be any positive number.
The answers given by the cards are all positive numbers.

n^2	$0.8n$	$\sqrt{n}$	$\dfrac{n}{0.8}$	$\dfrac{1}{n}$

    a Which card will always give an answer less than n?

    b When n is 1, which cards will give the answer 1?

    c When n is 4, which cards will give an answer less than 4?

    d When n is less than 1, which cards will give an answer less than n?

4 *GCSE 1387 November 2006*

   a Write down the value of $4^{\frac{3}{2}}$.

   b Write $\sqrt{8}$ in the form $m\sqrt{2}$, where m is an integer.

   c Write $\sqrt{50}$ in the form $k\sqrt{2}$, where k is an integer.

   d Rationalise $\dfrac{1 + \sqrt{2}}{\sqrt{2}}$.

5 *2002 Exceptional performance*

You will need some squared dotty paper for this question.

   a An elastic band is fixed on four pins on a pinboard.

      Show that the total length of the band in this position is $14\sqrt{2}$ units.

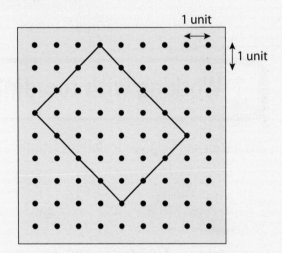

1 unit

1 unit

   b What is the length of the band in this new position?
Write your answer in its simplest form using roots.

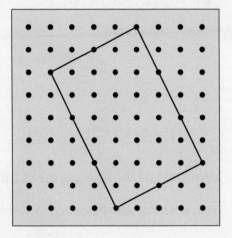

   c On dotty paper, outline a 9 by 9 array of dots to use as a pinboard.
Draw a square on the pinboard that has a perimeter of $4\sqrt{29}$.
Show your working.

   d Outline another 9 by 9 array of dots to use as a pinboard.
Now draw a trapezium on the pinboard that has a perimeter of $6 + 4\sqrt{2}$.
Show your working.

Linear graphs and inequalities

This unit will help you to:

- find the length and midpoint of a line joining two coordinate points;

- explore linear graphs;

- solve simultaneous equations;

- solve inequalities in two variables and use inequalities to solve problems.

1 Working with coordinates

This lesson will help you to find the lengths and midpoints of lines on a rectangular grid.

Exercise 1

In the right-angled triangle ABC, AC = 8 and BC = 4.

Use Pythagoras' theorem to find **the length of AB**.

$AB^2 = 8^2 + 4^2$

$AB^2 = 64 + 16 = 80$

$AB = \sqrt{80} = 8.94$ to 2 decimal places.

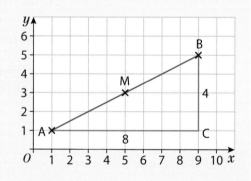

The **midpoint M of the line segment AB** is (5, 3).

Notice that 5, the x-coordinate of M, is the mean of the x-coordinates of A and B, i.e. $5 = \dfrac{1 + 9}{2}$.

Also 3, the y-coordinate of M, is the mean of the y-coordinates of A and B, i.e. $3 = \dfrac{1 + 5}{2}$.

In general:

- the **length of the line** joining (x_1, y_1) and (x_2, y_2) is $\sqrt{(x_2 - x_1)^2 + (y_2 - y_1)^2}$;

- the **midpoint of the line** joining (x_1, y_1) and (x_2, y_2) is $\left(\dfrac{x_1 + x_2}{2}, \dfrac{y_1 + y_2}{2} \right)$.

Example

Prove that the triangle on the right is isosceles.

The length of the line joining $(1, 2)$ to $(4, 6) = \sqrt{3^2 + 4^2} = 5$.

The length of the line joining $(4, 6)$ to $(8, 3) = \sqrt{4^2 + 3^2} = 5$.

The two lengths are equal so the triangle is isosceles.

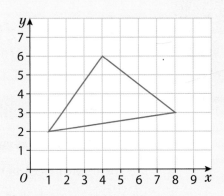

1 Find the length of the line joining each pair of points. Give your answer to 1 decimal place.

    a $(1, 3)$ and $(9, 9)$ **b** $(4, 3)$ and $(11, 17)$ **c** $(-5, 2)$ and $(1, 7)$

    d $(-8, 4)$ and $(2, -3)$ **e** $(-7, -4)$ and $(8, 5)$ **f** $(-9, -1)$ and $(7, -7)$

2 Find the midpoint of the line joining each pair of points.

    a $(2, 4)$ and $(10, 16)$ **b** $(1, 1)$ and $(9, 15)$ **c** $(-1, 2)$ and $(9, 6)$

    d $(-6, -2)$ and $(4, 11)$ **e** $(-5, 7)$ and $(3, -5)$ **f** $(-14, -1)$ and $(6, -17)$

3   **a** Find the midpoint K of the line BC.

    b A median of a triangle is the line segment joining a vertex to the midpoint of the opposite side.

      Draw one of the medians of the triangle by joining A to K.

      Find the length of AK.

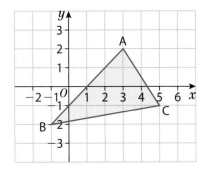

4   **a** A triangle is formed by joining the points $(-4, 1)$, $(4, 5)$ and $(0, -3)$.
      Prove that it is isosceles.

    b A shape is formed by joining the points $(4, -3)$, $(8, 1)$, $(12, -3)$ and $(8, -7)$.
      Prove that it is a square.

    c One end of a line is at $(-10, -5)$ and its midpoint is at $(-7, 1.5)$.
      What are the coordinates of the other end of the line?

    d A triangle is formed by joining $(3, 4)$, $(9, 9)$ and $(6, -3)$.
      Work out its area and perimeter.

    e Find the length of the line joining the midpoints of the lines AB and AC for
      A $(4, 3)$, B $(-4, -7)$ and C $(10, -5)$.

    f A rectangle is formed by joining the points $(-9, 4)$, $(3, 4)$, $(3, -2)$ and $(-9, -2)$.
      Prove that the diagonals bisect each other.

Extension problems

5   **a**   A is the point $(-3, -1)$ and B is the point $(3, 3)$.
Prove that the points C $(2, 4)$ and D $(-2, -2)$ lie on the circle with diameter AB.

      b   What shape is formed by joining the points $(2, 2)$, $(-3, 4)$, $(-6, 0)$ and $(-1, -2)$?

6   A is the point $(-5, 3)$, B is the point $(-4, -1)$ and C is the point $(1, -4)$.

      a   Find the coordinates of the midpoint of AC.

      b   The point D is such that ABCD is a parallelogram. Find the coordinates of D.

◉ Points to remember

- The length of the line joining (x_1, y_1) and (x_2, y_2) is $\sqrt{(x_2 - x_1)^2 + (y_2 - y_1)^2}$.

- The midpoint of the line joining (x_1, y_1) and (x_2, y_2) is $\left(\dfrac{x_1 + x_2}{2}, \dfrac{y_1 + y_2}{2} \right)$.

2 Exploring linear graphs

This lesson will help you to apply what you know about linear graphs.

Exercise 2

The graph of the linear equation $y = ax + b$ is a straight line with **gradient** a. The **intercept** on the y-axis is at $(0, b)$.

The red line is the graph of $y = 3x + 2$.
It has gradient 3 and the y-intercept is at $(0, 2)$.

Any line **parallel** to $y = 3x + 2$ has the equation $y = 3x + b$.
The blue line $y = 3x - 5$ is parallel to the red line.

Any line **perpendicular** to $y = 3x + 2$ has the equation $y = -\frac{1}{3}x + b$. The purple line $y = -\frac{1}{3}x + 7$ is perpendicular to the red line.

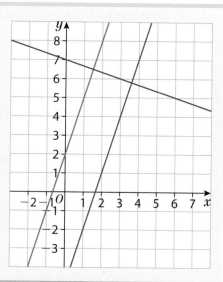

1   Write the gradient and intercept for each equation and sketch the graph.

     a $y = 5x - 8$ **b** $3x + y = 4$ **c** $2x + 4y - 5 = 0$

     d $\dfrac{y}{2} = 2x - 1$ **e** $\dfrac{x + y}{2} = 5$ **f** $\dfrac{4x - 2y}{3} = -3$

2 Find the equation of the line parallel to the given line passing through the given point.

   a $y = x - 1$ $(0, 4)$ **b** $y = 3x + 5$ $(0, -7)$

   c $3y + 2x = 14$ $(-2, -1)$ **d** $y = -4x - 7$ $(4, -8)$

   e $\dfrac{x - y}{2} = 1$ $(-1, -8)$ **f** $\dfrac{2x + 3y}{4} = 5$ $(6, -3)$

3 Find the equation of the line perpendicular to the given line passing through the given point.

   a $y = 2x - 3$ $(0, 5)$ **b** $y = -4x + 7$ $(8, 3)$

   c $y = 5x - 9$ $(-5, -3)$ **d** $y + 2x = 4$ $(6, -4)$

   e $2y - 3x - 1 = 0$ $(-6, 2)$ **f** $2x - y = 8$ $(-2, -2)$

4 Write the equation of the line passing through the given points.

   a $(0, 2)$ and $(4, 10)$ **b** $(1, 3)$ and $(3, -3)$

   c $(-2, 8)$ and $(1, -1)$ **d** $(-4, -5)$ and $(2, 7)$

   e $(6, -8)$ and $(10, 12)$ **f** $(-10, -12)$ and $(0, 0)$

5 A triangle is formed by joining the points A $(1, 5)$, B $(-7, 1)$ and C $(-3, -3)$.

   a What is the equation of BC?   **b** What is the midpoint, K, of BC?

   c What is the equation of KA?   **d** Find the length of BC.

   e Find the length of KA.   **f** What is the area of triangle ABC?

   g Check your answer to part **f** by using a different method to calculate the area.

Extension problem

6 **a** Prove that the triangle formed by the points $(4, 5)$, $(6, 7)$ and $(7, 2)$ is right-angled.

   b A is the point $(-3, 2)$ and B is the point $(5, 4)$.
       Find the equation of the tangent at A to a circle with diameter AB.

   c One marker buoy is placed at $(-8, 1)$ and another at $(4, -2)$.
       What is the equation of the set of points that are equidistant from both A and B?

Points to remember

  ⊙ The graph of $y = ax + b$ has gradient a and intercepts the y-axis at $(0, b)$.

  ⊙ Parallel lines have the same gradient.

  ⊙ Any line perpendicular to $y = ax + b$ has gradient $-\dfrac{1}{a}$.

3 Simultaneous linear equations

Did you know that...?

Relationships between two variables can be visualised using a coordinate grid.

René Descartes (1596–1650) was one of the first mathematicians to realise the power of using axes at right angles to each other. That is why the full name of points on such a grid is Cartesian coordinates.

This lesson will help you to solve simultaneous linear equations.

Exercise 3

Example 1

The two linear equations
$$10x + 3y = 20 \ldots\ldots\ldots (1)$$
$$12x - 4y = 5 \ldots\ldots\ldots (2)$$

have a solution where the lines cross.

Use the **method of elimination** to find the solution.

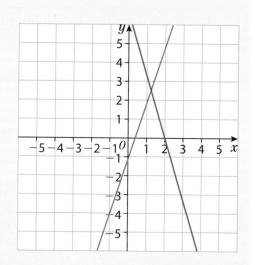

Multiply (1) by 4	$40x + 12y = 80 \ldots\ldots\ldots (3)$
Multiply (2) by 3	$36x - 12y = 15 \ldots\ldots\ldots (4)$

Add (3) and (4) $76x = 95$

Divide by 76 $x = \mathbf{1.25}$

Substitute in (2) $15 - 4y = 5$

Rearrange $4y = 10$

Divide by 4 $y = \mathbf{2.5}$

Check in (1) $(10 \times 1.25) + (3 \times 2.5) = 12.5 + 7.5 = 20$

Simultaneous equations can be used to solve problems.

Example 2

Gary and Kevin are buying tickets for a football match.
Gary buys 3 adult and 5 child tickets for £132.
Kevin buys 6 adult and 2 child tickets for £156.
Work out the cost of an adult's and a child's ticket.

Let x be the cost of an adult's ticket and y the cost of a child's ticket.

$$3x + 5y = 132 \ldots\ldots\ldots (1)$$
$$6x + 2y = 156 \ldots\ldots\ldots (2)$$

Multiply (1) by 2 $\quad 6x + 10y = 264 \ldots\ldots\ldots (3)$

Subtract (2) from (3) $\quad 8y = 108$

Divide by 8 $\quad\quad\quad y = 13.5$

Substitute in (1) $\quad\quad x = 21.5$

Check in (2) $6 \times 21.5 + 2 \times 13.5 = 156$

An adult's ticket costs **£21.50** and a child's ticket costs **£13.50**.

1 Solve these pairs of simultaneous linear equations.

a $\quad 5x - 2y = 4 \ldots\ldots\ldots\ldots (1)$
$\quad\quad 3x + 2y = 12 \ldots\ldots\ldots (2)$

b $\quad 7x + 2y = 17 \ldots\ldots\ldots (1)$
$\quad\quad 11x - y = 6 \ldots\ldots\ldots (2)$

c $\quad 2x - 5y = 11 \ldots\ldots\ldots (1)$
$\quad\quad 3x + 2y = 26 \ldots\ldots\ldots (2)$

d $\quad 3x - 4y = 6 \ldots\ldots\ldots (1)$
$\quad\quad 4x - 5y = 7 \ldots\ldots\ldots (2)$

e $\quad 3x - 2y = 21 \ldots\ldots\ldots (1)$
$\quad\quad 5x - y = 14 \ldots\ldots\ldots (2)$

f $\quad 2x + 3y - 13 = 0 \ldots\ldots (1)$
$\quad\quad 5x - 4y + 48 = 0 \ldots\ldots (2)$

2 Solve these pairs of simultaneous linear equations. Give your answers to 1 d.p.

a $\quad 2x - 5y = 6 \ldots\ldots\ldots\ldots (1)$
$\quad\quad 2x + 4y = 1 \ldots\ldots\ldots\ldots (2)$

b $\quad 3x + 2y = 9 \ldots\ldots\ldots\ldots (1)$
$\quad\quad 5x - 3y = 2 \ldots\ldots\ldots\ldots (2)$

c $\quad 5x - 3y = 2 \ldots\ldots\ldots\ldots (1)$
$\quad\quad 2x - 4y = 5 \ldots\ldots\ldots\ldots (2)$

d $\quad 10x + 4y = 18 \ldots\ldots\ldots (1)$
$\quad\quad 7x - 3y = 8 \ldots\ldots\ldots\ldots (2)$

e $\quad 6x - 5y = 7 \ldots\ldots\ldots\ldots (1)$
$\quad\quad 5x + 2y = 22 \ldots\ldots\ldots (2)$

f $\quad 3y - 6x = 25 \ldots\ldots\ldots (1)$
$\quad\quad 2y + 7x = 9 \ldots\ldots\ldots\ldots (2)$

3 The total area of four vertical sides of a rectangular box, of height 3 cm, is 72 cm². The length is increased by 10%. The width is decreased by 20%. The area stays the same.

Find the length and width of the box.

4 Jake has a bowl of identical grapefruit and another bowl of identical oranges. He weighs the fruit and finds that one orange is 50 g lighter than one grapefruit. He also finds that three grapefruit and two oranges weigh 800 g.

Find the weight of one grapefruit and the weight of one orange.

(5) 17 people fly to Greece for a holiday.

An adult fare is £300.
A child's fare is £160.

Altogether they pay £4260.

How many adults and how many children are travelling in the group?

(6) A rectangular lawn has a semicircular flowerbed at each end.

The distance all the way around the outside of the garden is 16.848 m.
The distance around the outside of the lawn is 13.2 m.

Find the dimensions of the rectangular lawn. Use $\pi \approx 3.14$.

Extension problems

(7) Pierre always takes 4 hours to drive from Paris via Orleans to his home town of Tours.

On Friday he averaged 60 km/h from Paris to Orleans and 80 km/h from Orleans to Tours.
On Monday he averaged 45 km/h from Paris to Orleans and 100 km/h from Orleans to Tours.

Find the length of each stage of his journey.

(8) The perimeter of a rectangle measures 36 cm. When the width of the rectangle is increased by 2 cm and the length is decreased by 3 cm, the area of the rectangle stays the same.

Work out the dimensions of the rectangle.

⊙ Points to remember

- ⊙ You can use the **method of substitution** to solve simultaneous equations algebraically.

- ⊙ Alternatively, you can use the **method of elimination** to solve the equations.

- ⊙ The intersection points of graphs can be used to find simple integer solutions but algebraic methods are needed for non-integer solutions.

4 Linear inequalities in one variable

This lesson will help you to solve linear inequalities in one variable.

Exercise 4

The inequality $x + 3 \leqslant 7$ has an infinite set of solutions: $x \leqslant 4$.
The solution set is shown like this on a number line

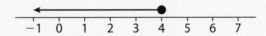

The inequality $x < 4$ does not include the number 4 and is shown like this:

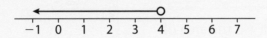

You can solve inequalities in the same way as you solve equations.

- You can add or subtract a positive or negative number to each side of an inequality.

- You can multiply or divide both sides of an inequality by a positive number, but when you multiply or divide an inequality by a negative number the inequality sign reverses.

Example

Find the values of x that satisfy $2x - 7 \leqslant 6x + 5$ and $4x - 11 < 4 + x$.

Solve both inequalities.

	$2x - 7 \leqslant 6x + 5$			$4x - 11 < 4 + x$
add 7	$2x \leqslant 6x + 12$		add 11	$4x < 15 + x$
subtract $6x$	$-4x \leqslant 12$		subtract x	$3x < 15$
divide by -4	$x \geqslant -3$		divide by 3	$x < 5$

The values of x satisfying both inequalities: $-3 \leqslant x < 5$

The integer solutions of these two inequalities are $-3, -2, -1, 0, 1, 2, 3, 4$.

---

① Solve the inequalities and represent the solution set using a number line.

a $x + 8 \leqslant 17$ **b** $x + 2 \leqslant 18 - x$ **c** $3x + 4 > 22$

d $3(2x - 5) \geqslant 2x - 3$ **e** $29 \leqslant 8 - 3x$ **f** $-2x + 9 < -3(x - 4)$

② Find the values of x that satisfy both inequalities.
Represent the solution set using a number line.

a $0 \leqslant 3x + 6$
   $2x + 1 \leqslant 3$

b $x - 3 < 0$
   $x + 5 > 0$

c $2x - 8 \leqslant 5x + 13$
   $4x - 23 \leqslant 10 + x$

d $2x - 8 \geqslant 5x + 13$
   $4x - 23 \geqslant 10 + x$

e $x - 7 \geqslant 4x - 16$
   $2x + 17 > -2x - 7$

f $6x - 4 \geqslant 8(x - 1)$
   $-x + 1 \leqslant 5$

g $6(3 - x) \leqslant 2(5 + x)$
   $3(x + 4) \leqslant 2x + 18$

h $15x - 1 > 5x + \frac{1}{4}$
   $4(x - 4) < 3x - 14$

i $8(x - 2) + 19 \leqslant \dfrac{15x + 8}{2}$
   $2x - 3 \leqslant \dfrac{10x + 1}{4}$

③ a Write the areas of A1 and A2 as expressions in x.

b For what values of x is the area of A1 greater than the area of A2?

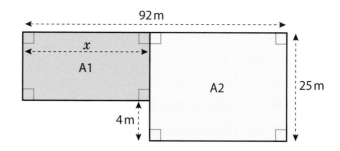

④ Grace pays her water bill each month.
Her bills vary from £30 to £65 per month.

Each bill consists of a £15 monthly charge plus 0.5 pence per litre of water used.

Find the maximum and minimum amount of water that Grace uses in a month.

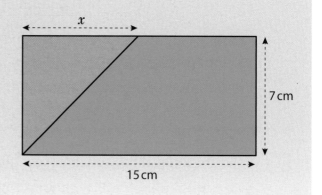

Extension problem

⑤ For what values of x is the area of the green trapezium greater than nine times the area of the mauve triangle?

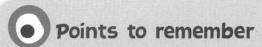

Points to remember

⊙ You can solve a linear inequality in one variable in much the same way as you solve a linear equation in one variable.

⊙ You can add or subtract a positive or negative number to each side of an inequality, so if $a \leqslant b$, then $a + c \leqslant b + c$ and $a - c \leqslant b - c$.

⊙ You can multiply or divide each side of an inequality by a positive number, so if $a \leqslant b$ and $c > 0$, then $ac \leqslant bc$.

⊙ When you multiply or divide each side of an inequality by a negative number the inequality sign reverses, so if $a \leqslant b$ and $c < 0$, then $ac \geqslant bc$.

⊙ You can represent the solution of a linear inequality on a number line.

5 Linear inequalities in two variables

This lesson will help you to solve linear inequalities in two variables.

Exercise 5

All the points satisfying an inequality in two variables can be shown using a graph:

⊖ a **solid** line is used for the graph of inequalities with $\leqslant$ or $\geqslant$;

⊖ a **dotted** line is used for the graph of inequalities with $<$ or $>$.

Example 1

Represent all the points satisfying $x + y \geqslant 5$.

Draw a **solid** line for $x + y = 5$.

Use one coordinate pair (e.g. (1, 1)) to check which side of the line the inequality is true. Shade the side where it is **not true**.

All the points satisfying $x + y \geqslant 5$ are in the **unshaded** region of the graph, including the points on the line.

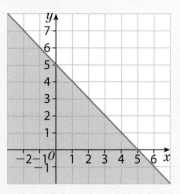

Example 2

Represent all the points satisfying $x + y > 5$.

Draw a **dotted** line for $x + y = 5$ and use one coordinate pair to check which side of the line the inequality is true.

All the points satisfying $x + y > 5$ are in the **unshaded** region of the graph **not** including the points on the line.

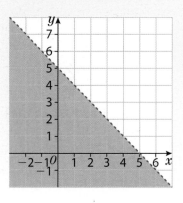

Example 3

Represent all the points satisfying the set of inequalities
$y \geqslant 3x - 2$, $y \geqslant 5 - x$ and $y < 6$.

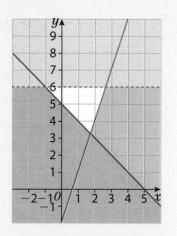

Draw $y = 3x - 2$ and $y = 5 - x$ as solid lines and $y = 6$ as a dotted line. Shade the unwanted regions.

All the points satisfying the set of inequalities
$y \geqslant 3x - 2$, $y \geqslant 5 - x$ and $y < 6$ are in the **unshaded** region.

The five integer solutions are at (0, 5), (1, 4), (1, 5), (2, 4), (2, 5).

You need copies of **A7.1 Resource sheets 5.1 and 5.2**.
You may use a graphics calculator to help you if your teacher wishes.

1. Use **Resource sheet 5.1**. Represent all the points satisfying the inequalities by shading the **unwanted region** on a graph. Use a new set of axes for each inequality.

   a $y \leqslant 2x + 5$ b $y \leqslant 4$ c $y \leqslant -x + 2$

   d $y - 2x < 5$ e $y \geqslant x$ f $2x - y < 4$

2. Write the inequalities representing the unshaded region of the graphs.

   a 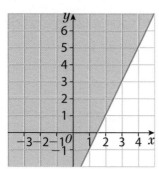   b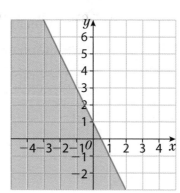

3. Use **Resource sheet 5.2**. Represent all the points satisfying these sets of inequalities by shading the unwanted regions on a graph. Use a new set of axes for each set of inequalities.

   a $y \leqslant 4$ b $y \geqslant 9$ c $y \geqslant x$
      $x \geqslant 3$ $x < 2$ $y < 2x + 1$
                                                       $x + y < 10$

   d $y < 3x - 2$ e $y - x \geqslant 3$ f $y < 7$
      $2y \geqslant x + 2$ $y + 2x < -2$ $2x + y \leqslant 7$
      $2x + y < 8$ $x > -5$ $2x + 5y > 10$

4. Use **Resource sheet 5.2**. Find the integer solutions to these sets of inequalities.

   a $y < 4$ b $x < 3$ c $x > -2$ d $y < 3$
      $x < 4$ $2y - x < 6$ $y - x > 1$ $2y + x \geqslant 5$
      $y + x > 4$ $y + x > 3$ $2y + x \leqslant 4$ $4y - x > 2$

(5) Frederik has £50 birthday money to spend.
He decides to pay for some music downloads from two websites.

Songs from website A cost 70p a download.
Songs from website B cost 50p a download.

Let x be the number of downloads from site A and y the number of downloads from site B.

a Explain why $70x + 50y \leqslant 5000$.

b Explain why $x \geqslant 0$ and $y \geqslant 0$.

c Sketch a graph to show the region that satisfies all three inequalities.

(6) A leisure club employs a maximum of 11 staff each evening to supervise the gym and pool. There must always be at least two staff in the pool and at least three in the gym.

Let x be the number of staff in the pool and y the number of staff in the gym.

a Write three inequalities to represent the information.

b Draw a graph to show the region which satisfies all three inequalities.

Extension problem

 A teacher is booking transport for a school visit for 185 pupils.

A large bus seats 25 pupils and costs £250.
A small bus seats 16 pupils and costs £175.
The total number of buses must not be greater than 10.

Let x be the number of large buses and y the number of small buses.

a Set up four inequalities to represent the information.

b Draw a graph to show the region which satisfies all four inequalities.

c Which solution minimises the cost?

Points to remember

⊙ The region representing an inequality can be shown on a coordinate grid.
⊙ To show the region, first draw the graph, using a solid or dotted line as appropriate.
⊙ Solid lines are used for $\geqslant$ and $\leqslant$ and dotted lines for $<$ and $>$.
⊙ Check points on each side of the line to see which region represents the inequality and then shade the unwanted region.

6 Optimisation problems

Did you know that...?

Using linear inequalities to solve problems is often called **linear programming**.

The ideas originated in the 1940s, motivated by the need to solve complex planning problems in wartime operations. Since then, linear programming has extended to finding solutions to problems in industrial and economic planning.

One of the early pioneers in this field was the Soviet mathematician **Leonid Kantorovich** (1912–1986). In 1975 he won a Nobel Prize for his work on the optimal allocation of scarce resources.

Leonid Kantorovich

This lesson will help you to write sets of inequalities to solve problems.

Exercise 6

Example

The cost of a single delivery of goods from two warehouses A and B to three shops P, Q and R are shown in the table below.

	P	Q	R
Warehouse A	£120	£40	£80
Warehouse B	£30	£100	£80

For delivery charges:

- **Shop P** spends at least £720 a week;
- **Shop Q** spends at least £800 a week;
- **Shop R** spends at most £1200 a week.

The number of deliveries a week from warehouse A is x and from warehouse B is y.

Form three inequalities and simplify them.

$120x + 30y \geqslant 720$ $4x + y \geqslant 24$

$40x + 100y \geqslant 800$ $2x + 5y \geqslant 40$

$80x + 80y \leqslant 1200$ $x + y \leqslant 15$

Draw a graph and represent the solution by shading the unwanted regions.

The minimum cost of deliveries is at (5, 6).

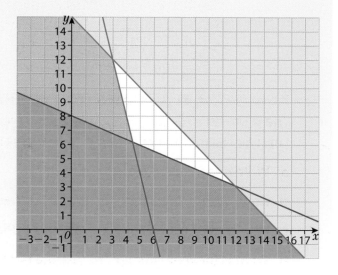

You need some graph paper.

1 The Staywarm wetsuit company makes two types of wetsuit, Type A and Type B.
Both wetsuits need cutting, shaping and stitching by three machines as shown below.

	Machine 1	Machine 2	Machine 3
Type A	30 minutes	60 minutes	48 minutes
Type B	60 minutes	30 minutes	48 minutes

No machine can run for more than 8 hours a day.

Let x be the number of Type A wetsuits and y the number of Type B wetsuits.
The profit made on a Type A suit is £12 and on a Type B suit is £9.

a Use the table to write three inequalities in x and y.

b Draw graphs and shade the unwanted regions.

c Find the maximum profit that can be made in a day.

d How many of each type of wetsuit will be made to give the maximum profit?

2 A farmer has 100 hectares of land to plant potatoes and cabbages.
He has £2900 to spend on preparing and planting the land.

It costs £50 per hectare to plant potatoes and £20 per hectare to plant cabbages.
The profit on a hectare of potatoes is £60 and on a hectare of cabbages is £45.
Let x be the number of hectares of potatoes and y the number of hectares of cabbages.

a Write two inequalities in x and y.

b Draw graphs and shade the unwanted regions.

c How many hectares of each vegetable does the farmer plant to get the most profit?

d What is the maximum profit that the farmer can make after paying for planting?

③ 72 teenagers visit an outdoor centre. They divide into groups to go walking and climbing.

The maximum size of a walking group is 8 and of a climbing group is 3.
One instructor from the centre must accompany each group.
A maximum of 18 instructors are available to accompany the groups.

The equipment costs are £8 for a walking group and £3 for a climbing group.

Let x be the number of walking groups and y the number of climbing groups.

a   Write two inequalities in x and y.

b   Draw graphs and shade the unwanted regions.

c   What is the minimum cost?

d   How many walking and climbing groups can be formed for this minimum cost?

Extension problem

Díd you know that...?

The hardest part of linear programming is understanding the real-life problem and turning it into a mathematical problem. This is called **mathematical modelling**.

Two other mathematicians who made contributions in this field were the American mathematicians **George B. Dantzig** (1914–2005), who also received the Nobel Prize for economics as a result of his work, and **John von Neumann** (1903–1957), who emigrated from Poland to the USA in 1930.

Their methods are now used widely in industry and economics, where the use of computer technology has made them very fast and efficient.

John von Neumann

4 A company buys a fleet of cars consisting of x Ford cars and y Honda cars.

A Ford car costs £20 000 and £160 a week to run.
A Honda car costs £24 000 and £100 a week to run.

The company has £180 000 to spend.
It wants to limit the running costs to not more than £1200 a week.

The company must buy at least four Fords and at least two Hondas to get a good deal.

a Write four inequalities in x and y.

b Draw graphs and shade the unwanted regions.

c Which combinations maximise the number of cars?

d Which combination in part **c** minimises the costs?

 Points to remember

⊙ Many real-life problems can be modelled using inequalities:
  – First decide what the variables are and assign letters to them.
  – Read through the problem and form a set of inequalities.
  – Draw the relevant graphs and shade any unwanted regions.
  – Find all the possible solutions in the unshaded region, then decide
    which of the possible solutions gives the best solution.

How well are you doing?

Can you:

- find the lengths and midpoints of lines on a rectangular grid?
- apply what you know about linear graphs?
- solve simultaneous equations?
- solve inequalities in two variables?

Linear graphs and inequalities (no calculator)

You need graph paper for question 6.

1 Work out the length of the line joining the points $(-10, 3)$ and $(14, 10)$.

2 *GCSE 1387 June 2007*

Work out the coordinates of the midpoint of the line joining the points $(4, 5)$ and $(-6, 3)$.

3 *GCSE 1387 November 2006*

A is the point $(0, 1)$.
B is the point $(10, 6)$.

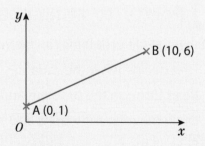

The equation of the straight line through A and B is $y = \frac{1}{2}x + 1$.

  a Write down the equation of another straight line that is parallel to $y = \frac{1}{2}x + 1$.

  b Write down the equation of another straight line that passes through the point $(0, 1)$.

  c Find the equation of the line perpendicular to AB passing through B.

(4) *2006 level 7*

Solve these simultaneous equations using an algebraic method.

$3x + 7y = 18$

$x + 2y = 5$

Show your working.

(5) *GCSE 1387 June 2007*

a m is an integer such that $-1 \leqslant m < 4$.

List all the possible values of m.

b i Solve the inequality $3x \geqslant x + 7$.

ii x is a whole number.

Write down the smallest value of x that satisfies $3x \geqslant x + 7$.

(6) *GCSE 1387 November 2005*

Copy the grid.

On your grid, show by shading, the region that satisfies all three of these inequalities.

$x < 3$

$y < 3x$

$y < x$

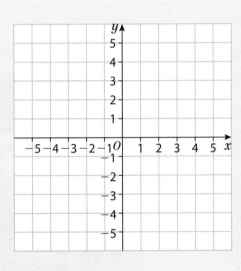

Functional skills 1

Can you post it?

This group activity will help you to:

- identify the mathematics in a situation;
- decide on the information, methods and tools to use;
- find and interpret results and draw conclusions.

Background

The Post Office has a service called **Standard Parcels**.

It states that for sending parcels through the post:

> **'Standard Parcels is ideal for items up to 1.5 m long and 20 kg in weight, provided that the combined length and girth doesn't exceed 3 m.'**

The 'length' is the greatest dimension of the parcel.

The 'girth' is the perimeter of the cross-section with the greatest area in a plane perpendicular to the length.

Work in a small group.

1 Can you send these packages using the Standard Parcels service?

a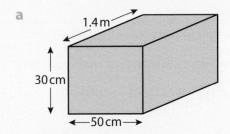

b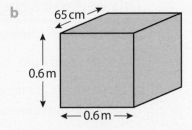

c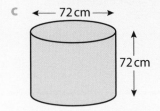

d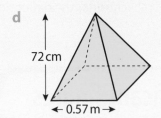

2 Henry is the UK distributor of digital photograph frames.
Each photograph frame is packed in a plastic box measuring 30 cm by 30 cm by 6 cm.
Each box and its contents weighs 0.5 kg.

Design a large container to hold 40 of the plastic boxes so that Henry can send them by Standard Parcels.

Extension problem

Work with a partner. You will need a graphics calculator or a computer with a function graph plotter and spreadsheet software.

3 Find the dimensions of a cuboid with a length of 1.5 m and the maximum possible volume so that it can be sent using Standard Parcels.

Be ready to discuss your solutions and the factors you have considered with other groups.

Decimals and accuracy

This unit will help you to:

○ use significant figures to approximate answers to calculations;

○ use standard form to calculate with very large or very small numbers;

○ work out the greatest and least possible values of calculations involving measurements;

○ consider the dimensions of a formula involving measurements.

1 Significant figures

This lesson will help you to use significant figures to approximate results of calculations.

Exercise 1

The first **non-zero** digit of a decimal number is called the **first significant figure**. The digit after the first significant figure (whether or not it is zero) is the **second significant figure**.

The **red** digit is the first significant figure. The **blue** digit is the second significant figure.

   34**5**6   **4**.**0**4   **1**0**.**456   **0**.**3**001   0.000 **7**2

Zeros at the front of a number are not counted as significant figures.

Zeros within a number are counted as significant figures.

Example 1

Round:

a 5.68 to two significant figures

   5.68 rounds to **5.7 to 2 s.f.**

   The **third** significant figure is **8**.
   As this is 5 or more, increase the 6 by 1.

b 0.3962 to three significant figures

   0.3962 rounds to **0.396 to 3 s.f.**

   The **fourth** significant figure is **2**.
   As this is less than 5, the 6 stays as it is.

c 0.0801 to two significant figures

   0.0801 rounds to **0.080 to 2 s.f.**

   The **third** significant figure is **1**.
   This is less than 5. The zero before 1 stays as it is.
   The zero at the end is the second significant figure.

It is a good idea to do an approximate calculation to check that your calculator answer is sensible. You can do this by rounding each number to 1 significant figure.

Example 2

Use your calculator to work out $\dfrac{2.4^3 + \sqrt{43.56}}{3.7^2 - 2.5^2}$.

Give your answer to 3 significant figures.

Estimate first: $\dfrac{2^3 + \sqrt{36}}{4^2 - 3^2} = \dfrac{8 + 6}{16 - 9} = \dfrac{14}{7} = 2$

Now calculate. Use the bracket, power and root keys.

(2 . 4 x^y 3 + √ 4 3 . 5 6) ÷

(3 . 7 x^2 − 2 . 5 x^2) =

The display shows 2.74516129, or **2.75 to 3 s.f.**

Your calculator may work differently.
Make sure you know how to use the keys.

In general, the number of significant figures in an answer should not be more than the number of significant figures in numbers in the problem. Usually, 2 or 3 significant figures are enough.

When you give answers, always say how many significant figures you have rounded to.

---

1. Round each number to one significant figure.

   a 5234   b 0.381   c 0.043   d 0.001 56   e 5.84

2. Round each number to two significant figures.

   a 58.15   b 0.0672   c 3.84   d 798   e 4957

3. Round each number to three significant figures.

   a 27.839   b 0.6751   c 0.020 96   d 73 574   e 0.9998

4. Copy and complete this table.

Number	Rounded to 1 s.f.	Rounded to 2 s.f.	Rounded to 3 s.f.
0.5897			
42.08			
0.042 99			

5 Estimate then calculate the value of each expression.

   i Work out an approximate value for each expression.

   ii Calculate the answer. Write all the figures on your calculator display.

   iii Write the answer correct to a sensible degree of accuracy.

   a $\dfrac{8.1^2}{5.23 \times 5.88}$ **b** $\dfrac{8.46 \times 5.79}{5.17^3}$ **c** $\dfrac{7.1^2 + \sqrt{864}}{39}$ **d** $\dfrac{\sqrt[3]{130} \times 2.9^2}{108.9 - \sqrt{83}}$

Work on the rest of the exercise **in pairs**.

6 Here is some information about the UK.

Number of households	24 million
Population	60 million
Number of children under 16	12 million
Number of secondary schools	4000

Give an estimate of each of these.
Write down any extra assumptions that you make and the calculations that you do.

a How many times does a person's heart beat in a year?

b If you breathe air at the rate of 0.6 litre for each breath, how much air do you breathe in a year?

c How many chips are eaten each day at lunchtime in UK schools?

d How many exercise books does a typical secondary school use in a year?

e How much water is flushed away from toilets in the UK in a single day?

f What is the total weight of burgers eaten each week in the UK?

g How much household rubbish is collected in the UK in a month?

Be prepared to justify your answers.

Extension problem

Did you know that...?

The **Sitka spruce** is the tallest of the world's spruce trees. It usually grows to a height of about 50–70 m.

The Kielder forest, in Northumberland, is the largest forest of spruce trees in England.

The spruce is felled when it is 50 years old. Its trunk, which has an average volume of 250 m³, can be as much as 5 m in diameter at the base. 10% of the volume of the trunk is bark. The rest can be used to make paper.

1 cubic metre of newly felled wood weighs about 920 kg. 1 kg of wood produces about 0.36 kg of newsprint.

7

a From 1990 to 2000, UK paper and cardboard consumption went up from 9.4 million tonnes to 12.9 million tonnes per year. Estimate the number of spruce trees that need to be felled to produce 12.9 million tonnes of newsprint.

b Estimate the number of spruce trees that need to be felled each day to produce:

  i *The Daily Telegraph*, which typically weighs 240 grams and has an average circulation of 0.9 million;

  ii *The Sun*, which typically weighs 148 grams and has an average circulation of 3.1 million.

Points to remember

- The **first significant figure** is the first non-zero digit.
- A number **rounded to one significant figure** has only one non-zero digit.
- In general, estimates of calculations are made by rounding numbers to one significant figure but sometimes other approximations of the numbers in a calculation are more sensible.
- In **exact calculations**, only the final answer is rounded, not the intermediate steps.
- In **approximate calculations**, the numbers can be rounded at any stage.
- Choose appropriate degrees of accuracy for answers to problems, based on the context. The most significant 2 or 3 digits are usually enough.

2 Standard form

This lesson will help you to use standard form to calculate with very large or very small numbers.

Did you know that...?

Large numbers are found in astronomy and cosmology. For example, the Big Bang theory suggests that the **Universe** is 13.7 billion years old (4.3×10^{17} seconds).

According to Hubble Space Telescope observations, the Universe that we can see is 93 billion light years across (4.65×10^{26} metres).

It contains about 5×10^{22} stars in around 125 billion (1.25×10^{11}) galaxies.

This astrophotograph is of the Fox Fur Nebula, Christmas Tree Cluster and Cone Nebula.

Exercise 2

A number written in **standard form** has the form $A \times 10^n$, where A is a number between 1 and 10 and n is an integer.

Example 1

Write 312 in standard form.

H	T	U	.	t	h
		3	.	1	2
3	1	2			

$312 = 3.12 \times 100 = 3.12 \times 10^2$ in standard form.

3.12 is the number between 1 and 10, so $A = 3.12$ and $n = 2$.

The 3 has moved two places to the left because it has been multiplied by 10^2.

Numbers in standard form can be written as ordinary numbers.

Example 2

Write 2.75×10^{-4} as an ordinary number.

$2.75 \div 10^4 = 0.000\ 275$

The digits move four places to the right, from the units place to the ten thousandths place.

You can write an approximate value of a number in the standard form $A \times 10^n$, where $A \leqslant 1 < 10$, by rounding A to 1 significant figure.

For example, 3.75×10^7 is approximately 4×10^7 correct to 1 significant figure.

Example 3

Estimate the value of $(8.97 \times 10^{11}) \div (1.987 \times 10^7)$.

Write each decimal correct to 1 significant figure, so $\dfrac{9 \times 10^{11}}{2 \times 10^7} = 4.5 \times 10^4$

1. Simplify these.

   a $(2^2)^4$ **b** $(5^2)^2$ **c** $(10^{-2})^3$ **d** $(-1^0)^{10}$

2. Simplify these.

   a $\dfrac{8^4}{8^7 \times 8^{-2}}$ **b** $\dfrac{9^{-2} \times 9^4}{9}$ **c** $\dfrac{4^{-5} \times 4^5}{4^{-2}}$ **d** $\dfrac{2^{-4} \times 2^2}{2^7 \times 2^{-11}}$

3. Write each number in standard form.

   a 36 000 000   **b** 0.000 47   **c** 339 000   **d** 24 300

   e 0.0007   **f** 37 819   **g** 0.0056   **h** 0.000 000 27

4. Write each standard form number as an ordinary number.

   a 2×10^9 **b** 3.142×10^{-4} **c** 2.7×10^6 **d** 5.06×10^{-1}

5. Write each number in standard form.

   a 267×10^3 **b** 54.2×10^{-5} **c** 0.55×10^{-3} **d** 12×10^{-4}

6. Write as a number in standard form.

   a $(2 \times 10^3)^4$ **b** $(5 \times 10^{-4})^2$ **c** $(2 \times 10^{-2})^5$ **d** $(4 \times 10^3)^3$

7. Evaluate these expressions.
   Give your answers in standard form correct to 3 significant figures.

   a $(1.6 \times 10^5) \times (6.7 \times 10^6)$ **b** $(3.21 \times 10^{15}) \times (4.6 \times 10^{-11})$

   c $(4.56 \times 10^{-6}) \div (2.3 \times 10^5)$ **d** $(1.35 \times 10^{-12}) \div (2.7 \times 10^{-5})$

   e $(3.51 \times 10^{-7}) \times (4.4 \times 10^7)$ **f** $(4.56 \times 10^9) \div (2.3 \times 10^{-8})$

8. Light travels at 3×10^8 metres per second.
   How long does it take to travel 6 centimetres?
   Give your answer in seconds in standard form.

9. The base of a microchip is in the shape of a rectangle.
   Its length is 1.75×10^{-3} mm and its width is 1.2×10^{-3} mm.
   Find the area of the base in square millimetres.
   Give your answer in standard form.

10. A memory stick can store 1 750 000 bytes of data.
    A hard disk can store 2.5×10^9 bytes of data.
    How many memory sticks are needed to store the 2.5×10^9 bytes of data?

11. The surface area of a sphere of radius r is given by the formula $S = 4\pi r^2$.
    The radius of the Earth is approximately 6.4×10^6 metres.
    What is the approximate area of the Earth's surface?
    Give your answer in standard form correct to 3 significant figures.

Extension problems

12. The distance of the Earth from the Sun is 1.5×10^8 km.
    The distance of the planet Uranus from the Sun is 2670 million km.
    Write in the form $1 : n$ the ratio:

    distance of the Earth from the Sun : distance of Uranus from the Sun

13. The M81 Galaxy in Ursa Major is 112 574 000 000 000 000 000 km from Earth.

    Light travels 9.46×10^{12} km in one year.
    How many light years does it take to travel from the M81 Galaxy to Earth?
    Give your answer in standard form correct to 2 significant figures.

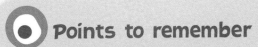

Points to remember

⊙ To multiply powers of a, add the indices, so $a^m \times a^n = a^{m+n}$.

⊙ To divide powers of a, subtract the indices, so $a^m \div a^n = a^{m-n}$.

⊙ To raise the power of a to a power, multiply the indices, so $(a^m)^n = a^{m \times n}$.

⊙ A number in **standard form** is of the form $A \times 10^n$, where $1 \leqslant A < 10$ and n is an integer.

⊙ The key for entering numbers in standard form is usually [EXP] or [∧]. Use the negative key [−] or the sign change key [+/−] for negative powers.

3 Accuracy of measurements

This lesson will help you to work out the greatest and least possible values of measurements.

 ### Did you know that...?

Le Grand K, a cylinder of 90% platinum and 10% iridium, made in London in 1889, is the **standard definition of the kilogram**. It is kept in a locked vault near Paris.

It is 39 mm in diameter and 39 mm tall but is changing. This could be caused by general handling, or by solvents used to clean it or pollutants that got into it at the time it was made.

The change, first noticed 30 years ago, is 50 parts in a billion, less than the mass of a grain of sugar.

A Conference on Weights and Measures in Paris in 2007 agreed to investigate whether the kilogram can be redefined.

The standard kilogram

Exercise 3

21.75   21.8   21.85

The diameter of a pan is measured with a ruler as 21.8 cm to the nearest millimetre. Its exact width can be any value between 21.75 cm and 21.85 cm.

21.8 cm is midway between 21.75 cm and 21.85 cm. 21.75 is the smallest value that rounds to 21.8. 21.75 cm is called the **lower bound**.

The length cannot be exactly 21.85 cm, since this would round to 21.9 cm, but this value is used as the **upper bound**.

Too many figures in answers to calculations can give a false impression of their accuracy.

For example, a pan with diameter 21.8 cm has a circumference of $\pi \times 21.8$ cm.
Using $\pi = 3.14$ leads to a circumference of 68.452 cm.

This has too many figures. You cannot measure a length with a ruler to one thousandth of a centimetre! In general, answers should have a similar number of significant figures to the numbers in a problem. A more sensible answer is 68.5 cm, correct to 3 significant figures, as lengths can be measured to the nearest millimetre.

① Write the maximum and minimum possible values for each of these.

   a There are 40 pasta pieces in a jar to the nearest 10.

   b There are 1100 grains of rice in a bag to the nearest 100.

   c There is 70 g of sugar in a packet to the nearest 10 grams.

   d The speed of a train is 90 mph to the nearest 10 mph.

   e A jug holds 1 litre of water to the nearest millilitre.

   f John is 1.60 metres tall to the nearest centimetre.

   g The mass of a large cake is 500 g to the nearest 10 g.

   h The mass of a small cake is 50 g to the nearest gram.

   i The length of a piece of elastic is 20 cm to 1 significant figure.

   j The length of a piece of elastic is 20 cm to 2 significant figures.

   k The length of a piece of elastic is 20.0 cm to 3 significant figures.

② For each rounded number, write the lower and upper bounds.

   a 8.5 (to 1 decimal place)   **b** 3.07 (to 2 decimal places)

   c 5900 (to 3 significant figures)   **d** 0.0246 (to 3 significant figures)

   e 67 (to the nearest whole number)   **f** 3 000 000 (to the nearest 10 000)

③ The length of a pencil is 14 cm correct to the nearest cm.
The length of a pencil case is 142 mm correct to the nearest mm.

Explain why the pencil may not fit in the case.

④ The width of an alcove is 82 cm correct to the nearest cm.
A shelf is 822 mm wide correct to the nearest mm.

Explain why the shelf might fit across the alcove.

5 Hilltown Rovers had crowds of 2400, 2000, 2600, 2300 and 2200 for their last five matches. Each figure is correct to the nearest 100.

   a What was the least possible total for the five matches?

   b What was the greatest possible total for the five matches?

6 Holly takes five tests for an exam. Each test is marked out of 100. The score for each test is correct to the nearest 5 marks.

Holly gets 45, 55, 65, 40 and 55 marks in the five tests.

To pass the exam Holly must have a total of at least 250 marks. Can Holly be certain that she will pass the exam?

7 There are 300 pasta pieces in a jar, to the nearest 10. They weigh 300 grams to the nearest 10 grams.

   a Between what bounds does the number of pasta pieces lie?

   b Between what bounds does the mass of the pasta pieces lie?

   c Why are the answers to parts **a** and **b** different?

Extension problems

8 A football pitch measures 95 metres by 52 metres. Each measurement is correct to the nearest metre.

What are the upper and lower bounds for:

   a the length of the pitch;

   b the width of the pitch;

   c the perimeter of the pitch;

   d the area of the pitch?

9 Mary wants to fit four kitchen units into a space 6.73 m long. Each unit is 1.68 m wide. Will the four units fit in the space? Explain your answer.

◉ Points to remember

⊙ Measurements may be inaccurate by **up to half a unit** in either direction, e.g. '4 kg to the nearest kilogram' has a least possible mass of 3.5 kg and a greatest possible mass of 4.5 kg.

⊙ The **upper and lower bounds** are the upper and lower limits of accuracy.

4 Upper and lower bounds

This lesson will help you to work out the greatest and least possible values of combined measurements.

The ancient Greeks could write numbers up to one hundred hundred (10 000), which they called a **myriad**. A myriad myriad, one hundred million (10^8), was their largest number.

Archimedes, 287–212 BC, proved that $10^a 10^b = 10^{a+b}$. He then invented ways of writing larger powers of ten.

In his book *The Sandreckoner*, which he wrote for King Gelo II, Archimedes worked out an upper bound for the number of grains of sand that would fit into the Universe. He showed that this was 10^{63}.

Exercise 4

You can find the upper and lower limits of **combined measurements**.

This table shows how to find the **maximum and minimum values** when two numbers a and b are added, subtracted, multiplied or divided.

Operation	Maximum	Minimum
$a + b$	$a_{max} + b_{max}$	$a_{min} + b_{min}$
$a - b$	$a_{max} - b_{min}$	$a_{min} - b_{max}$
$a \times b$	$a_{max} \times b_{max}$	$a_{min} \times b_{min}$
$a \div b$	$a_{max} \div b_{min}$	$a_{min} \div b_{max}$

Example

A skating rink measures 74 m by 57 m. Each measurement is to the nearest metre. Find the maximum and minimum values of its area.

To find the minimum area of length × width, take the smallest values of the length and the width.

Minimum area = 73.5 × 56.5 = **4152.75 m²**

To find the maximum area of length × width, take the largest values of the length and width.

Maximum area = 74.5 × 57.5 = **4283.75 m²**

Where appropriate, give your answers to a sensible degree of accuracy.

1 The radius of a plate is 9.7 cm to the nearest millimetre.
What is:

  a the least possible length of the diameter;

  b the greatest possible length of the diameter;

  c the greatest possible length of the circumference;

  d the least possible area of the plate?

2 The sides of a cuboid box are 6 cm, 8 cm and 10 cm to the nearest centimetre.
Find the minimum and maximum values of the volume of the box.

3 A car took 30.0 seconds to travel 4500 metres. The time was measured correct to 3 significant figures and the distance to 2 significant figures.

Work out the upper and lower bounds for the average speed of the car.

4 Patty cycles at a steady speed of 8 metres per second.
The speed is correct to the nearest metre per second.

Work out the upper and lower bounds for the time it takes Patty to cycle 500 metres.

5 The mass of a sculpture is 6460 kg correct to 3 significant figures.
Its volume is 2.8 m^3 correct to 2 significant figures.

Work out the upper and lower bounds of the density of the sculpture.

6 The population of a country is 42.6 million correct to 3 significant figures.
9.5 million of the population, to 2 significant figures, are less than 16 years old.

Calculate the difference between the upper and lower bounds of the percentage of the population who are less than 16 years old.

7 $n = 3.25$ correct to 2 decimal places. Work out the upper and lower bounds of:

  a $3n$ **b** $\dfrac{1}{n}$ **c** n^2 **d** $\sqrt{n}$

8 $p = 5.36$ to 2 decimal places and $q = 2.8$ to 1 decimal place.
Work out the upper and lower bounds of:

    a $p + q$ **b** $p - q$ **c** pq **d** $p \div q$

9 $e = 3.6$ to 1 decimal place and $f = 5.60$ to 2 decimal places.
Work out the upper and lower bounds of:

    a e^2 **b** $3e + 2f$ **c** $2e - f$ **d** $\dfrac{e + f}{e}$

10 $p = 5.2$, $q = 1.9$ and $r = 2.0$, all correct to 1 decimal place.
Work out the upper and lower bounds of:

    a $p + q + r$ **b** $p - qr$ **c** $4q - p$ **d** $p \div q$

Extension problem

11 The time, T seconds, it takes a pendulum to swing once is given by:

$$T = 6.283 \times \sqrt{\frac{l}{g}}$$

where l is the pendulum's length in metres and g m/s^2 is the acceleration due to gravity.

The pendulum of a clock has a length of 1.25 m correct to 3 significant figures.

Assume that g = 9.8 m/s^2 correct to 2 significant figures. Find the difference between the upper and lower bounds of T. Give your answer to a suitable degree of accuracy.

⊙ Points to remember

⊙ For two numbers a and b with bounds $a_{min} \leqslant a < a_{max}$ and $b_{min} \leqslant b < b_{max}$:

Operation	Maximum	Minimum
$a + b$	$a_{max} + b_{max}$	$a_{min} + b_{min}$
$a - b$	$a_{max} - b_{min}$	$a_{min} - b_{max}$
$a \times b$	$a_{max} \times b_{max}$	$a_{min} \times b_{min}$
$a \div b$	$a_{max} \div b_{min}$	$a_{min} \div b_{max}$

5 Dimensions

This lesson will help you to consider the dimensions of a formula involving measurements.

 Did you know that...?

A **dimension** describes a property of an object.

A *length* (or width or height) is one-dimensional.

An area, or 2D space, has two dimensions, *length* × *length*.

A volume, or 3D space, has three dimensions, *length* × *length* × *length*.

Dimensions can also be other physical parameters such as the *mass* or *electric charge* of an object.

Time can be added as a fourth dimension to a 3D space. Spacetime as used in relativity theory is four-dimensional.

Exercise 5

Perimeter and circumference are both lengths.

The perimeter of a rectangle is given by the expression $2l + 2w$.
Each term in the expressions $2l + 2w$ is *a number* × *a length*.

The circumference of a circle is given by πd.
The term πd is *a number* × *a length*.

Both the expressions have the **dimension *length***.
Numbers, such as 2 and π, have no dimensions.

The area of a rectangle is given by the expression lw.

The area of a circle is given by πr^2.

Both expressions are of the form *a number* × *a length* × *a length*.

Both expressions have the **dimensions *length* × *length***.

The volume of a cuboid is given by the expression lwh.

The volume of a cylinder is given by $\pi r^2 h$.

Each term consists of *a number* × *a length* × *a length* × *a length*.

Both expressions have the **dimensions *length* × *length* × *length***.

Example

If a, b and c represent lengths:

a What do $a + b$, $2a + 3b$ and $\pi(b + c)$ represent?

They represent **lengths** since each expression has dimension *length*.

b What do $ab + bc$, $a(b + c)$ and πab represent?

They represent **areas** since each expression has dimension *length* $\times$ *length*.

c What do $3b^2c$, $4a(ab + c^2)$ and $\pi a^2(b + c)$ represent?

They represent **volumes** since each expression has dimension *length* $\times$ *length* $\times$ *length*.

---

①

Length	Area
$1\,cm = 10\,mm$	$1\,cm^2 = 10 \times 10 = 100\,mm^2$
$1\,m = 100\,cm$	$1\,m^2 = 100 \times 100 = 10\,000\,cm^2$
$1\,km = 1000\,m$	$1\,km^2 = 1000 \times 1000 = 1\,000\,000\,m^2$

a How many mm^2 are there in $1\,m^2$? Give your answer in standard form.

b How many mm^2 are there in $1\,km^2$? Give your answer in standard form.

② Change to m^2:

    a $8\,km^2$ **b** $0.4\,km^2$ **c** $50\,000\,cm^2$ **d** $650\,cm^2$

③ **a** Find in cm^2 the area of a rectangle that measures $26\,cm$ by $1.8\,m$.

    b Find in cm^2 the area of a rectangle that measures $54\,mm$ by $9\,m$.

④ A hectare is $10\,000\,m^2$.

An acre is 4840 square yards.

There are 36 inches in a yard and an inch is exactly $2.54\,cm$.

Express 5 acres in hectares.

In questions 5 to 9, the letters a, b and c represent lengths.
Numbers such as 5, $\frac{1}{4}$ and π are numbers that have no dimensions.

⑤ Here are six expressions.

$$5bc \qquad\qquad a^2b \qquad\qquad \pi b^2 c$$

$$3b + 4c \qquad\qquad 2a(b + c) \qquad\qquad \frac{c^3}{a + b}$$

a Write down the expressions which could represent a length.

b Write down the expressions which could represent an area.

6 Here are six expressions.

A $3b + 2c$ **B** $\frac{1}{2}ab$ **C** $\pi(b + c)$

D $4abc$ **E** $10a^2$ **F** bc^2

  a Two of the expressions represent lengths. Which two are they?

  b Two of the expressions represent areas. Which two are they?

  c Two of the expressions represent volumes. Which two are they?

7 One of these five expressions could represent an area.

$a + bc$ $b(4 + c)$ $\pi b^3 + 2c^2$ $ac + \pi b^2$ $\dfrac{2b + c^2}{a}$

Which expression is it?

8 Each expression below represents either a length, an area or a volume.
For each expression, write whether it is a **length**, an **area** or a **volume**, or **none of these**.

  a $2a + c$ **b** $3ab$ **c** $4a(b + c)$ **d** a^2b

  e $6ba$ **f** $c^3 + ba$ **g** $\pi a + 2b$ **h** $\pi a^2(b + c)$

  i $\dfrac{(a + c)^2}{4b}$ **j** $\dfrac{abc}{(a + c)}$

9 One of these five expressions could not represent a volume.

$3a^2b$ $\dfrac{2b^4}{a + c}$ $\pi c^2(a + b)$ $(a + 2b)^2$ $\frac{1}{3}b^2c$

Which expression is it?

◉ Points to remember

- ◉ Numbers like 4 or π have no **dimensions**.
- ◉ The circumference of a circle with diameter d is πd.
  The expression πd is a number $\times$ a length.
  It has the dimension *length*.
- ◉ The area of a rectangle of length l and width w is lw.
  The expression lw has the dimension *length* $\times$ *length*.
- ◉ The volume of a cuboid of length l, width w and height h is lwh.
  The expression lwh has the dimension *length* $\times$ *length* $\times$ *length*.

How well are you doing?

Decimals and accuracy (no calculator)

1 *2007 level 8*

    a One light-year is approximately 9 430 000 000 000 kilometres.
Write this distance in standard form.

    b A star called Wolf 359 is approximately 7.8 light years from Earth.
About how many kilometres is this?
Write your answer in standard form.

2 *2003 level 8*

    The table shows information about some countries.

Country	Population	Area (km^2)
Canada	3.1×10^7	1.0×10^7
France	6.0×10^7	5.5×10^5
Gambia	1.4×10^6	1.1×10^4
India	1.0×10^9	3.3×10^6
United Kingdom	6.0×10^7	2.4×10^5
United States	2.8×10^8	9.3×10^6

    a Which country has the largest population?

    b Which country has the smallest area?

    c On average, how many more people per km^2 are there in the United Kingdom than in the United States?

    Show your working.

GCSE 1387 June 2005

Work out an estimate for the value of $\dfrac{637}{3.2 \times 9.8}$

(4) *2008 level 8*

Each expression below represents either a length, an area or a volume.

a, b and c all represent lengths.

For each expression, write whether it is a length, area or volume.

a $2a + c$ b $3ab$ c $4a(b + c)$ d a^2b

Decimals and accuracy (calculator allowed)

(5) *GCSE 1387 June 2007*

Kelly runs a distance of 100 metres in a time of 10.52 seconds.

The distance of 100 metres was measured to the nearest metre.
The time of 10.52 seconds was measured to the nearest hundredth of a second.

a Write down the upper bound for the distance of 100 metres.

b Write down the lower bound for the time of 10.52 seconds.

c Calculate the upper bound for Kelly's average speed.
Write down all the figures on your calculator display.

d Calculate the lower bound for Kelly's average speed.
Write down all the figures on your calculator display.

The two sides of a canal are straight, parallel and the same height.
Janet and Seb want to find the width of the canal.

They measure 100 m on the canal bank and stand facing each other at the points J and S.

Janet measures the angle she turns through to look at the post, P, as 25°.
Seb measures the angle he turns through to look at the post as 15°.

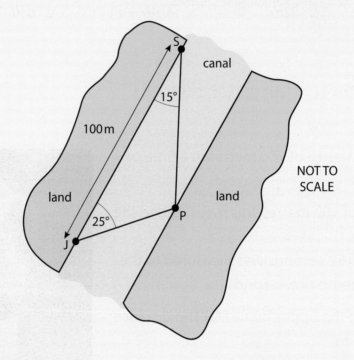

a Calculate the width of the canal.
   Show your working.

b Janet and Seb discuss the accuracy of their measurements.
   They decide their angles are correct to ±2°, and their distance is correct to ±1 m.

   Calculate the maximum width that the canal could be.
   Show your working.

Enquiry 1

This unit will help you to:

- choose and use different sampling methods;
- manage non-response and missing data;
- draw and interpret histograms;
- calculate a moving average for time series data.

1 Sampling

This lesson will help you use different methods to sample a population.

Did you know that...?

Finding out the opinions of the general public is big business. Companies carry out opinion polls and surveys on lots of topics, for example:

- voting intentions;
- confidence in the economy;
- attitudes to social issues.

These surveys can be carried out in person, over the telephone, by post or using the Internet.

Exercise 1

Primary data is data that you have collected yourself from a survey or experiment. **Secondary data** is data that someone else has collected. You may have found this data on a website, in a book or a CD ROM.

Qualitative data is non-numerical, e.g. 'red', 'blue', 'green', or 'car', 'train', 'bus'. **Quantitative data** is numerical, e.g. numbers or measurements, and can be discrete or continuous. **Discrete data** can only take certain values, whereas **continuous data** is measured and can take any value within an interval.

It is difficult to ask every person in a whole population their opinion. It is easier to ask a small number of people. This is called a **sample**. A sample that represents a population fairly and is not biased towards any particular group in the population is called a **representative sample**.

To choose a **representative stratified sample** of the population being investigated:

○ identify the different groups in the population;

○ work out the proportion of each group in the population;

○ identify a method of selecting members of each group at random to take part in the survey.

In a **random sample** each member of the population has an equal chance of being chosen. For example, if 50 out of 500 people (i.e. 10%) are needed for a sample,

○ each person could be allocated a number from 1 to 500, and then 50 random numbers from 1 to 500 chosen by using a random number generator;

○ the names of the people could be placed in a box and a name selected then replaced in the box, which continues until 50 different names are chosen;

○ the names could be listed in alphabetic order, and then every 10th name on the list chosen from a random starting point. This is called **systematic or selective sampling**.

Example 1

Here are the numbers of pupils in a junior school.

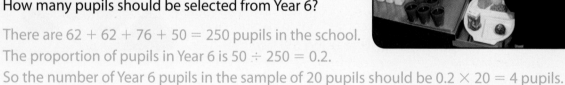

Year group	3	4	5	6
Number of pupils	62	62	76	50

a 20 pupils are to be selected using a stratified sampling method to take part in a survey of lunch preferences. How many pupils should be selected from Year 6?

There are 62 + 62 + 76 + 50 = 250 pupils in the school.
The proportion of pupils in Year 6 is 50 ÷ 250 = 0.2.
So the number of Year 6 pupils in the sample of 20 pupils should be 0.2 × 20 = 4 pupils.

b What else would you need to consider for the sample to be representative?

The sample size is 20 ÷ 250 = 8%.
To be properly representative, the numbers of boys and girls should be considered. For example, the numbers of boys and girls in the sample could be worked out from 8% of the boys and girls in each year group, rounded to the nearest whole number.

Example 2

A manufacturer of nails is sampling its nails to check they are the correct size. How should they take a 5% selective sample?

A 5% sample means that they need to select 1 in every 20 nails to check. The manufacturer should choose a number between 1 and 20 to decide which nail to start with, then select every 20th nail from then on.

1. A leisure centre manager wants to know what local people think about the centre's facilities.

    a Why will he need a sample of people?

    b How should he choose who to ask? What factors should he consider?

    c What type of sampling method should he use?

2. A delivery service wants to find out the opinions of the households in a street of 200 houses. They want a sample of 10%.

    a Explain how they could do this with a systematic sample.

    They then want to find out the opinions of a 10% sample of the 2000 households in the town.

    b Should they do this with a systematic or random sample? Explain your answer.

3. Here are some possible sources of data about the population.
    How suitable is each source if you want to get the views of people in the UK as a whole?

    a telephone directory   b electoral roll

    c email addresses   d catalogue mailing list

    e magazine subscription list

4. A headteacher wants to find out pupils' opinions on the amount of homework they get. This table shows the number of pupils in each year group.

Year	7	8	9	10	11
Number of pupils	105	125	160	110	100

    a Why is it important that the headteacher uses a stratified sample for the survey?

    b The headteacher wants to survey 60 pupils altogether.
      How many should be selected from each year group?

5. The table shows the gender of 120 people on four holiday tours.
    A sample of 30 people stratified by tour and gender is to be surveyed on their satisfaction.

	Tour A	Tour B	Tour C	Tour D	Total
Male	13	17	14	13	57
Female	18	10	15	20	63
Total	31	27	29	33	120

    a Work out the number of Tour D females in the sample.

    b Work out the number of Tour A males in the sample.

    c Work out the number of Tour C females in the sample.

6 Work on this question with a partner.

Here are the foot lengths in centimetres for 100 secondary pupils. This is a random sample generated from the Census at School data (www.censusatschool.org).

24	21	25.5	20	19	20	18.5	20	23	22
18	20	24	18	28	21	23	23	20	23
21	28	24	23.5	23	26	22.5	23	22	25.5
21	27.5	22.5	27	20	24	20.5		21	21
21	21	20	24	23	25	25	30	26	23
21.5		22.5	23	21	23	22	25		20
28	20	25	25	20	24	21	23	21	26
26	22	19	23	23	24	18	31	24	25
19.5	18	26.5	20	23	24	23	18	24	20
24	20	21	24	28	26	22	23	24	22.5

a Check the data – are there any errors or omissions?

b Use the random number generator function on your calculator.
Pick samples of sizes 2, 5, 10 and 15.
Work out the mean of each of your samples and record your results in a table.
If you have time, repeat the experiment for different samples of the same size.

c Compare your results with someone else.
What variation do you find in the mean for the different sample sizes?

d The actual mean for the data in the table is 22.8 cm.
Which sample size do you think is most appropriate to use as an approximation to the whole population?

⊙ Points to remember

⊙ **Sampling** is a way of finding out about the population as a whole without asking each person.

⊙ You need to decide which sampling method to use:
- in a **random sample**, each member of the population has an equal chance of being chosen;
- in a **systematic or selective sample**, every nth member is chosen from a random starting point;
- in a **stratified sample**, the population is divided into groups, then each group is randomly or selectively sampled.

2 Planning and collecting data

This lesson will help you to plan and collect suitable data for a statistical enquiry.

 Did you know that...?

The coding of crime data is particularly challenging as 35% cannot be matched easily to a specific address (e.g. robbery records where the only information known is that it occurred on the High Street).

80% of the time spent on analysing crime data is used on cleaning it so that it can be reliably used. Typical corrections needed to the address information are:
- correcting spelling mistakes;
- correcting address abbreviations;
- changing addresses only known locally to a format that can be recognised;
- reformatting records where the address information has been entered in the wrong place.

Source: www.crimereduction.homeoffice.gov.uk/

Exercise 2

Work in a small group of two or three.

 Statistical enquiry

In this activity, you will collect data to use later in this unit.

The data you find needs to be continuous, for example, times, distances or weights. It also needs to be suitable for sorting into groups, for example, the times of all the finishers in a marathon race, rather than just the winning times.

Some possible places to look for data are:

- World Sport Stacking Association – full records for the preliminary rounds of the World Championships are available at **www.worldsportstackingassociation.org/results.htm**

- athletics meetings – full results are available at **www.thepowerof10.info**

Pick some data that interests you and decide what you would like to find out. For example, you could use times for a marathon and for a half marathon and see if you think it takes people twice as long to run a marathon. Alternatively, you could look and see how much better the elite finishers are than the club runners in a race.

Make sure you have all the data you need. Check it to ensure that there are no obvious wrong or missing items of data. If there are, you will need to decide what to do about them.

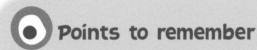
- Data needs to be selected carefully to be fit for purpose.
- Check for omissions, errors and unreasonable answers.

3 Drawing histograms

This lesson will help you to learn how to draw histograms.

Exercise 3

A **grouped frequency table** contains data that has been sorted into different groups.

Each group is called a **class**.

The set of values that data in a class can take is called the **class interval** and the range of the interval is called the **class width**. For example, for the interval $50 \leqslant t < 60$, where t represents times from 50 to 60 minutes, the class width is 10 minutes.

A **histogram** represents continuous data and is equivalent to a frequency diagram for discrete data. In a histogram, there are no gaps between the bars. There is a scale on the horizontal axis.

When the class widths for a data set are equal, the heights of the bars on the histogram represent the frequency.

Example

The table shows the finish times of the competitors in the Great Langdale Christmas Pudding 10 km race in 2007.

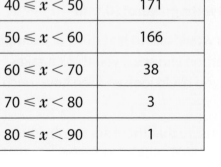

Time (min)	Frequency
$30 \leqslant x < 40$	74
$40 \leqslant x < 50$	171
$50 \leqslant x < 60$	166
$60 \leqslant x < 70$	38
$70 \leqslant x < 80$	3
$80 \leqslant x < 90$	1

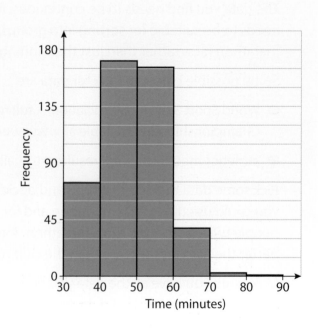

Draw a histogram to show this data.

You will need a ruler, a pencil and graph paper. You will also need your class work and, if you did the homework task, your homework from the last lesson.

1 Statistical enquiry

Use the **data you collected in the previous lesson for your statistical enquiry**.

a Draw grouped frequency tables for your data.

You will need to decide how many groups to have and what width to make the equal class intervals. Aim for between five and ten groups.

b Now draw a histogram to represent the data in each of your tables.
Make sure you that label the axes carefully.

2 Reaction times enquiry

Use the **data on the reaction times of 10 people that you collected for homework**.
Share your data with other pupils so that you each have at least 60 items of data.

a Draw a grouped frequency table for the data.

b Now draw a histogram to represent the data in your table.

3 The two tables below and the two at the top of the next page show the results for four different 5 km races, all in August 2007 (data source: www.thepowerof10.info).

Promenade 5 km Portsmouth	
Time (minutes)	Frequency
$14 \leqslant x < 15$	2
$15 \leqslant x < 16$	4
$16 \leqslant x < 17$	14
$17 \leqslant x < 18$	11
$18 \leqslant x < 19$	6
$19 \leqslant x < 20$	8
$20 \leqslant x < 21$	4
$21 \leqslant x < 22$	0
$22 \leqslant x < 23$	0
$23 \leqslant x < 24$	3
$24 \leqslant x < 25$	0
$25 \leqslant x < 26$	1
$26 \leqslant x < 27$	0
$27 \leqslant x < 28$	0
$28 \leqslant x < 29$	1

SWVAC 5 km Yeovilton	
Time (minutes)	Frequency
$14 \leqslant x < 15$	0
$15 \leqslant x < 16$	0
$16 \leqslant x < 17$	1
$17 \leqslant x < 18$	4
$18 \leqslant x < 19$	5
$19 \leqslant x < 20$	8
$20 \leqslant x < 21$	5
$21 \leqslant x < 22$	4
$22 \leqslant x < 23$	1

Millennium Bridge 5 km York	
Time (minutes)	Frequency
$14 \leqslant x < 15$	3
$15 \leqslant x < 16$	5
$16 \leqslant x < 17$	8
$17 \leqslant x < 18$	5
$18 \leqslant x < 19$	7
$19 \leqslant x < 20$	5
$20 \leqslant x < 21$	4
$21 \leqslant x < 22$	2
$22 \leqslant x < 23$	0

Vic Musgrove Fast 5 km Telford	
Time (minutes)	Frequency
$14 \leqslant x < 15$	0
$15 \leqslant x < 16$	6
$16 \leqslant x < 17$	11
$17 \leqslant x < 18$	4
$18 \leqslant x < 19$	7
$19 \leqslant x < 20$	6
$20 \leqslant x < 21$	1
$21 \leqslant x < 22$	2
$22 \leqslant x < 23$	2

a Draw a histogram to show the data for each of the four races.
Use the same scale on each set of axes.

b Compare the histograms.
What can you say about the results?
Be careful – the total number of runners varies between races.

 4 These two tables show the results for two different age groups in the preliminary rounds of the World Sport Stacking Association World Championships.

Individual Cycle age 10	
Time (s)	Frequency
$6 \leqslant x < 10$	22
$10 \leqslant x < 14$	59
$14 \leqslant x < 18$	70
$18 \leqslant x < 22$	23
$22 \leqslant x < 26$	8
$26 \leqslant x < 30$	5
$30 \leqslant x < 34$	1

Individual Cycle age 13–14	
Time (s)	Frequency
$6 \leqslant x < 10$	26
$10 \leqslant x < 14$	20
$14 \leqslant x < 18$	9
$18 \leqslant x < 22$	0
$22 \leqslant x < 26$	3
$26 \leqslant x < 30$	0
$30 \leqslant x < 34$	0

a Draw a histogram to show the data for each age group.
Use the same scale on each set of axes.

b Compare the histograms.
What can you say about the results?
Be careful – the total number of competitors is different for each age group.

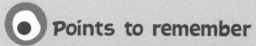
4 Choosing class intervals

This lesson will help you to choose appropriate class intervals for a histogram.

Exercise 4

A histogram can look very different depending on the class width you choose.

If the bars are wide, some of the important features of the distribution may be hidden. If the bars are narrow, the histogram may be too confusing to see any clear patterns and trends.

Example

This is the data for the Great Langdale Christmas Pudding 10 km race in 2007, grouped with two different class widths. Comment on the effect of changing the size of the class width.

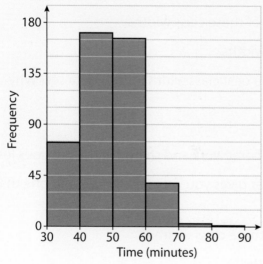
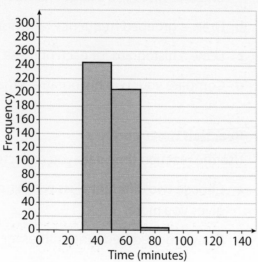

Choosing only three groups hides the detail of the histogram.
We can see in the more detailed histogram that there was a smaller group of fast runners – they don't show up in the other diagram.

You will need a copy of **S7.1 Resource sheet 4.1**, a ruler, pencil and graph paper. You will also need the data you collected earlier in the unit.

① **Group activity**

Use the data on **Resource sheet 4.1** for the results of a 5 km ladies race in Poole in 2007. The times are in minutes and seconds and are ordered.

Each of you should group the data. One of you should use class intervals of width 2, another width 3, another width 4, and another width 5.

a Draw a grouped frequency table for your data set.

b Draw a histogram for your data set.

c Compare your four histograms. What do you notice?

d Which histogram do you think is most useful for looking at the distribution of the finishing times of the runners? Explain why.

e Describe the advantages and disadvantages of grouping the data with your chosen class width.

② **Statistical enquiry**

Pick one of the sets of data you collected for your statistical enquiry.

a Choose two different class widths, one that gives you a small number of groups and one that gives you a larger number of groups.

b Draw a grouped frequency table for each of these class widths.

c Draw a histogram for each of these class widths.

d Compare your two histograms. What is the best class width for this data set? Why?

③ **Reaction times enquiry**

Use the reaction time data you collected for homework and shared in the previous lesson.

a Choose two different class widths, one that gives you very few groups and one that gives you more.

b Draw grouped frequency tables for both these class widths.

c Draw histograms for both these class widths.

d Compare your two histograms. What is the best class width for this data set? Explain why.

4 Use the data on **Resource sheet 4.1** for the Under 12s individual 3-3-3 competition from the World Sport Stacking Championships in 2007.
The times are in seconds and hundredths of seconds.

  a Draw a grouped frequency table for the data using the class intervals:
    $2.00 \leqslant x < 2.50$, $2.50 \leqslant x < 3.00$, $3.00 \leqslant x < 3.50$, $3.50 \leqslant x < 4.00$, $4.00 \leqslant x < 4.50$,
    $4.50 \leqslant x < 5.00$, $5.00 \leqslant x < 5.50$, $5.50 \leqslant x < 6.00$, $6.00 \leqslant x < 6.50$, $6.50 \leqslant x < 7.00$

  b Draw a histogram to represent this data using the class intervals in part **a**.

  c Draw another grouped frequency table, this time with the class intervals:
    $2.00 \leqslant x < 4.00$, $4.00 \leqslant x < 6.00$, $6.00 \leqslant x < 8.00$

  d Draw a histogram to represent this data using the class intervals in part **c**.

  e Which is the better choice of class interval? Why?

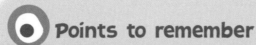

◉ Points to remember

- ◉ Choose the **number of class intervals** for a histogram carefully:
  - – too few means that any patterns and trends in the data will be hidden;
  - – too many means that the graph will be confusing and hard to interpret.

5 Using histograms

This lesson will help you to draw and interpret histograms with unequal class intervals.

 Did you know that...?

The term *histogram* was invented by the English mathematician and statistician **Karl Pearson** (1857–1936), who is known as one of the founders of statistics.

Karl Pearson was a lecturer at University College, London.

In 1895 he wrote that the word *histogram* was 'introduced by the writer in his lectures on statistics as a term for a common form of graphical representation, i.e. by columns marking as areas the frequency corresponding to the range of their base'.

When the class intervals are **unequal**, the **histogram** is drawn so that the area of each rectangle or bar is proportional to the frequency, not the height of the rectangle.

In the table below, the first and last groups are wider than the others. This means that for the area to be proportional to the frequency, the heights of their bars are less to compensate.

The height of each rectangle is called the **frequency density** of the class and the vertical axis is labelled 'frequency density'.

So frequency = area of rectangle

          = height of rectangle $\times$ class width

          = frequency density $\times$ class width

Rearranging this formula, frequency density $= \dfrac{\text{frequency}}{\text{class width}}$.

This data represents the times of 36 runners in a 5 km race.

Time (min)	Frequency	Class width	Frequency density $= \dfrac{\text{frequency}}{\text{class width}}$
$14 \leqslant t < 16$	4	2	$4 \div 2 = 2$
$16 \leqslant t < 17$	11	1	$11 \div 1 = 11$
$17 \leqslant t < 18$	4	1	$4 \div 1 = 4$
$18 \leqslant t < 19$	7	1	$7 \div 1 = 7$
$19 \leqslant t < 20$	6	1	$6 \div 1 = 6$
$20 \leqslant t < 23$	3	3	$3 \div 3 = 1$

To draw a histogram to represent the data:

☉ work out the width of each class interval (the class width);

☉ divide the frequency by the class width to find the frequency density, which gives the height of each bar;

☉ label the vertical axis 'Frequency density'.

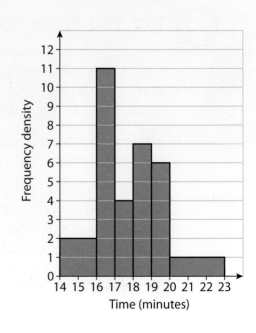

You will need some graph paper, a pencil and ruler.

1 The table shows the times that 70 competitors took in a Stacking cups competition.

Time (t, seconds)	Frequency	Class width	Frequency density = $\frac{\text{frequency}}{\text{class width}}$
$2 \leqslant t < 4$	4	2	$4 \div 2 = 2$
$4 \leqslant t < 6$	22		
$6 \leqslant t < 8$	16		
$8 \leqslant t < 12$	16		
$12 \leqslant t < 22$	12		

a Copy and complete the table.   **b** Draw a histogram to represent the data.

2 The table shows the times that 199 runners took to finish a sponsored run.

Time (t, minutes)	Frequency	Class width	Frequency density = $\frac{\text{frequency}}{\text{class width}}$
$6 \leqslant t < 8$	9	2	4.5
$8 \leqslant t < 10$	14		
$10 \leqslant t < 14$	60		
$14 \leqslant t < 18$	72		
$18 \leqslant t < 26$	36		
$26 \leqslant t < 34$	8		

a Copy and complete the table.   **b** Draw a histogram to represent the data.

3 The table shows the times, in seconds, that customers waited at a supermarket till.

Time (t, seconds)	Frequency	Class width	Frequency density = $\frac{\text{frequency}}{\text{class width}}$
$0 \leqslant t < 20$	16		
$20 \leqslant t < 40$	44		
$40 \leqslant t < 50$	55		
$50 \leqslant t < 60$	62		
$60 \leqslant t < 90$	18		

a Copy and complete the table.   **b** Draw a histogram to represent the data.

④ The histogram shows information about the weights of some pears.

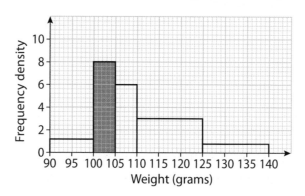

a How many pears does the shaded bar represent?

b Work out how many of the pears weigh less than 100 grams.

⑤ The histogram shows the ages of the members of a country club.

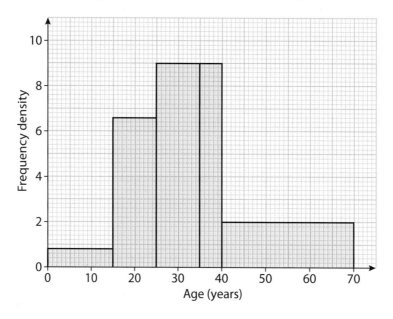

Draw a frequency table to represent the data.

6 Moving averages

This lesson will help you to calculate the trend in data over a period of time.

Exercise 6

A **time series graph** shows a set of readings taken over a period of time. The values are plotted against time on the x-axis. Sometimes time series graphs have repeated high and low points at regular intervals. To see whether the values are increasing, decreasing or staying the same, a **moving average** is calculated and plotted on the graph.

Example

The **table** and **time series graph** show the cups of hot soup sold by a cafe over 3 years.

Season	Year 1	Year 2	Year 3
Winter (W)	5900	5500	5100
Spring (Sp)	2400	2000	1600
Summer (Su)	1600	1200	1200
Autumn (A)	5700	5300	4900

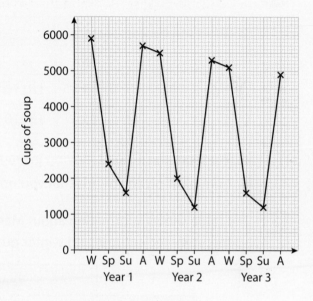

Has the number of cups of soup sold increased or decreased over the three years?

To find out, calculate the moving average.

The mean of the first four values (W, Sp, Su, A of Year 1) $= \frac{5900 + 2400 + 1600 + 5700}{4} = 3900$ cups.

The mean of the next four values (Sp, Su, A of Year 1 and W of Year 2) = 3800 cups.

The mean of the next four values (Su, A of Year 1 and W, Sp of Year 2) = 3700 cups, etc.

Since four consecutive values are used each time, these are **4-point moving averages**.

Plot the moving averages as points on the graph, and join the points.

Each moving average is plotted at the midpoint of the time period it covers. So the 1st moving average of 3900 cups is plotted halfway between Spring and Summer of Year 1.

It is clear that the number of cups of soup sold has decreased slowly over the three-year period.

This is called the **trend** of the graph.

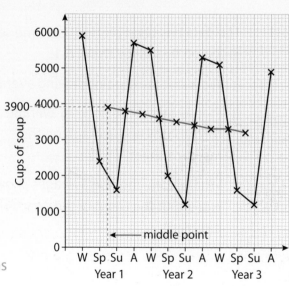

You will need a calculator, a pencil, a ruler and a copy of **S7.1 Resource sheet 6.1**.

1. The table shows the number of stamps that Jenny used each month throughout a year.

Month	Jan	Feb	Mar	Apr	May	Jun	Jul	Aug	Sep	Oct	Nov	Dec
Number of stamps	23	31	15	11	19	16	20	13	16	17	29	34

   a Work out the 6-point moving averages for this data.

   b Comment on any trends that you notice.

2. The table shows the quarterly profit in £ of Biggs Pet Shop over a two-year period.

	Quarter			
Year	1	2	3	4
1	£8170	£7900	£8260	£8420
2	£8210	£7960	£8320	£8560

   a Work out the 4-point moving averages for this data.

   b Comment on any trends that you notice.

3. The table shows information about Mark's quarterly electricity bill in £ for each of the spring, summer, autumn and winter quarters over a two-year period.

	Year 1				Year 2			
Quarter	1	2	3	4	1	2	3	4
Electricty bill	£200	£162	£80	£130	£216	£166	£96	£142

The data has been plotted as a time series graph on **Resource sheet 6.1**.

   a Work out the 4-point moving averages.

   b Plot all five of the moving averages on the copy of the graph on the resource sheet.

   c What do the moving averages show you about the trend of the quarterly gas bills?

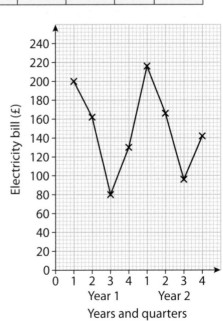

4 The table shows the percentage of men with full beards over a period of 30 years from 1882 to 1911 (data source: www-personal.buseco.monash.edu.au/~hyndman/TSDL/).

1882	44	1892	40	1902	52
1883	58	1893	53	1903	43
1884	34	1894	62	1904	67
1885	88	1895	68	1905	53
1886	43	1896	12	1906	91
1887	46	1897	48	1907	50
1888	42	1898	34	1908	73
1889	49	1899	28	1909	26
1890	93	1900	40	1910	95
1891	41	1901	59	1911	66

a Plot a time series graph to show this data.

b Calculate the 10-point moving averages.

c Plot these on the graph and draw in the trend line.

d Comment on the graph and the trend line.

 Points to remember

⊙ A **time series graph** shows a set of data collected over a period of time.

⊙ To look for trends in the data, plot the **moving averages**.

⊙ The set of **5-point moving averages** is the mean of the 1st to 5th values, followed by the mean of the 2nd to 6th values, followed by the mean of the 3rd to 7th values, and so on.

How well are you doing?

Can you:

- choose and use different sampling methods?
- draw and interpret histograms?
- calculate the moving average for time series data?

Enquiry 1 (calculator allowed)

You need some graph paper.

1 *GCSE 1387 June 2007*

The table shows the number of boys and the number of girls in each year group at Springfield Secondary School. There are 500 boys and 500 girls in the school.

Year group	Number of boys	Number of girls
7	100	100
8	150	50
9	100	100
10	50	150
11	100	100
Total	500	500

Azez took a stratified sample of 50 girls, by year group.
Work out the number of Year 8 girls in his sample.

2 The table shows the number of pupils in each year group of a large school.

A stratified sample of 100 pupils is to be surveyed about their views on the school meals service.

a Work out the number of pupils from each year group that should be sampled.

b How should the pupils from each year group be chosen?

Year group	Number of pupils
7	350
8	330
9	280
10	290
11	250

(3) All the pupils in a class ran in a 100 m race.
Their times are recorded in the table.

a Draw a histogram for the data.

b Comment on what the histogram shows.

Time (seconds)	Frequency
$10 \leqslant x < 12$	4
$12 \leqslant x < 14$	6
$14 \leqslant x < 16$	10
$16 \leqslant x < 18$	8
$18 \leqslant x < 20$	2

(4) The grouped frequency table shows the heights of a group of people of different ages.

Height (cm)	Frequency	Frequency density
$130 \leqslant x < 135$	5	1
$135 \leqslant x < 140$	8	1.6
$140 \leqslant x < 145$	12	2.4
$145 \leqslant x < 150$	15	3
$150 \leqslant x < 160$	14	1.4
$160 \leqslant x < 170$	7	0.7
$170 \leqslant x < 190$	3	0.15

a Draw a histogram for the data with frequency density as the vertical axis.

b Comment on what the histogram shows.

(5) *GCSE 1387 November 2007*

Month	Jan	Feb	Mar	Apr	May	Jun
Number of televisions	1240	1270	1330	1300	1330	x

The table shows the number of televisions sold in a shop in the first five months of 2006.

a Work out the first 3-month moving average for the information in the table.

b The fourth 3-month moving average of the number of televisions sold in 2006 is 1350.
The number of televisions sold in the shop in June was x.
Work out the value of x.

Functional skills 2

Where is the mathematics?

This group activity will help you to:

- identify the mathematics in a situation;
- identify mathematical questions to ask;
- choose appropriate language and forms of presentation to communicate conclusions.

Background

Maths is all around us.

Looking for the maths in a situation or in information will help you to appreciate how widely maths is used.

Problem 1

What mathematical questions could you ask about this picture?

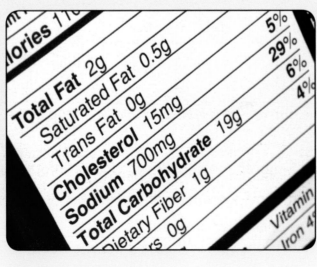

What answers to your questions would you give?

What mathematical questions could you ask about this picture?

What answers to your questions would you give?

What mathematical questions could you ask about this picture?

What answers to your questions would you give?

Be prepared to discuss your questions and answers with other groups.

Measures and mensuration

This unit will help you to:

- ◉ use formulae for the length of a circular arc and the area and perimeter of a sector of a circle;

- ◉ calculate and solve problems involving the surface area of cylinders and volumes of cones, pyramids and spheres;

- ◉ solve problems involving more complex 2D and 3D shapes, including segments of circles and frustums of cones.

1 Arcs and sectors of circles

This lesson will help you to use formulae for the length of an arc and the area of a sector of a circle.

Exercise 1

An **arc** is part of the circumference of a circle.

A **sector** is formed by an arc and two radii.

The **perimeter of a sector** is the sum of its arc length and two radii.

For a sector with an angle of 90° at the centre, (a quadrant), the arc length is $\frac{1}{4}$ of the circumference of the whole circle.

The area of the sector is $\frac{1}{4}$ of the area of the whole circle.

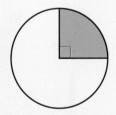

For a sector with an angle of 70° at the centre, the arc length is $\frac{76}{360}$ of the circumference of the whole circle.

The sector area is $\frac{70}{360}$ of the area of the whole circle.

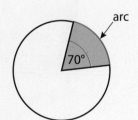

In general, for a sector with an angle of x degrees at the centre of a circle of radius r:

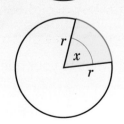

$$\boxed{\text{arc length} = \frac{x}{360} \times 2\pi r} \text{ and } \boxed{\text{sector area} = \frac{x}{360} \times \pi r^2}$$

Take $\pi = 3.142$ or use the π key on your calculator.

Where appropriate, give your answers to three significant figures.

1 Calculate **i** the length of the arc and **ii** the area of these sectors.

a 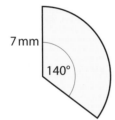 9 cm 50°

b 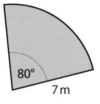 30° 4 cm

c 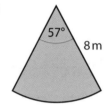 10 cm 68°

2 Calculate **i** the total perimeter and **ii** the area of these sectors.

a 7 mm 140°

b 80° 7 m

c 57° 8 m

3 A flowerbed is in the shape of a sector of a circle.

   a Calculate the total perimeter of the flowerbed.

   b Calculate the area of the flowerbed.

 135° 5.4 m

4 A circle is drawn inside a semicircle.

Prove that the shaded area of the semicircle is equal to the area of the small circle.

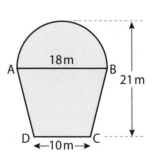

5 The diagram shows a shape made from trapezium ABCD and a semicircle with diameter AB.

AB = 18 m

CD = 10 m

The total height of the shape is 21 m.

Calculate the area of the whole shape.

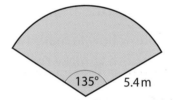 A 18 m B / 21 m / D ←10 m→ C

(6) Jenny is making bells for tree decorations. They are shaped like hollow cones.

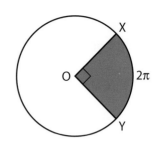

She takes a circle made from card, centre O. She cuts out the shaded sector, so that angle XOY is 90° and the length of the arc XY is 2π.

What is the area of the shaded sector that Jenny cuts out?

(7) A pendulum 40 cm long swings through an arc of 10°.

  a How far does the tip of the pendulum travel in one swing?

  b Find the shortest distance between the two furthest points reached by the tip.

(8) The outline of this fish is made up of six arcs of quadrants with radius 3 cm.

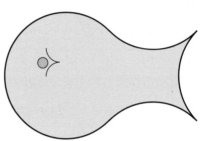

  a What is the length of the perimeter of the fish in terms of π?

  b What is the area of the fish?

  c Show how to make two straight cuts across the fish to make three pieces that can be rearranged to form a square.

Extension problems

(9) What percentage of the quadrant OAB is the circle?

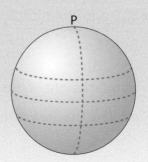

(10) P is a point on a sphere of radius 6 cm.

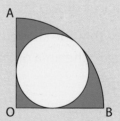

A pair of compasses is opened to a radius of 4 cm. A circle with centre P is drawn on the sphere. What is the radius of this circle?

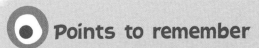

Points to remember

- **Circumference of circle** = $\pi \times$ diameter = $2 \times \pi \times$ radius
- **Length of arc** = (angle $\div$ 360) $\times$ circumference of the circle
- **Area of circle** = $\pi \times$ radius $\times$ radius = πr^2
- **Area of sector** = (angle $\div$ 360) $\times$ area of circle

2 Circle problems

This lesson will help you to solve problems involving areas of parts of circles, including segments.

Exercise 2

A **segment** of a circle is formed by a chord and an arc.

In the diagram, AB is a **chord** of a circle, centre O.

Segment area = area of sector OAB − area of triangle OAB

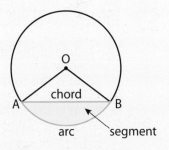

Take π = 3.142 or use the π key on your calculator.
Where appropriate, give your answers to three significant figures.

1. Find the area of each shaded segment.

   a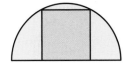

   b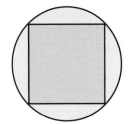

2. A square of area 20 cm² is drawn in a semicircle so that its vertices touch the perimeter.

   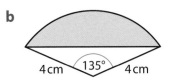

   Find the area of the square that could be drawn in a circle of the same radius.

3 The diagram shows three semicircles, each of radius 1.

What is the size of the total shaded area?

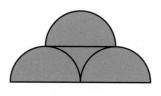

4 A sash window with a semicircular top is 1 m wide.

The upper 'half' of the window is lowered by 25 cm.

What is the area of the crescent-shaped opening?

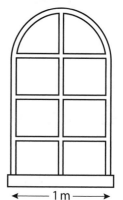

1 m

5 Six equal small circles are drawn in contact with a large circle as shown.

The radius of the large circle is 12 cm.

a What is the radius of the small circle?

b What is the ratio of the area of one of the small circles to the large circle?

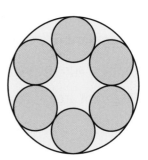

6 Six circles touch each other as shown.

The radius of the middle-sized circle is 4 cm.

a What is the radius of the large circle?

b What is the radius of the small circle?

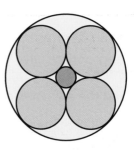

Extension problems

7 Which fills up a higher proportion of space:

a square peg in a round hole or a round peg in a square hole?

 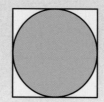

8 Two circles, each of radius 1 unit, are drawn so that the centre of each circle lies on the circumference of the other.

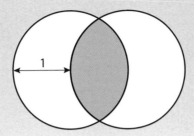

What is the area of the overlap?

3 Volume of 3D shapes

This lesson will help you to solve problems involving volumes of 3D shapes.

 Did you know that...?

Archimedes (287–212 BC) proved a famous result in his book *On the sphere and the cylinder*.

The volume of a sphere is four times the volume of a cone with a base equal to the greatest circle round the sphere and a height equal to the radius of the sphere.

Archimedes was the greatest mathematician of his time. His contributions to geometry revolutionised the subject. He was a very practical man who invented machines such as pulleys and a screw pumping device.

But he neglected himself. He often forgot to eat, drink or wash and had to be carried by force to the public baths.

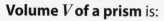
A **prism** is a 3D shape with polygonal faces. It always has the same cross-section. The diagram shows a hexagonal prism.

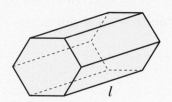

Volume V of a prism is:

V = area of cross-section × length, or
V = area of base × height

A **cuboid** is a prism with a rectangular cross-section.

Volume V of a cuboid, length l, width w and height h, is:

$V = lwh$

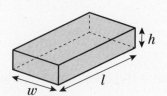

A **cylinder** is a 3D shape which can be regarded as a special case of a prism, with a circle as its cross-section.

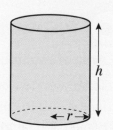

Volume V of a cylinder, radius r and length h, is:

$V = \pi r^2 h$

A **pyramid** is a 3D shape with a polygonal base. All the other faces are triangles with a common vertex, called the **apex**. The diagram shows a square-based pyramid.

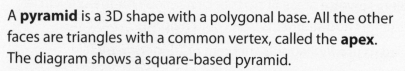

Volume V of a pyramid is:

$V = \frac{1}{3} \times$ area of base × perpendicular height

A **cone** is a 3D shape which can be regarded as a special case of a pyramid, with a circle as its base.

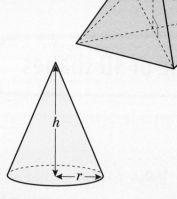

Volume V of a cone, radius r and height h, is:

$V = \frac{1}{3}\pi r^2 h$

A **frustum** is the solid remaining when a cone is cut by a plane parallel to its base and the top cone is removed.

A **sphere** is a 3D shape whose surface consists of all the points that are a given distance from a fixed point, the centre.

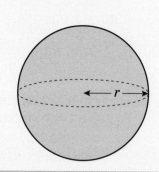

Volume V of a sphere of radius r is:

$V = \frac{4}{3}\pi r^3$

Take $\pi = 3.142$ or use the π key on your calculator.
Where appropriate, give your answers to three significant figures.

1 Calculate the volume of each cylinder. Give your answers correct to three significant figures.

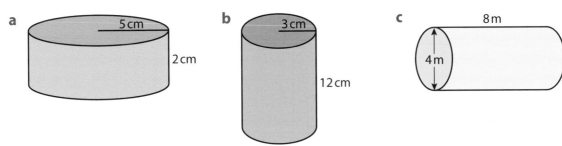

a 5 cm   2 cm

b 3 cm   12 cm

c 8 m   4 m

2 The diameter of a circular well is 90 cm.
To the nearest litre, how many litres of water are in the well if the water is 10 metres deep?

3 A cone, a hemisphere and a cylinder have a circular base of the same size and the same perpendicular height.
Show that the ratio of their volumes is $1 : 2 : 3$.

4 The height of a cone equals the radius of its base.

Two such cones are fitted inside a sphere so that the circumference of the bases just touches the sphere.

What fraction of the volume of the sphere is filled by the cones?

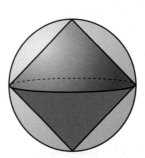

5 A sphere is placed inside a cube so that it just touches each of the six faces of the cube.

Does the sphere take up more or less than half the volume of the cube?

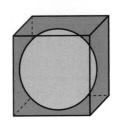

6 A cone and a cylinder have the same height.
The radii of their bases are in the ratio $3 : 2$.
Show that their volumes are in the ratio $3 : 4$.

7 A storage box measuring 48 cm by 36 cm by 18 cm is half full of oats.
How many times can a cylindrical measure 4 cm deep and 22 cm in circumference be filled with oats from the box?

8 The top of a child's plastic toy is a cone of height 10 cm.
The bottom of the toy is a hemisphere of radius 4 cm.

Calculate the volume of plastic needed to make the toy.

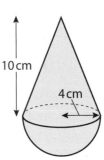

10 cm   4 cm

9 Two cylindrical water tanks, one with a base twice the diameter of the other, are joined at the bottom by a thin pipe with a tap.

The smaller tank is filled with water to a depth of 1 metre.

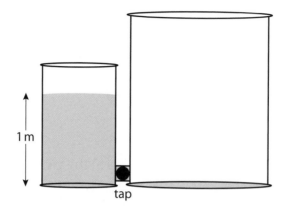

1 m

tap

What will be the common depth of water when the tap is opened?

10 A cone is filled with liquid to a depth of half its vertical height.
The cone is turned upside down.
How high up the vertical height of the cone will the liquid rise?

Extension problem

11 Two lead spheres, with radii 6 cm and 9 cm, are placed in the bottom of a cylinder with diameter 27 cm.

Water is poured into the cylinder so that it just covers both spheres.

What is the volume of water needed?

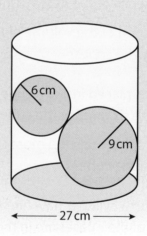

6 cm

9 cm

27 cm

● Points to remember

⊙ **Volume of a prism**
area of cross-section × length, or area of base × height

⊙ **Volume of a cylinder**, radius r, height h
area of cross-section × length, or area of base × height, or $V = \pi r^2 h$

⊙ **Volume of pyramid** is $\frac{1}{3}$ × area of base × height

⊙ **Volume of cone**, base radius r, height h
$\frac{1}{3}$ × area of base × height, or $V = \frac{1}{3}\pi r^2 h$

⊙ **Volume of a sphere**, radius r, is $V = \frac{4}{3}\pi r^3$

4 Surface area of 3D shapes

This lesson will help you to solve problems involving the surface area of cylinders, cones, pyramids and spheres.

 Did you know that...?

Archimedes also proved that:

'Every cylinder whose base is the greatest circle of the sphere, and whose height is equal to the diameter of the sphere, is $\frac{3}{2}$ of the sphere.
Its total surface area is $\frac{3}{2}$ the surface of the sphere.'

This means that if a cone and a sphere are fitted into the smallest cylinder that will enclose them:

- the volumes of the cone, sphere and cylinder are in the ratio $1:2:3$;

- the surface areas of the sphere and cylinder are in the ratio $2:3$.

Exercise 4

The net of the curved surface of a cylinder is a rectangle.

The length of this rectangle is equal to the circumference ($2\pi r$) of each circular end of the cylinder.

The two circular ends complete the net.

The total surface area is the sum of the area of the curved surface and the areas of the two circular ends.

Surface area A of cylinder, radius r and height h, is:

$$A = 2\pi rh + 2\pi r^2$$

Surface area A of a sphere of radius r is:

$$A = 4\pi r^2$$

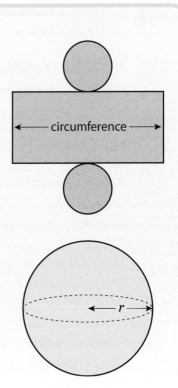

The net of a hollow cone is a sector of a circle. The radius l of the sector is the slant height of the cone and the arc length a is the circumference of the base of the cone.

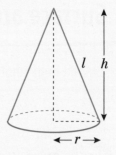

So $\dfrac{x}{360} \times 2\pi l = 2\pi r$, or $\dfrac{x}{360} \times l = r$

The area of the sector is $\dfrac{x}{360} \times \pi l^2 = \pi \times \left(\dfrac{x}{360} \times l\right) \times l = \pi r l$.

So the **area of the curved face of the cone**, radius r and slant height l, is the sector area $\pi r l$.

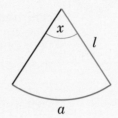

For a solid cone, the circular base of the cone is added to the net and the total surface area is the sum of the cone's curved surface area and the area of its base.

The total surface area A of the cone, radius r and slant height l, is:

$$A = \pi r^2 + \pi r l$$

Take $\pi = 3.142$ or use the π key on your calculator.
Where appropriate, give your answers to three significant figures.

1. Calculate the surface area of a sphere of radius 6.9 cm.

2. The surface area of a sphere is 60 cm². Calculate its radius.

3. The radius of the base of a cone is 5.3 cm and its slant height is 8.1 cm.
   Calculate its curved surface area.

4. The radius of the base of a cone is 3.7 cm and its slant height is 9.4 cm.
   Calculate its total surface area.

5. The height of a cylinder is equal to the radius of its base.
   Show that the curved surface of the cylinder is half of the whole surface.

6. A right-angled triangle has a hypotenuse of 17 cm, and a shortest side of 8 cm.
   The triangle is rotated about its third side to generate a cone.
   Find the surface area and volume of the cone.

7. The total surface area of a cylinder is 17 600 cm².
   The height of the cylinder is three times the diameter of the base.
   Work out the volume of the cylinder.

8. A canvas tent in the shape of a pyramid has a square floor of area 4 m².
   The perpendicular height of the tent is 3 m.
   Calculate the area of the canvas in the tent.

9 An aluminium can contains 330 ml of fizzy drink.

  a The can's diameter is 6 cm.
        What is the can's height?

  b Another can's height is 10 cm.
        What is its diameter?

  c Which of the two cans uses the least
        amount of aluminium?

  d Investigate the size of a can to hold 330 ml that
        uses the least amount of aluminium.

Extension problems

10 The length of a main diagonal through the centre
      of a large closed match box is 6 cm.

      The total surface area of the matchbox is 64 cm².

      What is the sum of all the edges of the match box?

11 To make a cylinder, you can cut three parts from a piece of card in several ways, e.g.

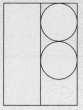
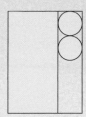
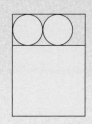

      Use a single sheet of A4 paper. Assume it measures 21 cm by 29.6 cm.
      Investigate how to make a cylinder with the greatest possible volume.
      What are the dimensions of the cylinder?

◉ Points to remember

- ⊙ The surface area of many 3D shapes can be worked out from their nets.
- ⊙ **Total surface area of cylinder**, radius r, height h, is $A = 2\pi rh + 2\pi r^2$.
- ⊙ **Curved surface area of cone**, base radius r, slant height l, is πrl.
- ⊙ **Total surface area of cone**, base radius r, slant height l, is $A = \pi r^2 + \pi rl$.
- ⊙ **Surface area of a sphere**, radius r, is $A = 4\pi r^2$.

5 Problem solving

This and the next lesson will help you to solve harder problems involving measures and mensuration.

Did you know that...?

The oldest mathematical text discovered is an Egyptian papyrus from around 2000 BC, now in the Pushkin Museum of Fine Arts in Moscow.

The **Moscow Papyrus** consists of 25 'word problems', apparently intended as entertainment, written on a scroll about 5 m long and from 4 cm to 8 cm in width.

One of the problems gives a method for finding the volume of a frustum.

'Given a truncated pyramid of 6 for the vertical height by 4 on the base by 2 on the top, ... square the 4, result 16; ... double the 4, result 8; ... square the 2, result 4. You are to add the 16, the 8, and the 4, result 28; ... take one third of 6, result 2; ... take 28 twice, result 56. See, it is 56. You will find it right.'

Pushkin Museum, Moscow

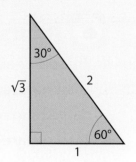

Exercise 5

Useful formulae

For any triangle PQR,

area of triangle = $\frac{1}{2}pq \sin R$

$$\sin 30° = \frac{1}{2}, \cos 30° = \frac{\sqrt{3}}{2}, \tan 30° = \frac{1}{\sqrt{3}}$$

$$\sin 60° = \frac{\sqrt{3}}{2}, \cos 60° = \frac{1}{2}, \tan 60° = \sqrt{3}$$

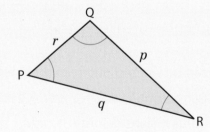

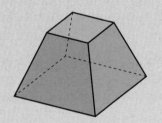

1 Two cylinders are made by bending a piece of A4 paper in two different ways, across its width or across its length.

Which cylinder has the greater volume?

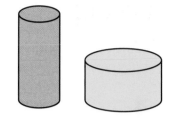

2 *2002 Exceptional performance*

This question is about calculating the area of a 50p coin.

 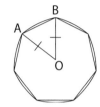

a The centre, O, of the 50p coin is the same distance, 1.39 cm, from all seven vertices. Show that the area of triangle AOB is approximately 0.76 cm².

b The edges of the 50p coin are not straight. Each edge is an arc of a circle.

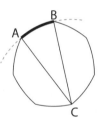

The centre of the circle is the opposite vertex of the 50p coin.

Show that length AC is approximately 2.71 cm.

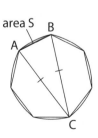

c Using values from parts **a** and **b**, find the area of sector ABC, and the area of triangle ABC.

Then show that the shaded area S is approximately 0.055 cm².

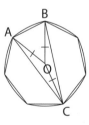

d Calculate the area of a 50p coin. Show your working.

When an air bubble rises through water its volume increases.

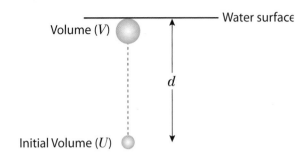

The formula that connects the volume (V) of an air bubble at the water surface, its initial volume (U) and the distance d it has risen is:

$$V = \left(\frac{d + 10.3}{10.3}\right)U$$

where V and U are in cm³ and d is in metres.

a At 50 metres below the water surface a bubble has a volume of 9.57×10^{-4} cm³.

What is the volume of the bubble at the water surface?

Give your answer in standard form.
Show your working.

b The volume of a bubble at the water surface is 4 times its initial volume.
By how many metres has the bubble risen?

c At the water surface a bubble has a volume of 2.46×10^{-2} cm³.

What was the initial volume of this bubble when it was 20 m below the water surface?

Give your answer in standard form.
Show your working.

d A spherical bubble, 35 metres below the water surface, had a radius of 6.92×10^{-2} cm.

Use the formula Volume $= \frac{4}{3}\pi r^3$ to calculate the volume of this bubble.

Give your answer in standard form.
Show your working.

e What is the radius of this bubble at the water surface?
Show your working.

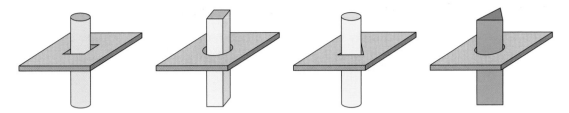

a A round peg, of radius r, just fits into a square hole.

What proportion of the hole is filled by the peg?

You may substitute an integer for r if you wish, and may give your answer as a decimal, a fraction or a percentage.

You must show your working.

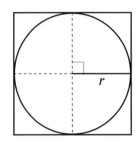

b A square peg just fits into a round hole, of radius r.

What proportion of the hole is filled by the peg?
Does the square peg fill a greater proportion of its hole than the round peg fills in part **a**?

You must show your working.

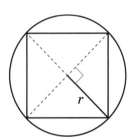

c A round peg, of radius r, just fits into an equilateral triangular hole.

What proportion of the hole is filled by the peg?

You must show your working.

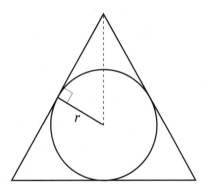

d An equilateral triangular peg just fits into a round hole, of radius r.

What proportion of the hole is filled by the peg?

Does the triangular peg fill a greater proportion of its hole than the round peg fills in part **c**?

You must show your working.

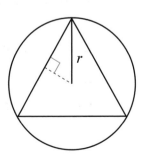

A log is a cylinder of diameter d.

From this log, a timber company wants to cut a beam of wood with square cross-sectional area. The cross-sectional area must be as large as possible.

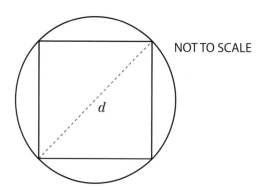

NOT TO SCALE

a Show that the side of the square is $\dfrac{d}{\sqrt{2}}$.

b If only the beam is used from the log, what proportion of the log will be wasted?

c The diameter of the log is 80 cm.

The company wants to cut planks of wood with a rectangular cross-section from the rest of the log.

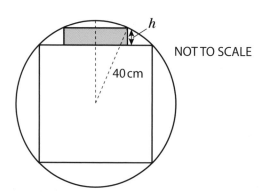

NOT TO SCALE

The cross-sectional area of each plank should be as large as possible, and the company needs to decide whether the height of the plank, h, should be 4 cm or 8 cm.

Calculate the cross-sectional area of the plank for both heights and decide whether 4 cm or 8 cm gives the larger cross-sectional area.
Your answer to part **a** may help you.

An ellipse has the equation $\dfrac{x^2}{16} + \dfrac{y^2}{9} = 1$.

The line $x = y$ intersects the ellipse at L and M.

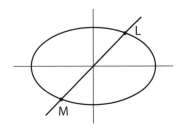

a Which equation A, B, C or D is equivalent to $\dfrac{x^2}{16} + \dfrac{y^2}{9} = 1$?

A $x^2 + y^2 = 144$ **B** $9x^2 + 16y^2 = 144$

C $16x^2 + 9y^2 = 144$ **D** $\dfrac{x^2 + y^2}{25} = 1$

b Half of the ellipse $\dfrac{x^2}{16} + \dfrac{y^2}{9} = 1$ is shaded.

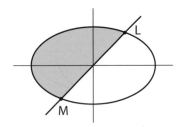

Use your answer to part **a** to find the coordinates of L and M.
Show your working.

c The approximate perimeter, P, of an ellipse is given by the formula.

$$P = 2\pi \sqrt{\tfrac{1}{2}(a^2 + b^2)}$$

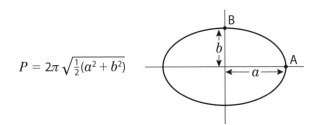

What are the coordinates of points A and B for the ellipse $\dfrac{x^2}{16} + \dfrac{y^2}{9} = 1$?

d What are the values of a and b for the ellipse $\dfrac{x^2}{16} + \dfrac{y^2}{9} = 1$?

e Use the formula in part **c** to find an approximate value for the total perimeter of the shaded area. Show your working.

f Two circles are drawn that just fit inside and outside the ellipse $\dfrac{x^2}{16} + \dfrac{y^2}{9} = 1$

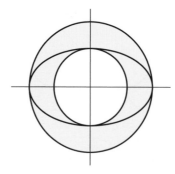

Calculate the shaded area between the two circles.

g An ellipse is drawn so that it just fits around the larger circle.
The larger ellipse is an enlargement of the smaller ellipse.

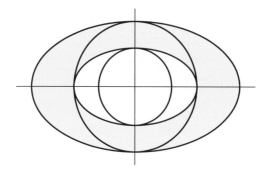

What is the scale factor of the enlargement?

h The area of an ellipse is πab.
Explain the relationship between the formula for the area of a circle and this formula.

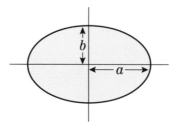

i Calculate the shaded area between the two ellipses shown in part **g**.
Show your working.

7 A full cylinder of water of height 15 cm and radius 4 cm is poured into an inverted cone of base radius 7 cm and depth 20 cm.

How deep is the frustum of empty space above the water in the cone?

8 A bucket in the shape of a frustum of a cone of depth 40 cm, top radius 14 cm and bottom radius 10 cm contains water to a depth of 8 cm.

How much does the water rise if a lead sphere of radius 4 cm is immersed in it?

Extension problems

 Did you know that...?

Benjamin Franklin was an American scientist and politician.

In 1770, Franklin did an experiment on a pond on Clapham Common in London.

He put one teaspoon of oil on the surface of the water. He found that the oil slick spread out until it covered half an acre of the surface.

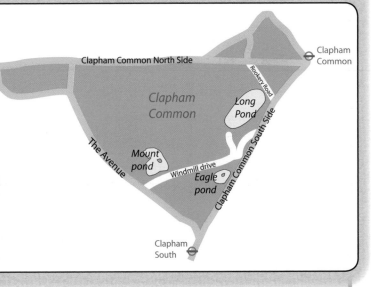

9 **a** Assume one teaspoon is 5 ml.
How deep was Benjamin Franklin's oil slick?
Give your answer in standard form to a sensible degree of accuracy.

b If Franklin had used 1 pint of oil, and the pond was a circle of radius 100 metres, approximately how deep would the oil slick be?

10 Consider two different sets of windscreen wipers as shown in the diagram.

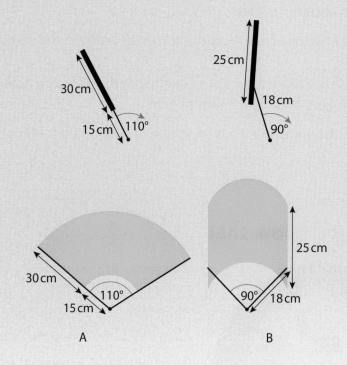

30 cm
15 cm 110°

25 cm
18 cm
90°

30 cm
15 cm 110°
A

25 cm
90° 18 cm
B

a Which wiper clears the greater area?

b Design a wiper with a 30 cm blade that clears more area than either of those above.

How well are you doing?

Measures and mensuration (calculator allowed)

1 *2001 level 8*

The diagram shows parts of two circles, sector A and sector B.

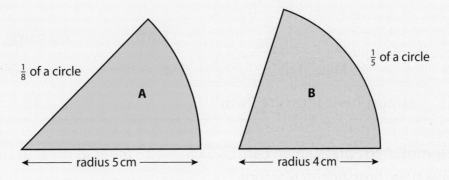

$\frac{1}{8}$ of a circle

A

radius 5 cm

$\frac{1}{5}$ of a circle

B

radius 4 cm

a Which sector has the bigger area?
Show working to explain your answer.

b The perimeter of a sector is made from two straight lines and an arc.
Which sector has the bigger perimeter?
Show working to explain your answer.

c A semicircle, of radius 4 cm, has the same area as a complete circle of radius *r* cm.

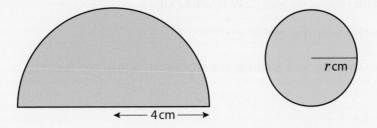

4 cm

r cm

What is the radius of the complete circle? Show your working.

2 *2003 level 8*

A cylinder has a radius of 2.5 cm. The volume of the cylinder is 4.5 cm³.

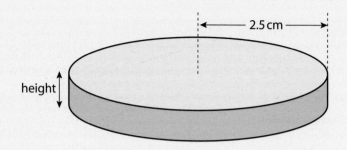

What is the height of the cylinder?

Show your working.

3 *1999 level 8*

Look at the table:

	Earth	Mercury
Mass (kg)	5.98×10^{24}	3.59×10^{23}
Atmospheric pressure (N/m²)		2×10^{-8}

a The atmospheric pressure on Earth is 5.05×10^{12} times as great as the atmospheric pressure on Mercury.

Calculate the atmospheric pressure on Earth.

b What is the ratio of the mass of Earth to the mass of Mercury?

Write your answer in the form $x:1$.

c The approximate volume, V, of a planet with radius r is given by:

$$V = \tfrac{4}{3}\pi r^3$$

Assume the radius of Mercury is 2400 km.

Calculate the volume of Mercury.

Give your answer, to 1 significant figure, in standard form.

4 *1999 level 8*

a This solid is a prism, with height $3x$.
The cross-section is shaded.

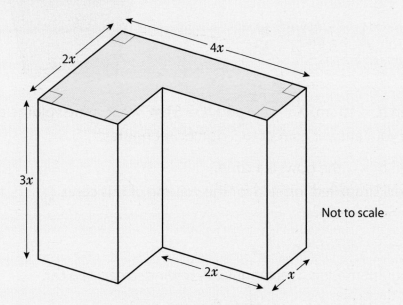

Not to scale

Write an expression for the volume of the solid.
Show your working and simplify your expression.

b The volume of this prism is given by the expression $8x^3 \sin a$.

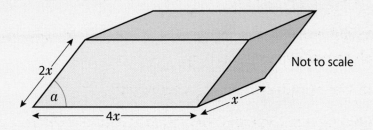

Not to scale

What value of a would make the volume of the prism $8x^3$?

c The prism has a volume of 500 cm³.
The value of a is 30°.

What is the value of x?
Show your working.

5 *2005 level 8*

A formula to find the volume, V,
of this bowl is:

$$V = \tfrac{1}{3}\pi h \frac{a^3 - b^3}{a - b}$$

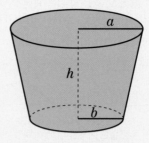

a When $a = 10\,\text{cm}$, $b = 7\,\text{cm}$ and $h = 5\,\text{cm}$, what is the volume of the bowl?
Give your answer correct to 3 significant figures.

b When $b = 0$, the bowl is a cone.
Write a simplified formula for the volume of this cone.

6 *2002 Exceptional performance*

The diagram models a rectangular rear windscreen of a car.

The windscreen wiper can rotate through 160°.

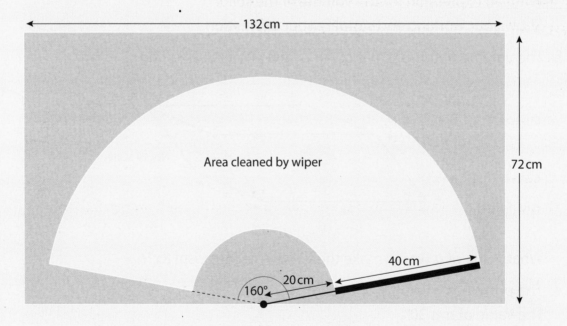

132 cm

72 cm

Area cleaned by wiper

160°   20 cm   40 cm

What percentage of the rear windscreen is cleaned by the wiper?
Show your working.

Expressions and formulae

This unit will help you to:

- simplify algebraic expressions;
- expand brackets;
- factorise algebraic expressions;
- work with algebraic formulae;
- use algebra to investigate mathematical problems;
- use algebra to derive formulae.

1 Simplifying expressions

This lesson will help you to simplify algebraic expressions.

Exercise 1

To **simplify** algebraic expressions:

- multiply out any brackets;
- collect like terms;
- divide the numerator and denominator of fractions by any common factors.

Example 1

a Simplify $x^5 \times x^9$.

$x^5 \times x^9 = x^{14}$

When you multiply powers of x, add the indices.

b Simplify $y^8 \div y^3$.

$y^8 \div y^3 = y^5$

When you divide powers of x, subtract the indices.

Example 2

Simplify $3a^2(2a + 5b) + 4ab(a + 7)$.

$6a^3 + 15a^2b + 4a^2b + 28ab$

Multiply out the brackets.

$= 6a^3 + 19a^2b + 28ab$

Collect like terms.

Example 3

Simplify $\dfrac{15c^3d}{5cd^2}$.

$\dfrac{15c^3d}{5cd^2} = \dfrac{15c^3d \div 5cd}{5cd^2 \div 5cd} = \dfrac{3c^2}{d}$

The highest common factor of $15c^3d$ and $5cd^2$ is $5cd$.

Divide the numerator and denominator by $5cd$.

---

1 Look at this pair of cards.

The **sum** of the expressions on the cards is $7x + 8$.

The **product** of the expressions on the cards is $56x$.

Write the sum and the product of the expressions on each pair of cards.

a 6 $3x + 2$

b $2y$ $3xy$

c x $x + 2y$

d $4y$ $3x + 5y$

e $\dfrac{x}{3}$ $\dfrac{x}{4}$

f  $\dfrac{3}{y}$ $\dfrac{5}{y}$

g $\dfrac{2}{a}$ $\dfrac{7}{b}$

h $\dfrac{5}{a}$ $\dfrac{2}{ab}$

---

2 Write these expressions in their simplest form.

a $b \times b \times b \times b$

b $a \times a \times b \times b \times b$

c $x^4 \times x^5$

d $x \times x^{10} \times x^4$

e $x^7 \div x^3$

f $ab^2 \times ab$

g $p^6q^3 \div p^4q$

h $2a^2 \times 3a^4$

i $4xy^3 \times 5xy$

---

3 Write these expressions in their simplest form.

a $b^{-2} \times b^{-5}$

b $x^3 \times x^{-7}$

c $p^6 \div p^{-3}$

d $a^{-6} \div a^{-8}$

e $a^{\frac{1}{2}} \times a^{\frac{3}{2}}$

f $b^{\frac{2}{5}} \times b^{\frac{3}{5}}$

g $a^{\frac{1}{2}}b^{\frac{3}{5}} \times a^{\frac{5}{2}}b^{\frac{7}{5}}$

h $x^{\frac{3}{4}} \div x^{\frac{1}{4}}$

i $a^{\frac{3}{7}}b^{\frac{8}{9}} \div a^{\frac{1}{7}}b^{\frac{5}{9}}$

4 Expand the brackets and, where possible, simplify the answers.

a $b(ab + a^2b)$

b $2a(b^2 + c^2) - ab^2$

c $x(y + z) - y(x + z)$

d $a(b^2 + c^2) - c(ac + b^2)$

e $3a(a + b) - 2b(a - 2b)$

f $5x(2x^2 + 2y) - 2y(5x - y^2)$

5 Simplify these expressions.

a $\dfrac{p^2}{p}$

b $\dfrac{x^4y}{x^3}$

c $\dfrac{2a^3}{3a^5}$

d $\dfrac{a^{-3}}{a^{-2}}$

e $\dfrac{2a^3b^2}{ab}$

f $\dfrac{a^6b^4}{a^2b}$

6 The **red graph** is $y = 2^x$.

The **blue graph** is $y = 3^x$.

a What is the name of graphs like these?

b Write the coordinates of the point that all graphs like these will pass through.

c Use the graphs to estimate the values of:

   i $2^{0.5}$

   ii $3^{-0.5}$

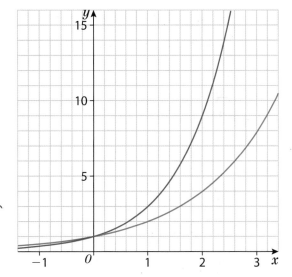

Extension problem

7 Simplify these expressions.

a $x^{\frac{1}{2}}(x^{\frac{1}{2}} + x^{\frac{1}{2}}y)$

b $a^{\frac{1}{2}}(a^{\frac{1}{2}} + b^2) - b^{\frac{1}{2}}(a^{\frac{1}{2}}b^{\frac{3}{2}} - b^{\frac{1}{2}})$

c $a^{-\frac{1}{2}} \div a^{-\frac{5}{2}}$

d $x^{-3}(x^3 + x^5y^2)$

⦿ **Points to remember**

- ⊙ Try to **simplify** algebraic expressions:
  - multiply out any brackets and collect like terms;
  - divide the numerator and denominator of any fractions by any common factors.
- ⊙ To multiply two powers of x, add the indices, so $x^a \times x^b = x^{a+b}$.
- ⊙ To divide two powers of x, subtract the indices, so $x^a \div x^b = x^{a-b}$.
- ⊙ To raise a power of x to a power, multiply the indices, so $(x^a)^b = x^{a \times b}$.

2 Expanding brackets

This lesson will help you to multiply a pair of linear expressions in brackets.

Exercise 2

'**F**irst **O**utside **I**nside **L**ast' (**FOIL**) will remind you how to multiply out two linear expressions.

$(3x + 4)(2x + 5)$

First:	$3x \times 2x = 6x^2$
Outside:	$3x \times 5 = 15x$
Inside:	$4 \times 2x = 8x$
Last:	$4 \times 5 = 20$

$(3x + 4)(2x + 5) = 6x^2 + 23x + 20$

Example 1

Expand the brackets $(3x - 4)(2x + 5)$.

First $6x^2$, Outside $15x$, Inside $-8x$, Last -20

$(3x - 4)(2x + 5) = 6x^2 + 7x - 20$

Example 2

Expand the brackets $(3x - 4)(2x - 5)$.

First $6x^2$, Outside $-15x$, Inside $-8x$, Last 20

$(3x - 4)(2x - 5) = 6x^2 - 23x + 20$

---

1 Which of these answers are wrong?

A $5(3a + 6) = 15a + 6$

B $9(3x + 2y) = 27x + 18y$

C $(x + y)^2 = x^2 + y^2$

D $(a + 5)(a + 8) = a^2 + 13a + 40$

E $(p + q)(p - q) = p^2 - q^2$

F $(x + 7)(x - 2) = x^2 - 5x - 14$

2 Expand the brackets.

a $(a + 3)(a + 4)$ b $(b + 1)(b + 9)$ c $(2x + 6)(3x + 2)$

d $(2y + 4)(5y + 10)$ e $(3p + 7)(2p + 5)$ f $(5z + 3)(2z + 4)$

3 Expand the brackets.

a $(a + 5)(a - 4)$ b $(b - 4)(b + 3)$ c $(4x - 1)(3x + 2)$

d $(3y + 3)(2y - 7)$ e $(2q - 7)(2q + 3)$ f $(6n + 1)(6n - 1)$

4 Expand the brackets.

a $(a - 1)(a - 2)$ b $(b - 2)(b - 3)$ c $(2x - 5)(8x - 1)$

d $(7y - 5)(7y - 8)$ e $(8w - 2)(3w - 5)$ f $(3w - 2)(3w - 2)$

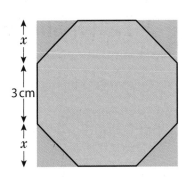

5 A regular octagon with sides 3 cm is cut out from a square piece of card.

    a Write an expression for the area of the square card.

    b Write an expression for the total area of the four triangles that are cut off to make the octagon.

    c Use your answers to parts **a** and **b** to write an expression for the area of the octagon.

    d Use Pythagoras' theorem to calculate the value of x.

    e Substitute the value for x in the expression in part **c** to find the area of the octagon.

Extension problems

6 Pythagoras' theorem states that the area of a square on the hypotenuse of a right-angled triangle is equal to the sum of the squares on the other two sides.

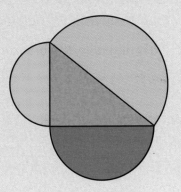

    a Does this theorem apply to semicircles on the sides of a right-angled triangle?

    b Investigate for other shapes on the sides of right-angled triangles.

7 Expand the brackets in these expressions and simplify.

    a $(a + b)^2 - (a - b)^2$ **b** $(a + b)^2 - (a - b)(a + b)$

    c $(2x + 3y)^2 - (x + 6y)^2$ **d** $(2x + 3)(6x - 5) - (3x + 1)(4x - 15)$

◉ Points to remember

- ⊙ A number or letter outside a bracket has to be multiplied by everything inside the bracket, e.g.

  $4(a + 7) = 4a + 28$ and $a(a + 5) = a^2 + 5a$.

- ⊙ To **expand the product of two linear expressions**, multiply everything in one bracket by everything in the other bracket.

- ⊙ You can use a multiplication grid to help you to multiply out brackets.

- ⊙ Alternatively, use **FOIL** to multiply **F**irst terms, **O**utside terms, **I**nside terms, **L**ast terms, e.g.

  $(a + 3)(a - 5) = a^2 - 5a + 3a - 15 = a^2 - 2a - 15$.

3 Factorising expressions

This lesson will help you to factorise quadratic expressions.

Exercise 3

A **quadratic expression** is of the form $ax^2 + bx + c$, where $a \neq 0$.
Examples of quadratic expressions are $z^2 + 7z + 12$, $4a^2 - 9$, $8w^2$.

In some cases a quadratic expression can be **factorised** into two brackets: $(x \pm m)(x \pm n)$.

To **factorise** the quadratic expression $x^2 + bx + c$, find a factor pair of c with a sum of b:

- if c is positive, both signs in the brackets are the same as the sign of b, i.e.

    for c positive and b positive, the brackets are $(x + \ )(x + \ )$
    for c positive and b negative, the brackets are $(x - \ )(x - \ )$

- if c is negative, the brackets are $(x + \ )(x - \ )$.

Example 1

Factorise $x^2 + 7x + 12$.

Since c is positive and b is positive, $x^2 + 7x + 12 = (x + ...)(x + ...)$.
The factor pair of 12 with a sum of 7 is 3 and 4.
So $x^2 + 7x + 12 = (x + 3)(x + 4)$.

Example 2

Factorise $x^2 - 7x + 12$.

Since c is positive and b is negative, $x^2 - 7x + 12 = (x - ...)(x - ...)$.
The factor pair of 12 with a sum of -7 is -3 and -4.
So $x^2 - 7x + 12 = (x - 3)(x - 4)$.

Example 3

Factorise $x^2 + x - 12$.

Since c is negative, $x^2 + x - 12 = (x + ...)(x - ...)$.
The factor pair of -12 with a sum of $+1$ is $+4$ and -3.
So $x^2 + x - 12 = (x + 4)(x - 3)$.

Example 4

Factorise $x^2 - x - 12$.

Since c is negative, $x^2 - x - 12 = (x + ...)(x - ...)$.
The factor pair of -12 with a sum of -1 is -4 and $+3$.
So $x^2 - x - 12 = (x + 3)(x - 4)$.

You will need a graph plotter or graphics calculator for questions 5 and 6.

1 Factorise these expressions.

    a $x^2 + 6x + 5$ **b** $x^2 + 6x + 8$ **c** $x^2 + 11x + 30$ **d** $x^2 + 15x + 56$

2 Factorise these expressions.

    a $x^2 - 8x + 15$ **b** $x^2 - 9x + 14$ **c** $x^2 - 15x + 54$ **d** $x^2 - 12x + 32$

3 Factorise these expressions.

    a $x^2 + x - 20$ **b** $x^2 + x - 6$ **c** $x^2 - 2x - 48$ **d** $x^2 + 7x - 30$

    e $x^2 - 4x - 21$ **f** $x^2 + 16x - 36$ **g** $x^2 - 19x - 20$ **h** $x^2 + x - 72$

4 **a** Factorise the expression $x^2 - x - 6$.

    b Use a graph plotter to generate the graph of $y = x^2 - x - 6$.

    c Use the graph to find the values of x when $y = 0$.

    d How do these values of x relate to your answer in part **a**?

5 **a** Factorise the expression $x^2 - 6x - 7$.

    b Use your answer to part **a**.
    Find the values of x where the graph of $y = x^2 - 6x - 7$ cuts the x-axis.
    Check your answer by drawing the graph.

Extension problem

6 Factorise these expressions.

    a $2x^2 + 11x + 12$ **b** $6x^2 + 23x + 7$ **c** $8x^2 - 8x + 2$ **d** $6x^2 - 8x - 8$

⊙ Points to remember

- ⊙ A **quadratic expression** can sometimes be written as the product of two linear expressions, e.g. $a^2 - 8a + 15 = (a - 3)(a - 5)$.

- ⊙ To **factorise** the quadratic expression $x^2 + bx + c$, find a factor pair of c with a sum of b:
  - if c is positive, both signs in the brackets are the same as the sign of b, i.e.
    for c positive and b positive, the brackets are $(x + \ )(x + \ )$
    for c positive and b negative, the brackets are $(x - \ )(x - \ )$
  - if c is negative, the brackets are $(x + \ )(x - \ )$.

4 Working with formulae

This lesson will help you to work with algebraic formulae.

Did you know that...?

A formula is a way of expressing a rule or generalisation.

The Greek mathematician **Heron** (or **Hero**) lived in the first century AD. He devised a famous formula for finding the area A of a triangle with sides a, b and c. First he found the value s of half the perimeter of the triangle:

$$s = \tfrac{1}{2}(a + b + c)$$

and then he used it in the formula:

$$A = \sqrt{s(s - a)(s - b)(s - c)}.$$

Exercise 4

Example

A triangle has sides 4 cm, 6 cm and 8 cm.
Use Heron's formula to find the area of the triangle.

$s = \tfrac{1}{2}(4 + 6 + 8) = 9$
$A = \sqrt{9(9 - 4)(9 - 6)(9 - 8)}$
$\quad = \sqrt{135} = 11.6\ \text{cm}^2$ (to 1. d.p.)

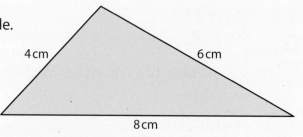

1. Without looking them up, write the formulae for:

   a the area of a parallelogram with base a and perpendicular height h;

   b the area of a trapezium with parallel sides a and b and perpendicular distance h between them;

   c the volume of a cylinder with base radius r and perpendicular height h;

   d the total surface area of a cuboid with length l, width w and height h;

   e the length l of an arc of a circle of radius r and angle x at the centre of the circle;

   f the area A of a sector of a circle of radius r and angle x at the centre of the circle.

2 Find the areas of these triangles with sides a, b and c.
Use Heron's method as shown in the example at the beginning of this exercise.
Give your answers to 2 decimal places.

a $a = 5\,\text{cm}$, $b = 7\,\text{cm}$, $c = 10\,\text{cm}$ **b** $a = 6\,\text{cm}$, $b = 8\,\text{cm}$, $c = 12\,\text{cm}$

c $a = 5.5\,\text{cm}$, $b = 6.5\,\text{cm}$, $c = 8\,\text{cm}$ **d** $a = 14\,\text{cm}$, $b = 18\,\text{cm}$, $c = 20\,\text{cm}$

3 Make the letter in brackets the subject of each formula.

a $A = \pi r^2$ (r) **b** $V = \pi r^2 h$ (h) **c** $C = \frac{5}{9}(F - 32)$ (F)

d $\cos x = \dfrac{A}{H}$ (H) **e** $\cos x = \dfrac{A}{H}$ (A) **f** $T = 2\pi\sqrt{\dfrac{l}{g}}$ (l)

g $a^2 = b^2 + c^2$ (b) **h** $v^2 = u^2 + 2as$ (s) **i** $F = \frac{9}{5}(C + 40) - 40$ (C)

4   **a** Use Pythagoras' theorem.
Find a formula for the height of an equilateral triangle with side a.

b Write a formula for the area of an equilateral triangle with side a.

c Write a formula for the area of a regular hexagon with side a.

d A prism has a perpendicular height h and a regular hexagon base of side a.
Write a formula for the volume of the prism.

e A box in the shape of a prism of height 12 cm has a regular hexagon base of side 10 cm.
What is the volume of the box?

5   **a** The diagonals of a kite are perpendicular to each other.
A kite has diagonals of lengths a and b.
Find a formula for the area A of the kite in terms of a and b.

b A quadrilateral that is not a kite has diagonals of lengths a
and b that are perpendicular to each other.
Find a formula for the area A of the quadrilateral
in terms of a and b.

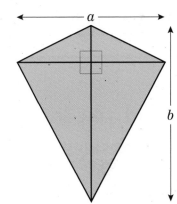

6 The diagram shows an arrowhead drawn in a circle of radius r.
The distance between the tips of the arrowhead is also r.

Find a formula for the area A of the arrowhead.

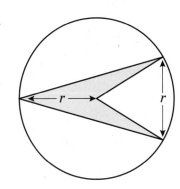

Extension problem

 a A regular nonagon with side a is made from 9 congruent isosceles triangles. Use trigonometry to find a formula for the height of one of the triangles.

b Write a formula for the area of one of the isosceles triangles.

c Write a formula for the area of a regular nonagon with side a.

d An n-sided regular polygon is made from n congruent isosceles triangles. Use trigonometry to find a formula for the height of one of the isosceles triangles.

e Write a formula for the area of one of the isosceles triangles.

f Write a formula for the area of the n-sided regular polygon with side a.

Points to remember

⊙ A **formula** is a way of expressing a relationship using symbols.

⊙ When a formula is written as $d = st$, then d is called the **subject** of the formula.

⊙ You can rearrange a formula to make a different letter the subject, e.g. $s = \dfrac{d}{t}$ or $t = \dfrac{d}{s}$.

⊙ When you substitute values into a formula, check that any quantities are in the correct units.

5 Investigations

 Did you know that...?

A **magic square** uses consecutive integers, starting from 1. The numbers in each row, column and diagonal have the same sum. This sum is called the **magic number**.

Magic squares were discovered as long ago as 400 BC in China.

In 1275, the Chinese mathematician **Yang Hui** found a simple rule for making a 4 by 4 magic square.

16	3	2	13
5	10	11	8
9	6	7	12
4	15	14	1

Write the numbers 1 to 16 in order in a 4 by 4 square.
Then swap the numbers in the opposite corners of the outside 4 by 4 square, and swap the numbers in the opposite corners of the inner 2 by 2 square.

This lesson will help you to use algebra to investigate mathematical problems.

One approach to an **investigation** is to try lots of examples, look for patterns, make a conjecture, test it, then try to justify the result.

Another approach is to identify and define the variables and set up and manipulate an expression or equation to prove a result.

A useful formula to use sometimes is for the nth triangular number:

$1 + 2 + 3 + \dots + n = \frac{1}{2}n(n + 1)$

Example

a Prove that the magic number for any 3 by 3 magic square is 15.

The sum of the numbers in a 3 by 3 magic square is:

$1 + 2 + 3 + \dots + 9 = \frac{1}{2} \times 9 \times 10 = 45$

6	7	2
1	5	9
8	3	4

Let the magic number be m.
The numbers in each row of the magic square add up to m.
So the numbers in 3 rows add up to $3m$.
So $3m = 45$ and $m = 15$.

b Prove that the magic number for any 4 by 4 magic square is 34.

The sum of the numbers in a 4 by 4 magic square is:

$1 + 2 + 3 + \dots + 16 = \frac{1}{2} \times 16 \times 17 = 136$

16	3	2	13
5	10	11	8
9	6	7	12
4	15	14	1

Let the magic number be m.
The numbers in each row add up to m.
So the numbers in 4 rows add up to $4m$.
So $4m = 136$ and $m = 34$.

c Find a formula for the magic number for any n by n magic square.

The sum of the numbers in an n by n magic square is:

$1 + 2 + 3 + \dots + n^2 = \frac{1}{2} \times n^2 \times (n^2 + 1)$

Let the magic number be m.
The numbers in each row add up to m.
So the numbers in n rows add up to nm.
So $nm = \frac{1}{2} \times n^2 \times (n^2 + 1)$ and $m = \frac{1}{2}n(n^2 + 1)$.

d Use your formula to show that the magic number for a 5 by 5 magic square is 65.

Substituting $n = 5$ in the formula $m = \frac{1}{2}n(n^2 + 1)$ gives $m = \frac{1}{2} \times 5 \times 26 = 65$.

Work with a partner.

1 Think of a number.

Follow the instructions on the right.

Prove that the answer will always equal the number your started with.

> **Instructions**
> Treble your number.
> Subtract 6.
> Multiply the result by 2.
> Divide by 3.
> Add 4.
> Divide by 2.

2 **a** Take any four consecutive numbers.

Put three + or − signs between them.

Carry on until you have found all eight possibilities.

For example,	4, 5, 6 and 7.
For example,	$4 + 5 + 6 + 7$
	$4 + 5 + 6 - 7$
	$4 + 5 - 6 + 7$
	$4 + 5 - 6 - 7$
	$4 - 5 + 6 + 7$
	$4 - 5 + 6 - 7$
	$4 - 5 - 6 + 7$
	$4 - 5 - 6 - 7$

Now work out the eight answers.

For example, $4 + 5 + 6 + 7 = 22$

$4 + 5 + 6 - 7 = 8$

Check your answers.

> ### Rules for the answers
>
> ◉ Three of your answers should be 0, −2 and −4.
>
> ◉ Another three answers should be double each of the first three of your consecutive numbers.
>
> ◉ Another answer should be −2 times the fourth of your consecutive numbers.
>
> ◉ Your last answer should be double the sum of your middle two consecutive numbers.

b Try a different set of four consecutive numbers.
Do the answers to the calculations follow the same rules?

c Prove that for any four consecutive numbers, the answers to the eight calculations will always follow the same rules.

3　**a**　Take any three consecutive integers.
Find their sum. Is it divisible by 3?
Is it true that the sum of three consecutive integers is always divisible by 3?
Explain your answer.

　　b　Prove that the sum of any five consecutive integers is always a multiple of 5.

　　c　Prove that the sum of any four consecutive integers is never a multiple of 4.

4　The sequences in this question are related to the sequence of triangular numbers.

　　a　Equilateral triangles are made from sticks.
The first triangle uses 3 sticks, the second
triangle uses 9 sticks and so on.

　　　Find a formula for the number of sticks
in the nth triangle.

  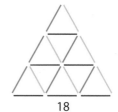
  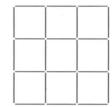

3　　　　　9　　　　　18

　　b　Squares are made using the same sticks.
The first square uses 4 sticks, the second
square uses 12 sticks and so on.

　　　Find a formula for the nth square.

Extension problem

5　**a**　Jack noticed that the numerical value for the perimeter of a
4×4 square is the same as the numerical value for the area.

　　　Find a formula for an n-sided regular polygon with
this property.

　　b　Extend the investigation to 3D shapes.

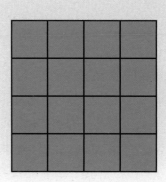

⦿ Points to remember

- ⊙ One approach to an **investigation** is to try lots of examples, look for patterns, make a conjecture, test it, then try to justify the result.
- ⊙ Another approach is to identify and define the variables and set up and manipulate an expression or equation to prove a result.
- ⊙ A good solution to an investigation is concise and elegant as well as clear and well explained.

6 Deriving formulae

This lesson will help you to use known formulae to derive new formulae.

Exercise 6

For a sector with angle x at the centre of a circle radius r:

$$\text{arc length} = \frac{x}{360} \times 2\pi r$$ and $$\text{angle } x = \frac{\text{arc length}}{2\pi r} \times 360$$

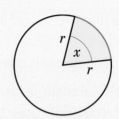

 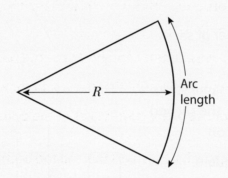

The curved face of a cone with base radius r can be made from card by cutting out a sector of a circle then bending the card.

The slant height of the cone l is the same as the radius R of the sector of the circle.

The arc length of the sector is the same as the circumference of the base of the cone: $2\pi r$.

The angle at the centre of the sector is $\frac{r}{R} \times 360°$.

You will need card, compasses, protractor, sticky tape, rice and a tennis ball for this exercise.

1. You are going to find the volume of a cone.

   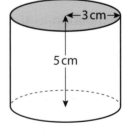 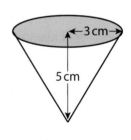

   a Use card to make a cylinder with base radius 3 cm and height 5 cm.
   Your cylinder will need a base.

   What is the volume of the cylinder?

   b Make a cone which has the same base radius and height as the cylinder.
   Your cone does not need a base.

   What is the volume of the cone?

   c Use the cone to fill the cylinder with rice.

   d How many level cones of rice do you need to fill the cylinder?

   e Explain how you can use your answer to part **d** to work out a formula for the volume of a cone with base radius r and perpendicular height h.

2 You are going to find the volume of a sphere.

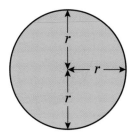 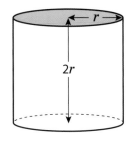 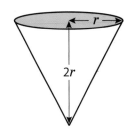

a Measure the diameter of the tennis ball. To do this, place a ruler on each side, hold them parallel to each other and measure the distance between the rulers.

b Use card to make a cylinder which has the same base diameter and height as the ball. It should fit snugly around the ball.

c Make a cone with the same base diameter and height as the ball.

d Place the ball inside the cylinder. Make sure that it is a snug fit with no gaps.

e Count how many cones full of rice will fill the spaces of the cylinder around the ball. Fill the top first.
Empty the rice out, turn the cylinder over, and then fill the bottom.

f Use your answer to part **e** to derive a formula for the volume of any sphere with radius r.

3 The volume V of a cone, radius r and height h, is:

$$V = \tfrac{1}{3}\pi r^2 h$$

In this question, use a value of 3 for π.

a What is the volume of an ice-cream cone with base radius 2 cm and perpendicular height 10 cm?

b The top of a conical glass has a diameter of 6 cm.
Approximately how many times can it be filled to a depth of 9 cm from a 1 litre bottle?

c A cone has a volume of 768 cm³ and a base radius of 8 cm.
Find its height.

d Write a formula to find the height h of a cone when you know that its volume is V and its base radius is r.

e A cone has a volume of 1400 cm³ and a height of 14 cm.
Find its radius.

f Write a formula to find the radius of a cone when you know that its volume is V and its height is h.

④ The volume V of a sphere, radius r, is:

$$V = \frac{4}{3}\pi r^3$$

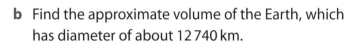

In this question, use a value of 3 for π.

a Find the approximate volume of a squash ball with radius 1.9 cm.

b Find the approximate volume of the Earth, which has diameter of about 12 740 km.

c The volume of a ball is 256 cm³.
What is its radius?

d Write a formula to find the radius of a sphere when you know its volume.

⑤ The radius of the top of a circular plant pot is 9 cm.
The radius of its base is 3 cm.
Its height is 8 cm.

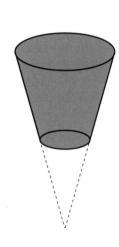

Find the volume of the container.

 Points to remember

⊙ When you derive formulae, first represent any unknown quantities with letters.

⊙ You can use formulae that you know to help you to derive new formulae.

⊙ Simplify any results to help you to remember and use them.

How well are you doing?

1 *2007 level 7*

I am going to use a wooden beam to support a load.
The cross-section of the beam is a rectangle.

The formula below gives the greatest load, M kg, that a beam of this length can support.

$$M = 5d^2w \quad \text{where} \quad \begin{array}{l} d \text{ is the depth of the beam in cm} \\ w \text{ is the width of the beam in cm} \end{array}$$

I can place the cross-section of the beam in two different ways.

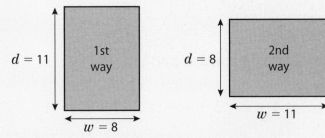

a In which way will the beam be able to support the greater load?

b Calculate the difference.

2 *2000 level 8*

a Explain how you know that $(y + 3)^2$ is not equal to $y^2 + 9$.

b Multiply out and simplify these expressions.

    i $(y + 2)(y + 5)$ **ii** $(y - 6)(y - 6)$ **iii** $(3y - 8)(2y + 5)$

3 *2007 level 8*

Use the equation in the box to help you write the missing expressions in terms of y.

$$x + (x + 1) + (x + 2) = y$$

The first one is done for you.

a $5 + x + (x + 1) + (x + 2) = y + 5$ **b** $(x + 5) + (x + 6) + (x + 7)$

c $2x + 2(x + 1) + 2(x + 2)$ **d** $(x + a) + (x + 1 + a) + (x + 2 + a)$

4 *2002 level 8*

a Simplify the expression $\dfrac{a^3b^2}{a^2b^2}$.   **b** Simplify the expression $\dfrac{a^3b^2 - a^2b^3}{a^2b^2}$.

c Show that $\dfrac{a^2 - b^2}{a - b}$ simplifies to $a + b$.

5 *2008 level 8*

Look at this factorisation.

$$x^2 + 5x + 6 = (x + 2)(x + 3)$$

Copy and complete this to make a correct factorisation.

$$x^2 + 7x + \ldots = (x + \ldots)(x + \ldots)$$

Now write different numbers to make a correct factorisation.

$$x^2 + 7x + \ldots = (x + \ldots)(x + \ldots)$$

6 *GCSE 1387 November 2007*

Here are the first 4 lines of a number pattern.

$$1 + 2 + 3 + 4 = (4 \times 3) - (2 \times 1)$$
$$2 + 3 + 4 + 5 = (5 \times 4) - (3 \times 2)$$
$$3 + 4 + 5 + 6 = (6 \times 5) - (4 \times 3)$$
$$4 + 5 + 6 + 7 = (7 \times 6) - (5 \times 4)$$

n is the first number in the nth line of the number pattern.

Show that the number pattern is true for the four consecutive integers:

$$n, (n + 1), (n + 2) \text{ and } (n + 3)$$

Trigonometry 1

This unit will help you to:

- ◉ use Pythagoras' theorem to solve problems in 2D and 3D;

- ◉ use trigonometric ratios in right-angled triangles to:
  - find an unknown angle;
  - find a side which is the denominator in the ratio.

1 Pythagoras' theorem in 3D

This lesson will help you use Pythagoras' theorem to solve problems in two and three dimensions.

Exercise 1

 Did you know that...?

A variation on Pythagoras' theorem can be used to measure the 'distance' between two colours. Colours are often defined by their RGB (red, green, blue) number. For example red is (255, 0, 0), black is (0, 0 ,0), white is (255, 255, 255) and other colours are made of various proportions of red, green and blue.

Imagine a particular shade of blue has RGB number (111, 255, 255) and a shade of pink has RGB (255, 85, 163). What is the 'distance' between the two colours?

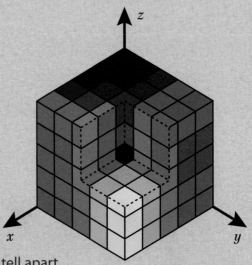

Square the differences between the R, G and B numbers and add them:

$(255 − 111)^2 + (255 − 85)^2 + (255 − 163)^2 = 58\,100$

Then take the square root of the answer to get distance between pink and blue = 241.

Humans cannot spot the difference between two colours that are separated by a distance of 4 or less. Even those colours with a difference of 30 are hard to tell apart.

You can read more about the distances between colours on the website

betterexplained.com/articles/measure-any-distance-with-the-pythagorean-theorem/

Pythagoras' theorem

In any right-angled triangle, the longest side of the triangle, opposite the right angle, is called the **hypotenuse**.

Pythagoras' theorem states that the square on the hypotenuse is the sum of the squares on the other two sides.

This can be written $a^2 + b^2 = c^2$.

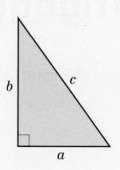

To use Pythagoras' theorem to find lengths in 3D shapes you need to identify suitable right-angled triangles and apply the theorem to them.

Example

ABCDEFGH is a cuboid with length 12 cm, breadth 9 cm and height 14 cm.

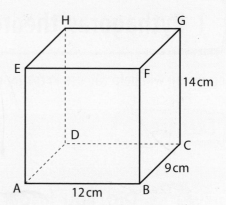

a Calculate the length of AC.

Look for a right-angled triangle where AC is one side and the lengths of the other two sides are known.

ABC is a suitable triangle.

So draw triangle ABC, marking the known lengths.

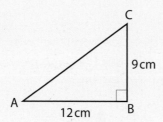

In triangle ABC, using Pythagoras' theorem,

$AC^2 = AB^2 + BC^2 = 12^2 + 9^2 = 144 + 81 = 225$

$AC = \textbf{15 cm}$

b Calculate the length of AG.

Look for a right-angled triangle where AG is one side and the lengths of the other two sides are known.

ACG is a suitable triangle.

So draw triangle ACG, marking the known lengths.

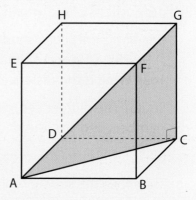

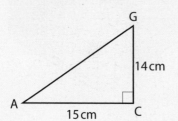

In triangle ACG, using Pythagoras' theorem,

$AG^2 = AC^2 + CG^2 = 15^2 + 14^2 = 225 + 196 = 421$

$AG = \sqrt{421} = \textbf{20.5 cm}$ (to 3 s.f.)

You need a scientific calculator.
Give your answers to 3 significant figures. Remember to round only the final answer.

1 The diagram shows a cuboid.
ABFE is a square with side 9 cm.
The length FG of the cuboid is 12 cm.

Calculate the length of:

a AF

b BG

c EC

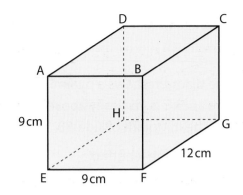

2 The diagram shows a prism of length 11 cm.
The cross-section is a right-angled triangle
with base 8 cm and height 4 cm.

Calculate the length of:

a VW

b WX

c WY

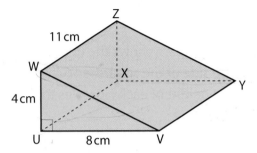

3 The diagram shows a prism of length 7 cm.
The cross-section is an equilateral triangle
with a side of 4 cm.

Calculate:

a the area of the triangular face

b the length of CE

c the length of AE

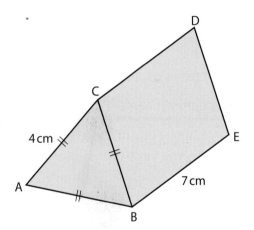

4 The diagram shows a square-based pyramid.
The apex V is 12 cm vertically above O, the
centre of the base.

Calculate the length of:

a WY

b XV

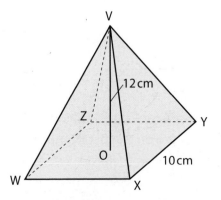

5 A ball of radius 4 cm floats in water. It is immersed to the depth of 6 cm.
Calculate the circumference of the water-line circle.

6 A sphere of diameter 12 cm rests on top of a hollow open cylinder of diameter 8 cm. How much higher than the top of the cylinder is the highest point of the sphere?

7 The diagram shows a pyramid with rectangular base. The apex E is vertically above O, the centre of the base. K is the midpoint of side AB.

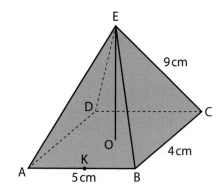

Calculate the length of:

a BD
b OE
c EK

8 The diagram shows the net of a square-based pyramid. The side of the square is 16 cm. The height of each isosceles triangle is 15 cm.

Calculate:

a the length of a sloping edge of the pyramid;

b the perpendicular height of the pyramid.

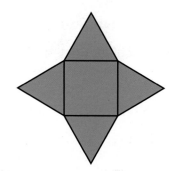

Extension problem

9 P is a point on a sphere of radius 6 cm.

A circle with centre P is drawn on the sphere.

To what radius must a pair of compasses be opened to draw the largest possible circle with centre P?

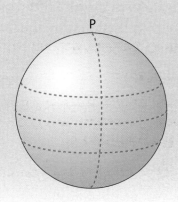

⊙ Points to remember

- In any right-angled triangle, the **hypotenuse**, the longest side, is opposite the right angle.

- **Pythagoras' theorem** states that in a right-angled triangle the square on the hypotenuse equals the sum of the squares on the other two sides:

$$a^2 + b^2 = c^2$$

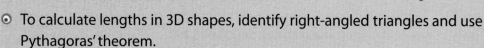

- To calculate lengths in 3D shapes, identify right-angled triangles and use Pythagoras' theorem.

2 Finding an unknown angle

This lesson will help you to use trigonometric ratios to calculate an unknown angle.

Exercise 2

 Did you know that...?

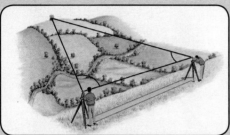

One application of trigonometry is in surveying. When they map an area, surveyors divide the area into triangles and measure lengths and angles from fixed points. The angles are measured with a tool called a **theodolite**. This gives enough information for all other necessary distances to be calculated using trigonometry.

In the 1800s, surveyors undertook to carry out the '**Great Trigonometric Survey**' to map out India. The two huge theodolites that they used were so large that it took 12 men to carry each of them. Using them, the project covered India with strips of triangles in two directions. It took decades to complete this work.

You can use the trigonometric ratios to calculate the unknown angles in right-angled triangles.

To do this you will need to use the **inverse functions** of sine, cosine and tangent:

$\sin^{-1}x$ means the angle whose sine is x
$\cos^{-1}x$ means the angle whose cosine is x
$\tan^{-1}x$ means the angle whose tangent is x

These inverse functions calculate the angle for a given ratio. For example:

$\tan x = 2.3$	$\sin x = 0.354$	$\cos x = 0.238$
so $x = \tan^{-1} 2.3 = 66.5°$	so $x = \sin^{-1} 0.354 = 20.7°$	so $x = \cos^{-1} 0.238 = 76.2°$

Example

The diagram shows a pentagon with one line of symmetry.
Calculate angle a.

In triangle ABF, the hypotenuse AB is 10 m and the adjacent side AF is 8 m, so use the cosine ratio.

$$\cos a = \frac{\text{adj}}{\text{hyp}}$$

$$\cos a = \frac{8}{10} = 0.8$$

$$a = \cos^{-1} 0.8 = 36.9° \text{ (to 3 s.f.)}$$

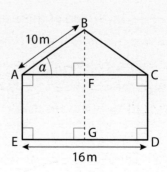

You need a scientific calculator. Give your answers to 1 decimal place.
In questions 2–9, draw and label the diagram. Remember to show your working.

(1) Use your calculator to work out the size of angle x.

a $\tan x = 0.967$ **b** $\tan x = 0.248$ **c** $\tan x = 1.3$ **d** $\tan x = 0.91$

e $\cos x = 0.967$ **f** $\cos x = 0.23$ **g** $\cos x = 0.550$ **h** $\cos x = 0.404$

i $\sin x = 0.299$ **j** $\sin x = 0.767$ **k** $\sin x = 0.328$ **l** $\sin x = 0.622$

(2) A kite is flying on a 40 m string.
The kite is 25 m vertically above the ground.

What angle does the kite string make with
the ground?

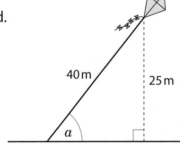

(3) A seesaw is 4.2 m long.
The centre support is 1.1 m high.

One end of the seesaw is resting on the ground.
What angle does the seesaw make with
the horizontal?

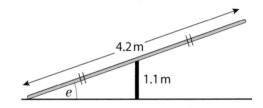

(4) The general rule for safety with ladders is 'one out for four up'.

a At what angle to the horizontal is a ladder safe?

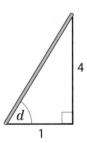

b Which of these ladders are safe?
Explain your reasoning.

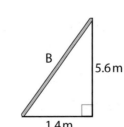

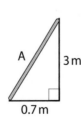

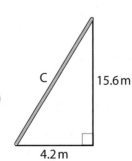

5 Mr Patek is planning his garden.
It is based on a rectangle 45 m by 60 m,
with equal triangular flowerbeds in each corner.

Calculate angles b and c.

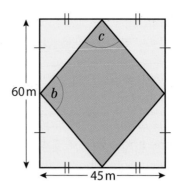

6 From the top of a ship's mast 20 m high a
buoy can be seen 50 m west of the ship.

a What is the angle of depression of the
buoy from the top of the mast?

b A second buoy, also due west, is 75 m
further from the ship than the first buoy.
What is the angle of depression of the
second buoy from the top of the mast?

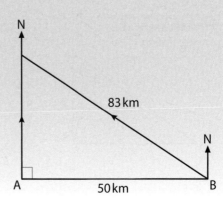

7 A helicopter is flying at night over level ground at a height of 2000 m.
It is lit up by two searchlights 1 km apart due south of it.
The angle of elevation of the helicopter from the first searchlight is 42°.
What is the angle of elevation of the helicopter from the second searchlight?

Extension problems

8 A ship travels 95 km on a bearing of 035° and
then 46 km on a bearing of 125°.

On what bearing should it travel to return to its
starting point?

9 Two ships, A and B, are travelling at the same speed.

Ship A travels due north.
Ship B starts 50 km due east of ship A and travels in
a straight line.

The two ships meet after ship B has travelled 83 km.

On what bearing did ship B travel?

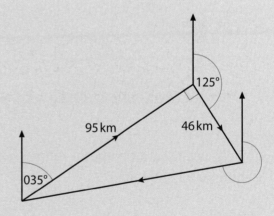

Points to remember

⊙ To find an unknown angle of a right-angled triangle, given two sides, choose the ratio that refers to the two sides relative to the unknown angle.

⊙ **sin⁻¹**x means the angle whose sine is x,
cos⁻¹x means the angle whose cosine is x,
tan⁻¹x means the angle whose tangent is x.

⊙ Give your answer to a suitable degree of accuracy (usually three significant figures for lengths and one decimal place for angles).

3 Finding an unknown side

This lesson will help you to find missing lengths in triangles when the unknown is the denominator in the trigonometric ratio.

Exercise 3

The **angle of elevation** is the angle up from the horizontal towards a point.

The **angle of depression** is the angle down from the horizontal towards a point.

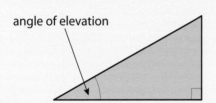
angle of elevation

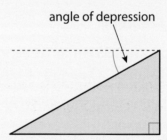
angle of depression

You can use the trigonometric ratios in right-angled triangles when the unknown side is the denominator in the ratio.

Example

Find the length x.

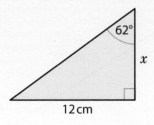

You know the opposite side and you want to find the adjacent side so use the tangent ratio.

$$\tan x = \frac{\text{opposite}}{\text{adjacent}}$$

$$\tan 62° = \frac{12}{x}$$

Multiply both sides by x: $x \tan 62° = 12$

Divide both sides by $\tan 62°$: $x = \dfrac{12}{\tan 62°} = $ **6.38 cm** (to 3 s.f.)

You need a scientific calculator. Give your answers to 3 significant figures.
Remember to draw and label a diagram and to show your working.

1 The diagram shows the side view of a potting shed.

Find the length of the roof, a.

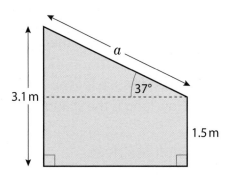

2 A man is standing at the top of a cliff 76 m high. He can see a small boat out at sea.

The angle of depression of the boat from the top of the cliff is 46°.

How far out to sea is the boat?

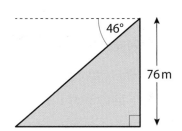

3 Find lengths b and c in the diagram.

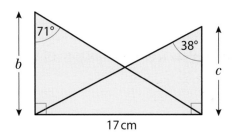

4 A hang glider's altitude is 120 m. His angle of elevation is 22°.

He glides down to land in a straight line.

Find the horizontal distance d he travels before landing.

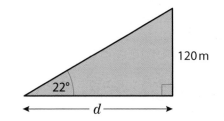

5 A symmetrical roof has a pitch of 37°. Its horizontal width is 9.6 m.

Find the sloping length of the roof e.

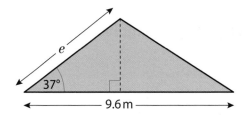

6 A right-angled ramp is built for wheelchair access.
It has an angle of incline of 8° and covers a horizontal distance of 4 m.
How long is the ramp?

7 A large balloon is tethered 67 m above the ground.

The tether rope is taut and forms a straight line.
It makes an angle of 62° with the horizontal ground.

How long is the tether rope?

8 When the sun is at an angle of 49°, a vertical pole 1.44 m long makes a shadow.
How long is the shadow?

Extension problem

9 A river runs east to west.

Pete is standing on the south bank.
He sees a spire on the far bank at a bearing of 020°.

a Pete walks 200 m east along the bank to find a seat.
He sees that the spire is now north-west of him.

Work out the width of the river.

b The top of the spire is 40 m from the ground.
It is at an angle of elevation of 40° from Pete.

How far is Pete from the bottom of the tower?

⊙ Points to remember

- The **angle of elevation** is the angle up from the horizontal towards a point.
- The **angle of depression** is the angle down from the horizontal towards a point.
- You can use the trigonometric ratios to find unknown angles and sides in right-angled triangles.

How well are you doing?

Trigonometry 1 (calculators allowed)

1   *2005 level 8*

a Calculate the length w.

b Calculate the size of angle x.

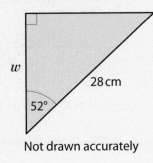

Not drawn accurately

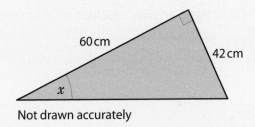

Not drawn accurately

2   A cone has radius 5 cm and slant height 12 cm.
Calculate:

a the vertical height, h, of the cone

b the size of angle a

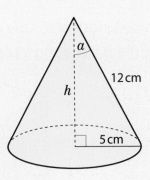

3   Calculate the values of x and y
in these diagrams.

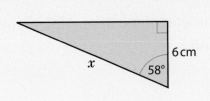

4 *GCSE 1387 November 2007*

The diagram shows an equilateral triangle.

The area of the equilateral triangle is $36\,\text{cm}^2$.

Find the value of x.
Give your answer correct to 3 significant figures.

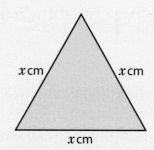

Diagram NOT drawn accurately

5 *GCSE 1387 November 2007*

AB is parallel to DC.

AD = 9 cm, DC = 3 cm.

Angle BCD = 35°.
Angle ABD = 90°.

Calculate the size of angle BAD.
Give your answer correct to one decimal place.

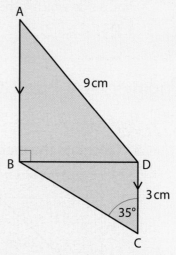

Diagram NOT drawn accurately

6 *2004 level 8*

The side length of a cube is 10 cm.
The cube is cut along a plane through three of the vertices to make a pyramid.

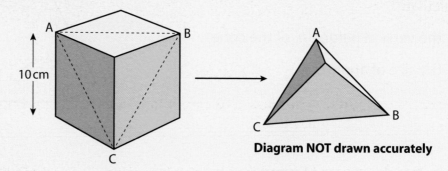

Diagram NOT drawn accurately

Calculate the perimeter of the base, ABC, of the pyramid.
Show your working.

Proportional reasoning

This unit will help you to:

- ⊙ solve harder problems involving percentages, including compound interest and reverse percentage changes;
- ⊙ use direct and inverse proportion and work with proportional relationships.

1 Percentage problems

This lesson will help you to solve more complex percentage problems.

Did you know that...?

Percentages have been widely used since the end of the 15th century to work out interest, profit and loss, and taxes.

However, the idea had much earlier origins. When the Roman emperor **Augustus** levied a tax on all goods sold at auction, *centesima rerum venalium*, the rate was $\frac{1}{100}$. Other Roman taxes were $\frac{1}{20}$ on every freed slave and $\frac{1}{25}$ on every slave sold.

Although the Romans did not use percentages as such, they used fractions which easily converted to hundredths.

Exercise 1

You can use the **unitary method** or **decimal multipliers** to find the original quantity.

Example 1

The price of a new washing machine is £376. This includes Value Added Tax (VAT) at 17.5%. Work out the cost of the washing machine before VAT was added.

Method 1: Unitary method

£376 represents 117.5%.

£376 ÷ 117.5 = £3.20 represents 1%. Find the value of 1%.

100% = £3.20 × 100 = £320 Find the value of 100%.

Method 2: Using a multiplier

A 17.5% increase is represented by 1.175.

£376 ÷ 1.175 = £320   Divide £376 by 1.175.
                             This gives you the price before VAT.

Banks and building societies usually pay **compound interest**. When the interest is paid, it is added to the account, so that the interest earns interest in the subsequent year.

Example 2

£400 is invested in a bank account at an annual rate of compound interest of 5%.
What is its value after 3 years?

Using the multiplier 1.05:

    after 1 year there will be £(400 × 1.05) = £420 in the account
    after 2 years there will be £((400 × 1.05) × 1.05) = £441 in the account
    after 3 years there will be £(((400 × 1.05) × 1.05) × 1.05) = £463.05 in the account.

To find the amount in the account after 3 years the original £400 has been multiplied by 1.05 × 1.05 × 1.05, which is equivalent to 1.05^3.

1. In a sale all prices are reduced by 15%.
   Harry pays £15.64 for a shirt.
   Calculate the normal price of the shirt.

2. The local shop is offering a discount of 10% on DVDs.
   Jessica buys three identical DVDs for £48.60.
   What was the original cost of one DVD?

3. **a** Jo got 65% of the total number of marks in a French test. She got 39 marks.
   Work out the total number of marks for the French test.

   b In the test, 8% of pupils score As, 12% score Bs, 23% score Cs, 27% score Ds, and six score Es or worse. How many pupils took the test?

4. The price of a new television is £423.
   This price includes Value Added Tax (VAT) at 17.5%.
   Work out the cost of the television before VAT was added.

5. £5000 is invested for 3 years at 4% per annum compound interest.
   Work out the total interest earned over the 3 years.

6. Mark buys a van that has a value of £12 000.
   Each year the value of the van will depreciate by 25%.
   Work out the value of the van at the end of 3 years.

7 A house costs £150 000 today.
Suppose the annual rate of inflation stays at 5% for 15 years.
What would you expect the same house to cost in 15 years' time?

8 Serena invests £500 on 1 January 2009 at a compound interest rate of 4.5% per annum.
What is the value of her investment after 20 years?

9 What is 20% of 30% of 40% of £100?

10 A shop buys a pair of jeans for £39.
The shop puts a price ticket on the jeans which would give them a $33\frac{1}{3}$% profit.
The jeans don't sell, so the shop reduces the price by 25% and puts them in a sale.
What do the jeans cost in the sale?

11 You are given a choice for an increase in pocket money: either an increase of 20% this year followed by 40% next year, or an increase of 40% this year followed by 20% next year.
Which will you choose and why?

12 A cuboid is 134 cm long, 49 cm wide and 94 cm high. Each dimension is increased by 50%.

a By what percentage has the volume of the cuboid increased?

b By what percentage has the surface area of the cuboid increased?

13 In the first week of June, my weekly charge for delivering milk increased by 50%.
The next week it increased by a further 20%.

a What was the total percentage increase in the delivery charge over the two weeks?

b In the third week of June the delivery charge fell by 50%.
It fell by a further 20% in the last week of June.
What was the overall percentage change in the delivery charge over the four weeks?

c If instead the falls in the third and last weeks of June were 20% and 50%, what would the overall percentage change in the delivery charge have been over the four weeks of June?

 14 A club is laying two new rugby pitches. The larger pitch is 10% wider and 10% longer than the smaller one.

a How much extra grass seed is used for the larger pitch as a percentage of the amount used for the smaller one?

b How much less grass seed is used for the smaller pitch as a percentage of the amount used for the larger one?

c How much extra white paint is used to mark all the white lines on the larger pitch as a percentage of the amount used for the smaller pitch?

Extension problem

15 **a** Jack bought a goat.

He expected to sell it at a price that would give him a 10% profit on his purchase.
However, he had to sell it for £50 less than he expected, a loss of 15% on what it cost him.

What did Jack pay for the goat?

b Jack increased the price of his goats' cheeses by 20%.
Sales dropped by 20%.
Does the money Jack receives from sales go up or down?
By how much?

c Jack loses 60% of his herd of goats. By the next day he has found 60% of those he lost.
What proportion of his herd of goats are still missing?

d Jo also keeps goats. She loses three-quarters of her herd.
The next day she finds all but 10% of her missing goats.
What percentage of her herd are still missing?

Points to remember

⊙ You can work out percentage increases and decreases, or reverse percentages, using the **unitary method** or **decimal multipliers**.

⊙ The unitary method involves finding 1% as an intermediate step.

⊙ **Compound interest** is paid on the original investment plus any previous interest, e.g. for compound interest of 3% for 5 years:

Final amount at end of 5 years = initial amount $\times 1.03^5$
Total interest at the end of 5 years = final amount − initial amount

2 Direct proportion 1

This lesson will help you to solve problems involving direct proportion.

 Did you know that...?

The symbol ∝ for 'is proportional to' looks like an eight on its side with a bit removed. It was first used in 1768 by the English mathematician, **William Emerson**, in a textbook called *Doctrine of Fluxions*.

William was born in 1701 at Hurworth in county Durham, where he lived most of his life.

He was taught by his father at the village school. After university, he took over his father's teaching post but he was unsuccessful as a teacher.

After William married he decided to earn his living through his study of mathematics. He wrote many books, never putting forward an idea that he had not previously tested in practice, nor publishing an invention without first proving its effects by making a model.

Exercise 2

When we convert miles to kilometres, the ratio of miles : kilometres is always the same. We say the number of kilometres is **directly proportional** to the number of miles. The symbol ∝ means '**is directly proportional to**', so the number of kilometres ∝ the number of miles.

miles : kilometres = 25 : 40
$\qquad\qquad\quad$ = 5 : 8

miles : kilometres = 100 : 160
$\qquad\qquad\quad$ = 5 : 8

miles : kilometres = 2.5 : 4
$\qquad\qquad\quad$ = 5 : 8

miles	kilometres
5	8
25	40
100	160
2.5	4

In general, if y is directly proportional to x, then

$y \propto x$, or $y = kx$,

where k is the **constant of proportionality**.

Since $y = kx$ the graph of y against x is a **straight line passing through the origin**.

The constant k is the **gradient** of this straight line.

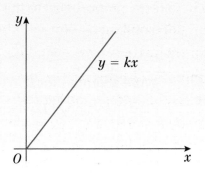

Example

Marks in a test are converted to percentages. Some results are shown in the table.

Mark (M)	0	28	56
Percentage score (P)	0	50	100

The marks are directly proportional to the percentages.

a Plot a graph to show the relationship between P and M.

The graph is shown on the right.

b Write the equation of the line to show the relationship between the mark M and the percentage score P.

The gradient of the line is approximately 1.8 so the equation of the line, which passes through the origin, is $P = 1.8M$.

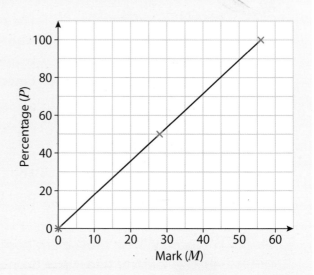

---

1 y is directly proportional to x.

a $y = 2$ when $x = 1$.
Find y when $x = 3$.

b $y = 7$ when $x = 4$.
Find x when $y = 4$.

c $y = 5$ when $x = 2$.
Find y when $x = 1.5$.

d $y = 6$ when $x = 4$.
Find x when $y = 10.5$.

e $y = 12$ when $x = 4$.
Find y when $x = 3.2$.

f $y = 8$ when $x = 1$.
Find x when $y = 4$.

2 Each table shows two variables, x and y, that are directly proportional to each other. For each table, write a formula connecting y and x, and find the missing value z.

a

x	7	11
y	9	z

b

x	46.9	83.1
y	22.1	z

c

x	13.6	17.9
y	z	28.2

3 The distance, D km, travelled by a truck is directly proportional to the amount, A litres, of diesel used.

When $A = 5$, $D = 25$.

a Write a formula for D in terms of A.

b Find the value of D when $A = 12.5$.

c How many litres of diesel are needed for a journey of 428 km?

4 The perimeter, P cm, of a regular pentagon is directly proportional to the length, l cm of one of its sides.

When $l = 16$ cm, $P = 80$ cm.

  a Write a formula for P in terms of l.

  b Find the value of P when $l = 18.6$ cm.

  c What is the length of the pentagon's side when the perimeter is 58.2 cm?

5 The mass, m grams, of a candlestick is directly proportional to its volume, v cm^3.

When $m = 525$ g, $v = 50$ cm^3.

  a Express m in terms of v.

  b Find the value of m when $v = 25$.

  c What is the candlestick's volume when the mass is 945 g?

6 The weight of a length of climbing rope is directly proportional to its length.
A 40 m length of rope has a weight of 2.4 kilograms.
Another length of the same rope is 55 m long.
Calculate the weight of the 55 m length of rope.

You will need graph paper for the next two questions.

7 Some different weights are hung on an elastic ribbon.
The extension of the elastic for different loads in newtons is shown in the table.

Load (N)	0	1	2	3	4	5
Extension (cm)	0	2.1	4.2	6.2	8.5	10.5

  a Plot a graph of extension (cm) against load (N). Draw a line of best fit on your graph.

  b Write the equation of the line showing the relationship between the load w and the extension x of the elastic.

  c Predict the extension for a load of 2.5 N.

  d Predict the load that would produce an extension of 9 cm.

8 A baby octopus is weighed from birth at midday for its first 5 days.
The results are shown in the table.

Day	1	2	3	4	5
Mass (kg)	1.7	3.1	4.5	5.9	7.3

  a Plot the points on a graph. Draw a suitable line through the points.

  b Write down the equation of the line showing the relationship between the mass m and the age a of the octopus.

  c If the octopus continued to grow at the same rate, at what age would it first weigh over 15 kg?

9 On 13 August 1999, the *Times Education Supplement* published this short article.

If the whole history of the Universe could be compressed into the space of one earth year, with the Big Bang occurring on 1 January, and the start of the second millennium AD at midnight on 31 December, the first galaxies would have begun to form on 2 January.

It was a long wait before the birth of our sun, on 10 September, and our own planet, the Earth, on 13 September. Life appeared around 15 October. The dinosaurs lived on 24 December, but it was not until 9:00 pm on 31 December that the first recognisable human beings evolved. At ten seconds to midnight, the Egyptians built the pyramids.

On this scale, the Sun will become a red giant making Earth inhabitable on 1 April next year.

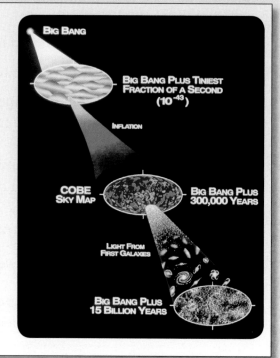

The Egyptians built the pyramids about 3000 BC. Roughly how long elapsed:

a between the birth of planet Earth and life appearing on it?

b between the evolution of the first recognisable humans and the building of the pyramids?

Points to remember

⊙ Two quantities y and x are **directly proportional** if their ratio $y : x$ stays the same as the quantities increase or decrease.

⊙ $y \propto x$ (y is directly proportional to x) can be written as $y = kx$, where k is the **constant of proportionality**.

⊙ The graph of the relationship between two variables that are directly proportional is a straight line through the origin.

⊙ You can use the **unitary method** to solve direct proportion problems by reducing the value of one of the variables to 1.

⊙ When you solve problems involving direct proportion:
  – make sure that corresponding quantities are in the same units;
  – ask yourself whether the answer should be larger or smaller than the quantity already given.

3 Direct proportion 2

This lesson will help you to solve problems involving the relationship $y = kx^2$.

Sometimes one quantity is directly proportional to the square or the cube of another quantity.

In general, if y is proportional to the square of x, then:

$y \propto x^2$ or $y = kx^2$

where k is the **constant of proportionality**.

Since $y = kx^2$, the graph is a **quadratic curve** passing through the origin.

Similarly, if y is proportional to the cube of x, then:

$y \propto x^3$ or $y = kx^3$

where k is the constant of proportionality.

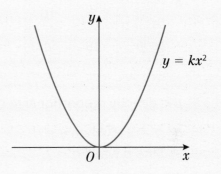

Example

The rate of heat loss, H calories per second, from a cube of side a cm is proportional to the square of the side. Some results are shown in the table.

Side of cube (a cm)	2	4	6
Heat loss (H calories per second)	0.4	1.6	3.6

a Write a formula to show the relationship between the heat loss H and the length of an edge of the cube a.

$H \propto a^2$, so $H = ka^2$, where k is a constant.

Since $H = 3.6$ when $a = 6$, substituting these values gives $k = \dfrac{3.6}{6^2} = \dfrac{1}{10}$. So $H = \dfrac{1}{10}a^2$.

b Sketch a graph to show the relationship between H and a.

The graph is shown on the right.

c Find the value of a when $H = 90$.

Substituting $H = 90$ in $H = \dfrac{1}{10}a^2$ gives $90 = \dfrac{1}{10}a^2$.

Multiplying by 10 gives $900 = a^2$, so $a = 30$, as $a > 0$.

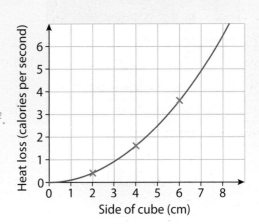

1 y is directly proportional to the square of x.

   a $y = 2$ when $x = 1$.
   Find y when $x = 3$.

   b $y = 18$ when $x = 3$.
   Find y when $x = 7$.

   c $y = 12$ when $x = 2$.
   Find y when $x = 3.5$.

   d $y = 5$ when $x = 2$.
   Find x when $y = 1$.

   e $y = 5$ when $x = 5$.
   Find x when $y = 20$.

   f $y = 1$ when $x = 0.5$.
   Find x when $y = 9$.

2 Each table shows two variables, a and b; b is proportional to the square of a.
For each table, write a formula for b in terms of a, and find the missing value c.

a

a	7	10
b	49	c

b

a	0.5	1.5
b	10	c

c

a	3	16
b	c	128

3 p is directly proportional to the cube of q.

   a $p = 216$ when $q = 3$.
   Find p when $q = 7$.

   b $p = 54$ when $q = 6$.
   Find q when $p = 128$.

   c $p = 2$ when $q = 10$.
   Find q when $p = 0.25$.

4 The area, $A\,\text{cm}^2$, of a square is proportional to the square of its perimeter, $P\,\text{cm}$.
When $P = 20$, $A = 25$.
Find a formula for A in terms of P.

5 The area, $A\,\text{cm}^2$, of a regular octagon is proportional to the square of the diagonal through the centre, $d\,\text{cm}$.

When $A = 8\sqrt{2}$, $d = 4$.

   a Write a formula for A in terms of d.

   b Find the value of A when $d = 8$.

   c Find the value of d when $A = 100\sqrt{2}$.

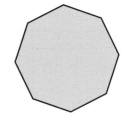

6 Christmas puddings are cooked in spherical tins.
The time, T minutes, that a pudding takes to cook is proportional to the cube of the radius of the tin, $r\,\text{cm}$.

When $r = 4$, $T = 60$.

   a Write a formula for T in terms of r.

   b Find the value of T when $r = 8$.

   c What is the radius of a pudding that takes 3 hours to cook? Give your answer to 1 decimal place.

7 The kinetic energy, K joules, of a moving object is directly proportional to the square of its velocity, v metres per second.

When $v = 6$, $K = 90$.

a Find the value of v when $K = 40$.

b Sketch a graph to show the relationship between the kinetic energy and the velocity of the object.

8 The melting rate of an ice cube, R grams per second, is proportional to the square of the length of an edge, a mm.

When $a = 25$, $R = 1$.

a Show that $R = 0.0016 \times a^2$.

b Find the melting rate when the edge of the cube is 20 mm.

c Find the length of the edge of the cube when the melting rate is 2 grams per second.

9 The volume, V cm^3, of a regular tetrahedron is directly proportional to the cube of the length of an edge, l cm.

When $l = 2$, $V = \dfrac{2\sqrt{2}}{3}$. Show that when $l = 15$, $V = \dfrac{1125\sqrt{2}}{4}$.

10 a is proportional to the cube of b. When $b = 8$, $a = 1000$.

a Write a formula for a in terms of b.

b Find the value of b when $a = 1728$.

11 The area of a circle, A cm^2, varies directly as the square of its radius r cm.

Sketch a graph:

a to show the relationship between the area and its radius

b to show the relationship between the area and the square of its radius.

Extension problems

12 On a map with scale 1 : 25 000 a lake has an area of 13 cm^2.
What is the area of the same lake on a map with scale 1 : 100 000?

13 In a scale model of a new city development, the footprint of the development is $\frac{1}{50}$ of the actual footprint on the ground. What is the ratio of the volume of the scale model to the volume of the full-size development?

4 Inverse proportion

This lesson will help you to solve problems involving inverse proportion.

Exercise 4A

Example 1

Six girls take 4 days to paint the village hall. How long would it take eight girls?

6 girls take 4 days.
1 girl takes $4 \times 6 = 24$ days.   1 girl takes longer than 6 girls.
8 girls take $24 \div 8 = 3$ days.   8 girls take less time than 1 girl.

Example 2

Four men take 5 days to dig a ditch 300 metres long.
What length of ditch could be dug by six men working for 8 days?

4 men take 5 days to dig 300 m.
1 man takes $5 \times 4 = 20$ days to dig 300 m.   1 man takes longer than 4 men.
1 man in 1 day digs $300 \div 20 = 15$ m.   1 man in 1 day digs less than in 20 days.
1 man in 8 days digs $15 \times 8 = 120$ m.   1 man digs more in 8 days than in 1 day.
6 men in 8 days dig $120 \times 6 = 720$ m.   6 men would dig more than 1 man.

1. Two men can paint a room in 6 hours.
   How long would five men take?

2. A box of emergency rations can feed twelve soldiers for 6 days.
   For how long would the same box of rations feed eight soldiers?

3. Four taps fill a storage tank in 36 minutes.
   How long will it take three taps to fill the same storage tank?

4. A phone card gives 120 minutes of calls at peak times.
   Off-peak calls cost one third of peak time calls.
   How many minutes of off-peak calls will the phone card give?

(5) Three men lay 30 m² of paving in 4 days.
How many days would it take two men to lay 45 m² of paving?

(6) Members of a family brush their teeth twice a day.
The family uses four tubes of toothpaste in 9 weeks.
They decide to brush their teeth three times a day for 4 weeks.
How many tubes of toothpaste will they need?

(7) A delivery company charges £240 to deliver four sofas to a
furniture store 300 miles away.
They deliver five sofas for a cost of £180 to a second store.
How far away is the second store?

(8) In 1 hour, eight markers can mark 90 Key Stage 3 test papers.
How many test papers can 15 markers mark in 90 minutes?

Exercise 4B

When one quantity increases at the same rate as another quantity decreases, the quantities are **inversely proportional** to each other.

In general, if y is inversely proportional to x, then:

$$y \propto \frac{1}{x} \text{ or } y = \frac{k}{x}$$

where k is the **constant of proportionality**.

When $k > 0$, the graph of $y = \frac{k}{x}$ looks like this:

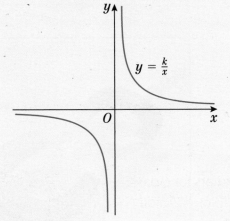

$y = \frac{k}{x}$

If y is inversely proportional to the square of x, then:

$$y \propto \frac{1}{x^2} \text{ or } y = \frac{k}{x^2}$$

where k is the **constant of proportionality**.

When $k > 0$, the graph of $y = \frac{k}{x^2}$ looks like this:

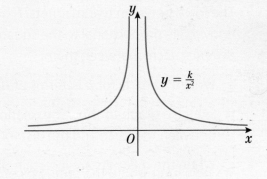

$y = \frac{k}{x^2}$

Example

y is inversely proportional to x.

$y = 8$ when $x = 2$.

Find y when $x = 4$.

$y \propto \frac{1}{x}$ or $y = \frac{k}{x}$, where k is a constant.

Substituting $y = 8$ and $x = 2$ gives $k = 8 \times 2 = 16$.

Substituting $k = 16$ and $x = 4$ gives $y = 16 \div 4 = 4$.

1 p is inversely proportional to q.

$p = 15$ when $q = 0.15$.

Calculate the value of p when $q = 6$.

2 m is inversely proportional to n.

$m = 6$ when $n = \frac{1}{2}$.

Which of the following belongs to the same relationship?

A $(3, \frac{1}{4})$ **B** $(12, 1)$ **C** $(3, 1)$ **D** $(3, 6)$ **E** $(\frac{1}{12}, 1)$

3 For rectangles with the same area, the length, l cm, of the rectangle is inversely proportional to the width, w cm, of the rectangle.

When $l = 4.8$, $w = 2.5$.

a Write a formula for l in terms of w.

b Sketch a graph to show the relationship between the length and width of the rectangle.

c Find the value of w when $l = 3.75$.

d For what value is $l = w$?

4 The temperature, $T°C$, at a distance, d metres, from a source of heat is inversely proportional to the square of the distance.

When $d = 6$, $T = 100$.

a Find T when $d = 4$.   **b** Find d when $T = 400$.

5 The force between two magnets, F newtons, is inversely proportional to the square of the distance, d cm, between them.

a Write a formula for F in terms of d.

b Sketch a graph to show the relationship between the force and the distance.

c When the magnets are a certain distance apart, the force is 10 newtons.
What is the force when this distance is doubled?

d When the magnets are 3 cm apart, the force is 2 newtons.
Find the force when they are 5 cm apart.

6 The electrical resistance R of a wire varies inversely as the square of its diameter d.
A wire of diameter 4 mm has a resistance of 4 ohms.

   a Find the resistance of a wire with diameter 1.2 cm.

   b Find the diameter of the wire when the resistance is 8 ohms.

   c What happens to the resistance when the diameter of the wire is doubled?

7 The weight of an object in space varies inversely as the square of its distance from Earth.
An astronaut weighs 26 kg when a spacecraft is 10 800 km from Earth.
What does the astronaut weigh when the spacecraft is 6600 km from Earth?

Extension problems

8 The time needed to pump out a flood is inversely proportional to the number of pipes used.

A flood is pumped out by 7 pipes. If an extra pipe is used, the flood can be pumped out 5 minutes faster.

How many extra hosepipes must be used so that the flood is pumped out 12 minutes faster?

9 The average speed to travel a fixed distance is inversely proportional to the time taken.
A family travels exactly half their car journey in 2 hours.
They stop for lunch for 1 hour, and then take 3 hours over the second half of the journey.

   a How were the average speeds related on each part of the journey?

   b The average speed for the first half of the journey was 72 kilometres per hour.
      What was the average speed for the whole journey?

⦿ Points to remember

- ⊙ Two quantities a and b are **inversely proportional** if a increases as b decreases at the same rate, so their product is constant.
- ⊙ If y is inversely proportional to x, then $y = \dfrac{k}{x}$, where k is a constant.
- ⊙ If y is inversely proportional to x^2, then $y = \dfrac{k}{x^2}$, and $x = \dfrac{\sqrt{k}}{\sqrt{y}}$, so x is inversely proportional to $\sqrt{y}$.
- ⊙ When you solve word problems involving inverse proportion, ask yourself if the answer should be larger or smaller than the quantity already given.

5 Proportion and square roots

This lesson will help you to solve problems involving direct or inverse proportion and square roots.

Exercise 5

Sometimes one quantity is **directly proportional to the square root** of another quantity.

In general, if y is directly proportional to $\sqrt{x}$, then:

$$y \propto \sqrt{x} \text{ or } y = k\sqrt{x}$$

where k is the **constant of proportionality**.

When $k > 0$, the graph of $y = k\sqrt{x}$ looks like the graph on the right.

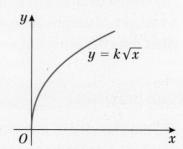

Sometimes one quantity is **inversely proportional to the square root** of another quantity.

In general, if y is inversely proportional to the square root of x, then:

$$y \propto \frac{1}{\sqrt{x}} \text{ or } y = \frac{k}{\sqrt{x}}$$

where k is the **constant of proportionality**.

When $k > 0$, the graph of $y = \dfrac{k}{\sqrt{x}}$ looks like the graph on the right.

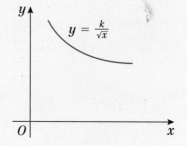

Example

y is inversely proportional to the square root of x.

$y \propto \dfrac{1}{\sqrt{x}}$ or $y = \dfrac{k}{\sqrt{x}}$, where k is a constant.

$y = 5$ when $x = 64$.

Substituting $y = 5$ and $x = 64$ gives $k = 5 \times 8 = 40$.

Find y when $x = 25$.

Substituting $k = 40$ and $x = 25$ gives $y = 40 \div \sqrt{25} = 8$.

---

① y is directly proportional to the square root of x.

a $y = 4$ when $x = 9$.
Find y when $x = 81$.

b $y = 20$ when $x = 16$.
Find y when $x = 49$.

c $y = 6$ when $x = 4$.
Find y when $x = 25$.

d $y = 4$ when $x = 1$.
Find x when $y = 8$.

e $y = 21$ when $x = 49$.
Find x when $y = 27$.

f $y = 10$ when $x = 4$.
Find x when $y = 25$.

g $y = 5$ when $x = 1$.
Find y when $x = 36$.

h $y = 5$ when $x = 5$.
Find x when $y = 20$.

i $y = 8$ when $x = 4$.
Find x when $y = 27$.

2 n is directly proportional to the square root of m. Copy the table and fill in the missing values.

m	1	4			25
n		$\frac{1}{2}$	$\frac{3}{4}$	1	

3 p is inversely proportional to the square root of q.

a $p = 22$ when $q = 25$.
Find p when $q = 4$.

b $p = 2$ when $q = 36$.
Find p when $q = 100$.

c $p = 0.5$ when $q = 64$.
Find q when $p = 0.8$.

4 The time, T seconds, it takes a pendulum to swing once is directly proportional to the square root of the length of the pendulum, l metres.

When $T = 0.8$, $l = 0.16$.

a Write a formula for T in terms of l.

b Find the value of T when $l = 1.44$.

c What length of pendulum will give a swing of 1 second?

5 The time taken, t seconds, for a particle to slide a distance d metres down a smooth slope is directly proportional to the square root of the distance.

When $t = 1.5$, $d = 6.25$.

a Find a formula for t in terms of d.

b Rearrange the formula to find d in terms of t.

6 The speed, v metres per second, at which a ball hits the ground is directly proportional to the square root of the height, h metres, from which it is dropped.

a Express v in terms of h and a constant k.

b The ball is dropped from a height of 2 metres. It hits the ground at a speed of 6 metres per second. Find the value of k.

c The ball is dropped from a height of 8 m. What is its speed when it hits the ground?

d The ball hits the ground with a speed of 10 metres per second. From what height was it dropped?

7 The oscillation frequency, f cycles per second, of a spring is inversely proportional to the square root of the mass of the spring, m kg.

When $m = 2.56$, $f = 2$.

Find f when $m = 4$.

8 For $k > 0$, each of the graphs below matches one of these equations:

$$y = kx \qquad y = k\sqrt{x} \qquad y = \frac{k}{x} \qquad y = kx^2$$

Match each graph to its equation.

Graph A

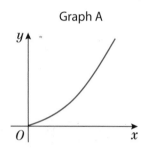

Graph B

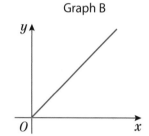

Graph C

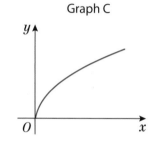

Graph D

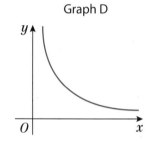

Points to remember

⊙ $y \propto \sqrt{x}$ (y is directly proportional to $\sqrt{x}$) can be written as $y = k\sqrt{x}$, where k is a constant.

⊙ $y \propto \dfrac{1}{\sqrt{x}}$ (y is inversely proportional to $\sqrt{x}$) can be written as $y = \dfrac{k}{\sqrt{x}}$, where k is a constant.

How well are you doing?

Proportional reasoning (no calculator)

1. *1999 level 8*

   In 1995, the Alpha Company employed 4000 people.
   For each of the next 2 years, the number of people employed increased by 10%.

1995	employed 4000 people
1996	employed 10% more people
1997	employed 10% more people

   a Tony said: 'Each year, the Alpha company employed another 400 people.'
     Tony was wrong. Explain why.

   b Which of the calculations below shows how many people worked for the company in 1997?

$4000 \times 0.1 \times 2$	4000×0.1^2	$(4000 \times 0.1)^2$
$4000 \times 1.1 \times 2$	4000×1.1^2	$(4000 \times 1.1)^2$

   c Look at these figures for the Beta Company:

1995	employed n people
1996	employed 20% fewer people
1997	employed 10% more people

   Write an expression using n to show how many people the company employed in 1997.
   Show your working and write your expression as simply as possible.

② 2005 level 8

Here are sketches of five different graphs.

Graph A

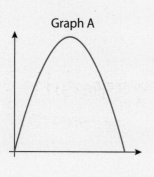

Graph B

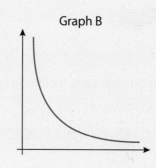

Graph C

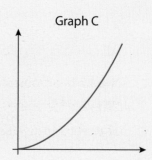

Graph D

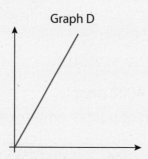

Graph E

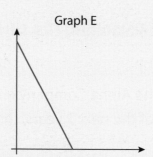

Which graph best matches each relationship below?

For each relationship, give the letter of the correct graph.

a The circumference of a circle plotted against its diameter.

b The area of a circle plotted against its radius.

c The length of a rectangle of area 30 cm² plotted against its width.

③ GCSE 1387 June 2003

The force, F, between two magnets is inversely proportional to the square of the distance, x, between them.

When $x = 3$, $F = 4$.

a Find an expression for F in terms of x.

b Calculate F when $x = 2$.

c Calculate x when $F = 64$.

Proportional reasoning (calculator allowed)

4 *2001 level 8*

A shop had a sale.
All prices were reduced by 15%.

A pair of shoes cost £38.25 in the sale.
What price were the shoes before the sale?
Show your working.

5 *GCSE 1387 June 2007*

James invested £2000 for three years in an Internet Savings Account.
He is paid 5.5% per annum compound interest.
Work out the total interest earned after three years.

6 *1997 level 8*

These plant pots are mathematically similar.

The internal dimensions are shown.

a Calculate the value of m.
Show your working.

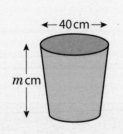
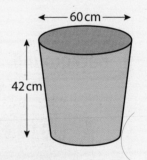

b The capacity, C, of a plant pot in cubic
centimetres is given by the formula:

$C = \frac{1}{2}\pi h(a^2 + ab + b^2)$

In the larger plant pot $a = 60$, $b = 36$ and $h = 42$.

How many litres of compost are needed
to fill the plant pot? Show your working.

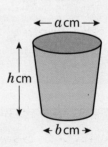

c Think about the ratio of the widths of the two plant pots.
Explain why the ratio of the capacity of the smaller pot
to the capacity of the larger pot is $8:27$.

Functional skills 3

Sports injuries

This group activity will help you to:

- ☉ choose and combine representations from a range of perspectives;
- ☉ select and apply a range of methods, operations and tools, including ICT;
- ☉ examine patterns and relationships;
- ☉ recognise limitations in the accuracy of results and conclusions;
- ☉ interpret and communicate results and solutions.

Background

Sports participation is a major cause of serious injury among young people. Sports activities are the second most frequent cause of injury for both male and female adolescents.

In the USA, each year it is estimated that more than five million children seek treatment in hospital emergency rooms because of sports injuries.

Young people's sports injuries

This table (source: www.nyssf.org) shows the percentage of injuries treated at hospital for different age groups. The table is in an Excel spreadsheet **Sports injuries** for you to analyse.

Sport	Number of injuries	Percentage aged 0–4	Percentage aged 5–14	Percentage aged 15–24
Archery	3 110	2.8	22.7	27.5
Basketball	631 186	0.6	31.5	46.4
Cycling	577 621	7.1	55.0	15.2
Boxing	9 183	0.0	8.6	54.4
Dancing	38 427	3.5	19.2	36.3
Diving	11 124	2.3	40.8	31.2
Football	169 734	0.5	14.2	15.9
Hockey	4 666	1.7	43.3	49.3
Gymnastics	31 446	3.8	77.3	16.0
Horse riding	64 692	1.5	20.2	15.3
Ice skating	33 741	2.4	46.4	18.8
Rugby	8 361	0.0	0.1	65.9
Skateboard	54 532	2.7	50.7	39.5
Skiing	81 787	0.5	14.2	15.9
Swimming	49 331	5.2	40.1	20.7
Trampoline	95 239	9.6	69.6	14.0

Problems

Work with a partner. You need a computer and the Excel file **Sports injuries**.

1. What do you notice about the data in the table above?
   Give as many details as you can.
   Try to explain or give reasons for the things that you notice.

2. a. Which is the most dangerous sport for each of the three age groups?
   Justify your answer.

   b. Which sports would you recommend for each age group?

   c. How well do you think these figures reflect the accident rates for different sports?
   Are there other considerations, that are not included?

Be prepared to discuss your conclusions with other pairs.

G 7.3

Geometrical reasoning

This unit will help you to:

- prove the circle theorems and use them to solve problems;
- prove that triangles are congruent;
- verify standard ruler and compass constructions;
- solve problems involving similar shapes.

1 Tangents and chords

This lesson will help you to learn properties of tangents, chords and radii.

Did you know that...?

Euclid of Alexandria lived around 300 BC. He is often called the Father of Geometry. His book *The Elements* showed many examples of geometrical proofs.

Euclid's Proposition 32 in Book 1 of *The Elements* states:

Of every triangle, when one of the sides is extended the external angle is equal to the two interior and opposite angles and the three interior angles of the triangle are equal to two right angles.

Can you see how the diagram proves the proposition?

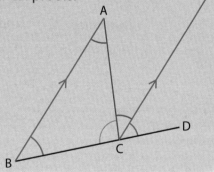

Exercise 1

Here are some facts about tangents, chords and radii that you can use to solve problems.

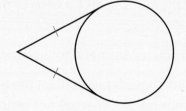

The **tangent** at a point on a circle is perpendicular to the radius at the point.

The tangents to a circle from a point outside the circle are equal in length.

The perpendicular from the centre of a circle to a **chord** bisects the chord.

You can use properties of tangents, chords and radii to find unknown angles and lengths.

Example

TA and TB are tangents to a circle with centre O.
C is the midpoint of the chord AB.
Angle TBC = 68°

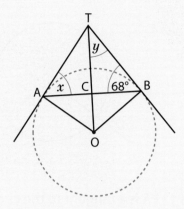

a Find the size of angle x.

AT = BT (equal tangents to a circle)

So triangle ATB is isosceles.

So angle x = angle TBA = 68°

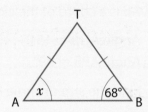

b Find the size of angle y.

Angle TCB = 90° (the line from the centre to the midpoint of a chord is perpendicular to the chord)

So angle y + 68° + 90° = 180° (angles in a triangle)

So angle y = 22°

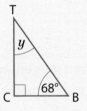

The diagrams are not drawn accurately.

1 PA is a tangent at A to the circle, centre O.
Find the size of each angle marked with a letter. Give reasons for your answers.

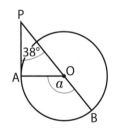

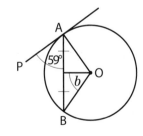

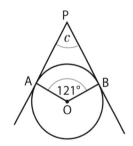

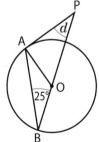

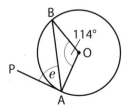

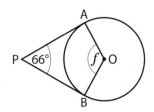

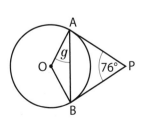

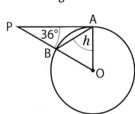

2 O is the centre of the circle.
Find the size of each angle marked with a letter. Give reasons for your answers.

a

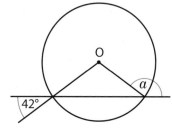

42°

b

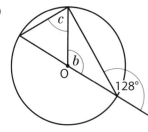

c
b
128°

c

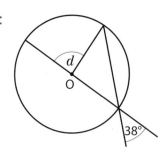

d
38°

3 PA is a tangent to the circle, centre O.
AB is a chord of the circle.

Angle AOB = 151°
Angle APB = 69°

Find the size of angle PBA.

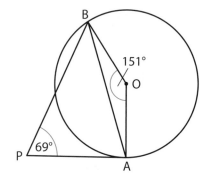

B
151°
O
P 69°
A

4 PA is a tangent to the circle at A.
AB is a diameter of the circle.
AP = AB

D is a point on PB such that angle BAD = 68°.

Calculate the size of angle PDA.

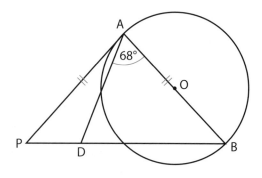

A
68°
O
P
D
B

5 A and B are points on the circumference of a
circle, centre O.

CA is a tangent to the circle at A.
OBC is a straight line.

a Calculate angle y when angle $x = 70°$.
Explain each step of your calculation.

b Show that when triangle OAB is equilateral,
triangle ABC is isosceles.

c Prove that $y = 2x - 90°$.

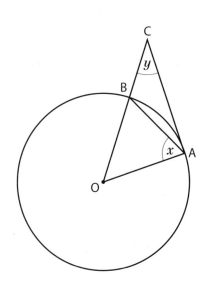

C
y
B
x
A
O

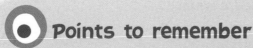

Points to remember

⊙ The **tangent** at a point is perpendicular to the radius at the point of contact.

⊙ The tangents to a circle from a point outside the circle are equal in length.

⊙ The perpendicular from the centre of a circle to a **chord** bisects the chord.

⊙ The line joining the midpoint of a chord to the centre of the circle is perpendicular to the chord.

2 Circle theorems

This lesson will help you to prove and use some of the circle theorems.

Exercise 2

Theorem 1: The angle at the centre of a circle is twice the angle at the circumference

To prove that angle AOB = 2 × angle ACB

Proof

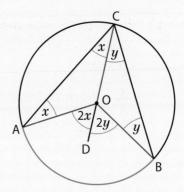

Join CO and extend to D.

OA = OB = OC (radii)

Triangle OAC is isosceles, so angle OAC = angle OCA = x
Triangle OBC is isosceles, so angle OBC = angle OCB = y

Angle AOD = angle OAC + angle OCA = $2x$
(exterior angle of triangle)
Similarly, angle BOD = $2y$

Angle AOB = $2x + 2y = 2(x + y)$ = 2 × angle ACB

Theorem 2: The angle in a semicircle is a right angle

To prove that angle ACB = 90°

Proof

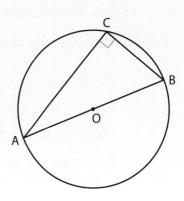

Angle AOB = 180°
(AOB, a diameter of the circle, is a straight line through O)

Angle AOB = 2 × angle ACB
(angle at the centre is twice the angle at the circumference)

So angle ACB = $\frac{1}{2}$ × angle AOB = $\frac{1}{2}$ × 180° = 90°

Theorem 3: Angles in the same segment are equal

To prove that angle APB = angle AQB

Proof

Angle APB = $\frac{1}{2}$ × angle AOB
(angle at the centre is twice the angle at the circumference)

Similarly, angle AQB = $\frac{1}{2}$ angle × AOB
So angle APB = angle AQB

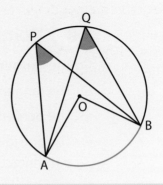

Example 1

AB is a chord of a circle, centre O.
P is a point on the circumference.

Angle PAO = 37°
Angle PBO = 12°

Work out the sizes of angles AOB and APB.

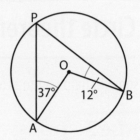

Not drawn accurately

In triangle AOP:

    AO = OP (radii of circle)
    Angle APO = angle OAP = 37° (isosceles triangle)

In triangle BOP:

    BO = OP (radii of circle)
    Angle BPO = angle OBP = 12° (isosceles triangle)

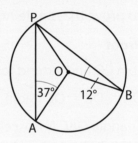

Not drawn accurately

Angle APB = angle APO + angle BPO = 37° + 12° = 49°

So angle AOB = 2 × 49° = **98°** (angle at the centre is twice the angle at the circumference)

Example 2

A, B, C and D are points on the circumference of a circle.
Angle CBD = 74° and angle BDC = 56°.

Work out the sizes of angles BAD and BCD.

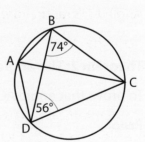

In triangle BDC:

    Angle BCD = 180° − (74° + 56°) = **50°** (angle sum of a triangle)

    Angle CAD = angle CBD = 74° (angles in the same segment)

    Angle BAC = angle BDC = 56° (angles in the same segment)

    Angle BAD = angle CAD + angle BAC = 74° + 56° = **130°**

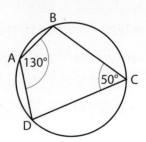

The diagrams are not drawn accurately.

(1) The diagrams show three circles each with centre O.
Calculate the angles marked a to e. Give reasons for your answers.

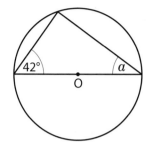
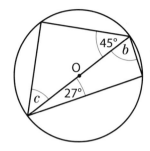
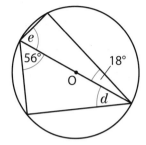

(2) The diagrams show three circles each with centre O.
Calculate the angles marked a to f. Give reasons for your answers.

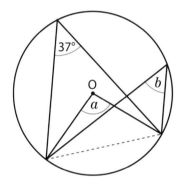
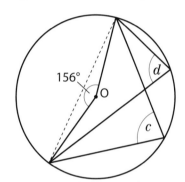
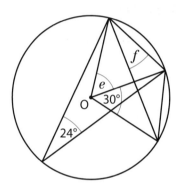

(3) The diagram shows two circles that intersect at P and Q.

B is the centre of the larger circle.
C is the centre of the smaller circle.

ABCD is a straight line.

Prove that the line AP is a tangent of the smaller circle.

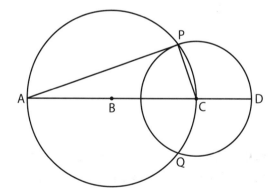

(4) The diagram shows two circles.
A is a point of intersection.

The centre of the larger circle is B.

C is a point on the circumference of the smaller circle such that AC is a tangent to the larger circle.

Prove that BC is a diameter of the smaller circle.

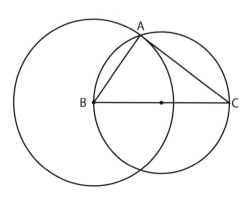

5 A, B, C and D are points on the circumference of a circle, centre O.

AC is a diameter of the circle.
Angle BDO $= x$
Angle BCA $= 2x$

Work out in terms of x the size of:

a angle BDA   **b** angle AOD   **c** angle ABD

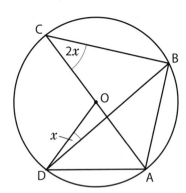

Extension problem

6 AB is the diameter of a circle, centre O.
P is a point on the circumference of the circle.
Angle APO $= x$ and angle BPO $= y$.

a Work out in terms of x and y the size of:

 i angle PAO   **ii** angle PBO

b Write down and simplify an expression in terms of x and y for the sum of the angles in triangle APB.

c Explain why this shows that $x + y = 90°$.

d Explain why parts **a**–**c** of this question prove that the angle in a semicircle is a right angle.

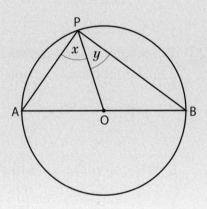

◉ Points to remember

⊙ The **angle at the centre of a circle** is twice the angle at the circumference.

⊙ The **angle in a semicircle** is a right angle.

⊙ **Angles in the same segment** are equal.

3 More circle theorems

This lesson will help you to prove and use more of the circle theorems.

Exercise 3

A quadrilateral whose vertices all lie on the circumference of a circle is called a **cyclic quadrilateral**.

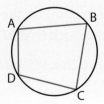

Theorem 4: Opposite angles of a cyclic quadrilateral sum to 180°

To prove that in the cyclic quadrilateral ABCD:

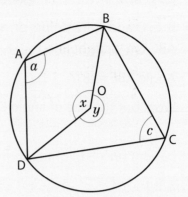

angle DAB + angle BCD = 180°, i.e. $a + c = 180°$
angle ABC + angle CDA = 180°

Proof

Join points B and D to the centre of the circle, O.
Let angle BOD = x and reflex angle BOD = y.

$x = 2c$ and $y = 2a$
(angle at the centre is twice the angle at the circumference)

$y + x = 360°$ (sum of angles at a point)

So $2a + 2c = 360°$ and, dividing by 2, $a + c =$ **180°**

Also, angle ABC + angle CDA = **180°**
(the sum of the angles of a quadrilateral is 360°)

The diagram shows a **tangent** and a **chord** of a circle.

w is **the angle between the tangent and the chord**.

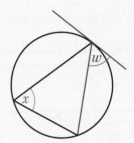

The segment on the opposite side of the chord from w is called the alternate segment.

x is **the angle in the alternate segment**.

Theorem 5: The angle between a tangent and a chord at the point of contact is equal to the angle in the alternate segment

To prove that angle TAB = angle BCA, i.e. $w = x$

Proof

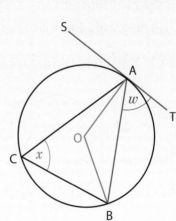

Join points A and B to the centre of the circle, O.

Angle OAT = 90° (tangent is perpendicular to radius)

So angle OAB = 90° − w

OA = OB (radii of the circle)

So angle OBA = angle OAB = 90° − w (isosceles triangle AOB)

Angle AOB = 2x (angle at the centre is twice the angle at the circumference)

In triangle AOB, $2x + 90° - w + 90° - w = 180°$ (angle sum of triangle is 180°)

So $2x - 2w = 0$ and $w = x$

Example 1

B, C, D and E are points on a circle.
ABC is a straight line.

Angle ABE = 81°

Work out the size of angle CDE.

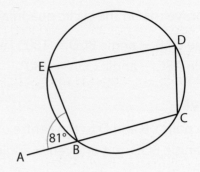

Angle CBE = 180° − 81° = 99°
(angles on a straight line sum to 180°)

Angle CDE = 180° − 99° = **81°**
(opposite angles of a cyclic quadrilateral sum to 180°)

Example 2

A, B and T are points on a circle.
PTQ is a tangent to the circle at T.

Angle PTB = 37°
Angle ATB = 68°

Work out the size of angle ABT.

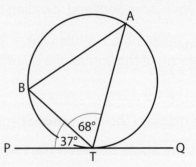

Angle BAT = angle PTB = 37°
(alternate segment theorem)

Angle ABT = 180° − (37° + 68°) = 75°
(the angle sum of triangle is 180°)

You will need a copy of **G7.3 Resource sheet 3.1**.

The diagrams are not drawn accurately.

(1) Calculate the angles marked with a letter. Give reasons for your answers.

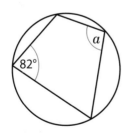
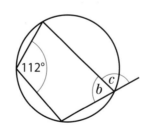
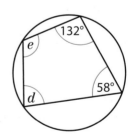

(2) Is this quadrilateral a cyclic quadrilateral?
Explain your answer.

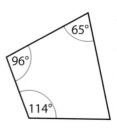

3 Work with a partner to complete **Resource sheet 3.1**.

4 A, B and C are points on the circumference of a circle, centre O.

PA and PB are tangents to the circle at A and B.

Angle ABP = 70°

Work out the sizes of angles x, y and z.
Give reasons for your answers.

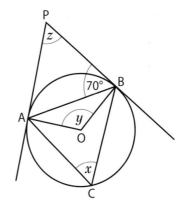

5 ABCT is a cyclic quadrilateral.
PTQ is a tangent to the circle at T.

Angle PTC = 51°
Angle BAC = 23°

Work out the size of angle BCT.
Give reasons for your answer.

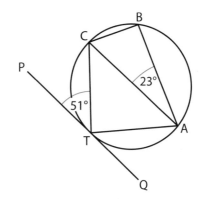

6 The diagram shows a circle, centre O.
ST is a chord.
PT and PS are tangents to the circle at T and S.
R is a point on the circumference of the circle.

Angle SPT = 58°.

a Work out the size of:

   i angle PTS   **ii** angle SOT

   iii angle OTS   **iv** angle SRT

b Explain why OSPT is a cyclic quadrilateral.

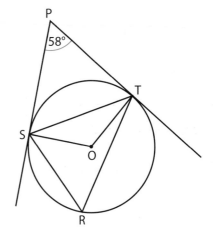

7 A, B, C and D are points on a circle.
AP and BP are tangents to the circle.

Angle BAD = 80°
Angle BAP = 70°

Find the size of:

   a angle BCD   **b** angle APB   **c** angle DCA

Give reasons for your answers.

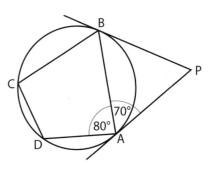

Extension problem

 8 A, B, C and D are points on a circle.
PAQ is a tangent.

Angle PAD = x and angle QAB = y.

a Express angle DAB and angle BCD
in terms of x and y.

b What do you notice?

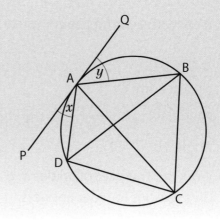

 Points to remember

⊙ When four points A, B, C and D lie on the circumference of a circle then
ABCD is a **cyclic quadrilateral**.

⊙ The sum of the opposite angles of a cyclic quadrilateral is 180°.

⊙ The angle between a tangent and a chord is equal to the angle in the
alternate segment. This is called the **alternate segment theorem**.

4 Using the circle theorems

This lesson will help you to use angle facts to solve problems.

Exercise 4

Here are some angle facts that you know:

⊙ The angle at the centre of a circle is twice the angle at the circumference.

⊙ The angle in a semicircle is a right angle.

⊙ Angles in the same segment are equal.

⊙ The sum of the opposite angles of a cyclic quadrilateral is 180°.

⊙ The tangent at a point on a circle is perpendicular to the radius at the point.

⊙ The tangents to a circle from a point outside the circle are equal in length.

⊙ The perpendicular from the centre of a circle to a chord bisects the chord.

⊙ The angle between the tangent and a chord is equal to the angle in the alternate segment.

You can use angle facts that you know to help you solve problems.

Example 1

A, B, C and D are points on the circumference of a circle, centre O.
Angle AOC = 96°

Work out angle ADC.

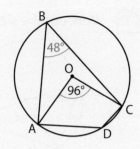

Angle ABC = angle AOC ÷ 2 = 96° ÷ 2 = 48°
(angle at the centre is twice the angle at circumference)

Angle ADC + angle ABC = 180°
(opposite angles of a cyclic quadrilateral)

So angle ADC = 180° − 48° = **132°**

Example 2

A, B and C are points on the circumference of a circle, centre O.
PA and PB are tangents to the circle. Angle ACB = 48°

Work out angle APB.

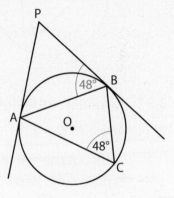

Angle PBA = angle ACB = 48° (alternate segment theorem)

PA = PB (tangents to a circle)

So triangle PAB is isosceles.

Angle APB = 180° − 2 × 48° = **84°** (angle sum in a triangle)

Example 3

ABCD is a cyclic quadrilateral and PAQ is a tangent.
Angle QAB = 32° and angle ABD = 18°.

Work out angle BCD.

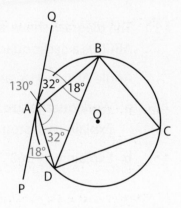

Angle ADB = angle QAB = 32°
(alternate segment theorem)

Angle BAD = 180° − 18° − 32° = 130° (angle sum in a triangle)

Angle BCD = 180° − 130° = **50°** (opposite angles in a cyclic
                        quadrilateral)

There is another way of working out angle BCD.

Angle PAD = angle ABD = 18° (alternate segment theorem)

Angle BAD = 180° − 32° − 18° = 130° (angles on a straight line)

Angle BCD = 180° − 130° = **50°** (opposite angles in a cyclic quadrilateral)

The diagrams are not drawn accurately.

1 Work out the size of each angle marked with a letter. Give reasons for your answers.

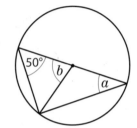 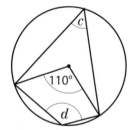 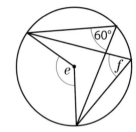

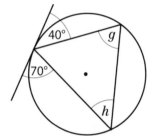 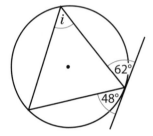 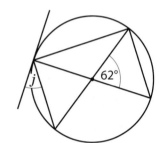

2 A, B and P are on the circumference of a circle, centre O.

Angle APB = 33°

Work out the size of angle OAB.
Explain each step in your working.

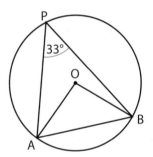

3 The diagram shows a circle, centre O.
ABCD is a cyclic quadrilateral.

Angle ADC = 118° and angle AOC = x.

a Work out the size of angle x.
Explain each step in your working.

b Explain why 360° − x = 2 × 118°.

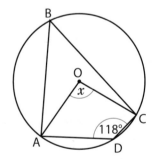

4 A, B and C are points on the circumference
of a circle, centre O.

PA and PB are tangents.
PB is parallel to AC and angle APB = 38°.

a Work out the sizes of angles x and y.
Give reasons for your answers.

b Show that triangle ABC is isosceles.

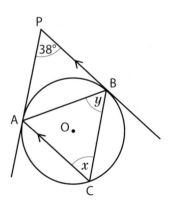

5 A, B and C are points on the circumference
of a circle, centre O.
PA and PB are tangents.

Angle AOB = 140°
Angle OBC = 15°

a Explain why OAPB is a cyclic quadrilateral.

b Work out the size of:

    i angle APB   **ii** angle ACB   **iii** angle OAC

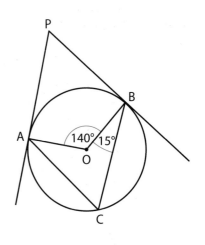

Extension problems

6 A, B, C, D and E are points on the circumference
of a circle, centre O.
EC is a diameter that is parallel to AB.

Angle AOB = 100°

Show that angle CDB = angle ADE.

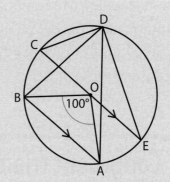

7 A, B and C are points on the circumference
of a circle, centre O.
PQ touches the circle at A.

Angle QAC = 46°
Angle APB = 18°

Work out the size of angle OAB.
Give reasons for your answers.

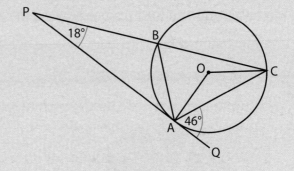

8 A, B, C and T are points on the circumference of a circle.
AB is parallel to TC.
Angle BAC = 25°
The line STP is the tangent at T to the circle.

CAP is a straight line and AT = AP.

Prove that:

a angle APT = 25°   **b** angle BTS = 75°

Give reasons for your answers.

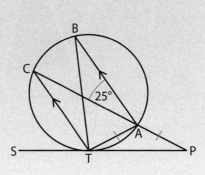

Points to remember

⊙ Once a fact has been proved, it can be used to prove further facts.

⊙ These facts can be used to solve problems involving angles in circles:

- The angle at the centre of a circle is twice the angle at the circumference.

- The angle in a semicircle is a right angle.

- Angles in the same segment are equal.

- The sum of the opposite angles of a cyclic quadrilateral is 180°.

- The tangent at a point on a circle is perpendicular to the radius at the point.

- Tangents to a circle from a point outside the circle are equal in length.

- The perpendicular from the centre to a chord bisects the chord.

- The angle between the tangent and a chord is equal to the angle in the alternate segment.

5 Congruent triangles

This lesson will help you to recognise when triangles are congruent.

Did you know that...?

Congruent triangles are used in architecture to make rigid structures.

The Hearst Tower, Manhattan

The Gherkin, London

The Hearst Tower in Manhattan was designed by **Sir Norman Foster** and completed in 2006. The triangular frame is called a diagrid.

Norman Foster was born in Manchester in 1935 and trained as an architect at Manchester University. He also designed the building known as The Gherkin, in the City of London.

Shapes are **congruent** if they are exactly the same shape and size. Corresponding sides are equal in length and corresponding angles are equal in size. The only difference could be in the position or orientation of the shapes, or whether one is a reflection of the other.

For two triangles to be congruent, one of four conditions must be met. Each condition includes the three pieces of information needed to construct a **unique** triangle.

1 **Three sides are equal.**

   This condition is called **SSS**.

2 **Two angles and a corresponding side are equal.**

   This condition is called **ASA**.

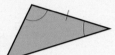

3 **Two sides and the included angle are equal.**

   This condition is called **SAS**.

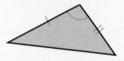
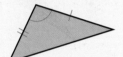

4 **A right angle, the hypotenuse and one other side are equal.**

   This condition is called **RHS**.

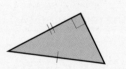

Example

Explain why each pair of triangles is congruent.

a

b
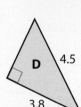

c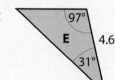
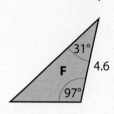

d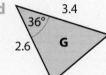

Triangle **A** is congruent to triangle **B (SSS)**.

Triangle **C** is congruent to triangle **D (RHS)**.

Triangle **E** is congruent to triangle **F (ASA)**.

Triangle **G** is congruent to triangle **H (SAS)**.

The diagrams are not drawn accurately.

1 Look at triangles **A** to **H**. Identify three pairs of congruent triangles.
In each case, explain why they are congruent.

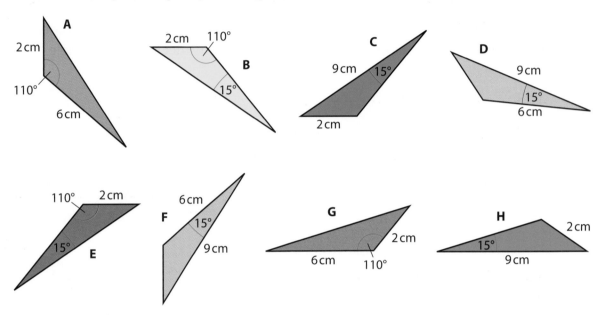

Explain why the remaining two triangles are **not** congruent.

2 Which of triangles **B**, **C** and **D** are congruent to triangle **A**?
Explain each answer.

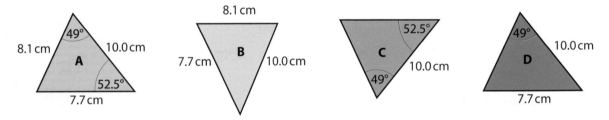

3 Explain why triangles **A** and **B** may not be congruent.

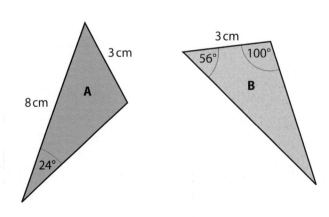

4 **A**, **B** and **C** are congruent triangles.

What is the size of angle x in triangle **C**? Give a reason for your answer.

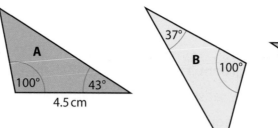
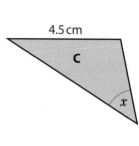

5 In triangle ABC, AD is the perpendicular bisector of BC.

  a Explain why triangles ABD and ACD are congruent.

  b What does this tell you about triangle ABC? Explain your answer.

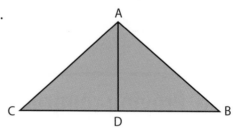

6 AED and CEB are straight lines. AE = CE and BE = DE.

Explain why triangles ABE and CDE are congruent.

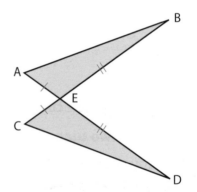

7 The diagram shows a regular hexagon ABCDEF.

  a Show that triangle ABC is congruent to triangle AFE.

  b Show that triangle ACD is congruent to triangle AED.

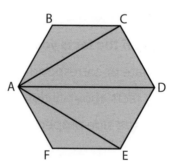

Extension problem

8 The diagram shows a triangle ABC.

D is the midpoint of AB.
E is the midpoint of DC.
BDE is an isosceles triangle.

Angle BDE = 80°

Show that triangle BEC is congruent to triangle AED.

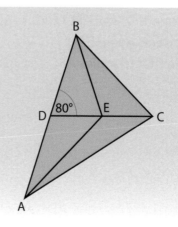

Points to remember

- Two or more shapes are **congruent** if they are the same shape and size.
- Triangles are congruent if they satisfy one of these conditions:

  SSS Corresponding sides are equal.

  SAS Two sides and the angle between them are equal.

  ASA Two angles and a corresponding side are equal.

  RHS A right angle, the hypotenuse and one other side are equal.

6 Proving congruency

This lesson will help you to prove that triangles are congruent.

Exercise 6

For two triangles to be **congruent**, one of the conditions for congruency must be true.

To prove that two triangles are congruent:

- mark equal lengths and equal angles on the diagram;
- make one statement at a time, giving a reason why it is true;
- state which of the four conditions for congruency is satisfied.

Draw on all the facts you know about properties of angles, lines or shapes. For example:

- alternate or corresponding angles when lines are parallel;
- angle facts about circles, chords and tangents;
- angle and side properties of shapes such as regular polygons, triangles or quadrilaterals.

Example 1

In a quadrilateral ABCD, AB = AD.
AC bisects angle BAD.
Prove that triangles ABC and ADC are congruent.

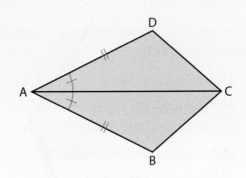

In triangles ABC and ADC:

AB = AD (given)

Angle BAC = angle DAC (given)

AC is common.

So triangles ABC and ADC are congruent **(SAS)**.

Example 2

In the diagram, AB and CD are parallel and equal.

Prove that triangle ABE is congruent to triangle CDE.

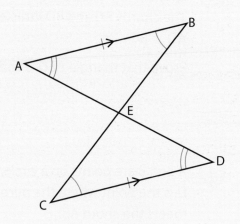

In triangles ABE and CDE:

Angle BAE = angle CDE (alternate angles)

Angle ABE = angle DCE (alternate angles)

AB = CD (given)

So triangles ABE and CDE are congruent **(ASA)**.

Example 3

ABC is an isosceles triangle.
E is a point on AB and D is a point on AC
such that BE = CD.

Prove that triangles EBC and DCB are congruent.

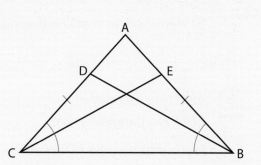

In triangles EBC and DCB:

BE = CD (given)

BC = BC (common)

Angle EBC = angle DCB (base angles of an isosceles triangle)

So triangles EBC and DCB are congruent **(SAS)**.

The diagrams are not drawn accurately.

① ABC is an isosceles triangle.
D is the midpoint of AC.

   a Prove that triangle ABD is congruent to triangle CBD.

   b What does this tell you about the lines AC and BD?

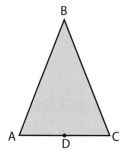

② The diagonals of a quadrilateral
bisect each other at right angles.

Use congruent triangles to prove
that the quadrilateral is a rhombus.

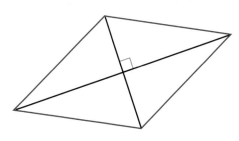

3 A, B, C and D are points on the circumference of a circle.
The chords AC and BD intersect at E.
AD = BC

Prove that triangle AED is congruent to triangle BEC.

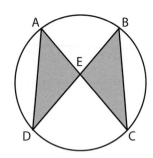

4 A and B are points on a circle, centre O.
D is the point where the perpendicular from O
meets the chord AB.

   a Prove that triangles OAD and OBD are congruent.

   b Hence prove that D is the midpoint of the chord AB.

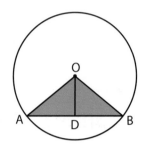

5 ABCD is a rectangle.
CDEF is a parallelogram.

Prove that triangle ADE is congruent to triangle BCF.

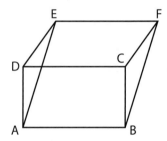

6 WXYZ is a quadrilateral.
WY is perpendicular to WX and ZY.
WZ = XY

   a Prove that triangles WYZ and YWX are congruent.

   b What does this tell you about quadrilateral WXYZ?
      Give reasons for your answer.

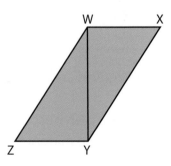

Extension problem

7 ABCD is a square.
E is a point on AB and F is a point on AD.
EC is perpendicular to FB.

Prove that triangle ABF is congruent to triangle BCE.

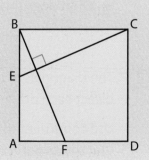

Points to remember

⊙ To **prove** that two triangles are **congruent**, show that one of these conditions is satisfied:

SSS Corresponding sides are equal.

SAS Two sides and the angle between them are equal.

ASA Two angles and a corresponding side are equal.

RHS A right angle, the hypotenuse and one other side are equal.

⊙ You can use congruent triangles to prove that the standard constructions work.

7 Similar shapes and solids

This lesson will help you to understand and use similarity.

 Did you know that...?

3D shapes can be mathematically similar. For example, the **Pyramids of Giza**, built around 3000 BC are similar solids because they are enlargements of each other.

The triangular faces are all at the same angle to the horizontal square bases.

Corresponding sloping faces are similar triangles and are parallel to each other.

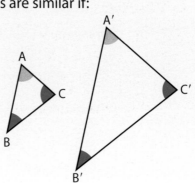

Exercise 7

Similar shapes are enlargements of each other so they are connected by a scale factor. They are the same shape but are different sizes. Two polygons are similar if:

⊙ the angles at corresponding vertices are **equal**;

⊙ corresponding sides are **in the same ratio**.

Triangle ABC and triangle A′B′C′ are **similar triangles**.

The angles in triangles ABC and A′B′C′ are the same.

The lengths of corresponding sides are in the same ratio, so:

$$\frac{A'B'}{AB} = \frac{B'C'}{BC} = \frac{C'A'}{CA} = k, \text{ where } k \text{ is the scale factor.}$$

Similar areas

The diagram shows two squares of side 1 cm and side 3 cm.

Area of square of side 1 cm = 1 cm²
Area of square of side 3 cm = 9 cm²

When lengths are multiplied by 3, area is multiplied by 9.

In general, for similar shapes,

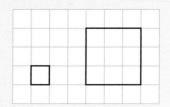

> **when lengths are multiplied by k, area is multiplied by k^2.**

For example, if the lengths of a shape are multiplied by 4, its area is multiplied by 4^2, that is 16.

Similar volumes

The diagram shows two cubes of side 1 cm and side 3 cm.

Volume of cube of side 1 cm = $(1 \times 1 \times 1)$ cm³ = 1 cm³
Volume of cube of side 3 cm = $(3 \times 3 \times 3)$ cm³ = 27 cm³

When lengths are multiplied by 3, volume is multiplied by 27.

In general, for similar solids,

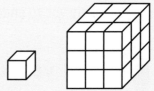

> **when lengths are multiplied by k, volume is multiplied by k^3.**

For example, if the lengths of a shape are multiplied by 4, its volume is multiplied by 4^3, that is 64.

Example 1

Cylinders **R** and **S** are similar.

The surface area of cylinder **R** is 40 cm².

Calculate the surface area of cylinder **S**.

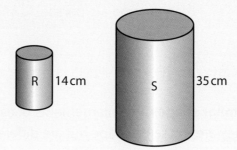

Scale factor = $\frac{35}{14} = \frac{5}{2} = 2.5$

Find the number by which the length of the small cylinder has been multiplied to get the length of the large cylinder (the scale factor, k).

$2.5^2 = 6.25$

Square the scale factor to find the number by which the area should be multiplied.

40 cm² $\times$ 6.25 = **250 cm²**

Multiply the surface area of cylinder **R** by 6.25 to find the surface area of cylinder **S**.

Example 2

Cones **P** and **Q** are similar.

The volume of cone **P** is 12.5π cm³.
The volume of cone **Q** is 100π cm³.

Calculate the value of x.

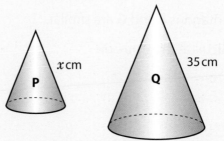

$\dfrac{100\pi}{12.5\pi} = 8$ Find the number by which the volume of **P** has been multiplied to get the volume of **Q** (k^3).

$k^3 = 8$ This number is (scale factor)³.

$k = \sqrt[3]{8} = 2$ The scale factor is the cube root of this number.

35 cm $\div\ 2 = \mathbf{17.5\ cm}$ Divide the height of the large cone by the scale factor to get the height of the small cone.

Example 3

Prisms **P** and **Q** are similar.

The surface area of prism **P** is 300 cm².
The surface area of prism **Q** is 588 cm².

The volume of prism **P** is 250 cm³.

Calculate the volume of prism **Q**.

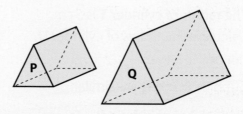

$\dfrac{588}{300} = 1.96$ Find the number by which the surface area of **P** has been multiplied to get the surface area of **Q** (k^2).

$k^2 = 1.96$ This number is (scale factor)².

$k = \sqrt{1.96} = 1.4$ The scale factor is the square root of this number.

$k^3 = 1.4^3 = 2.744$ Find the number by which the volume of **P** must be multiplied to get the volume of **Q** (k^3).

250 cm² $\times\ 2.744 = \mathbf{686\ cm^3}$ Multiply the volume of **P** by this number to get the volume of **Q**.

The diagrams are not drawn accurately.

1   In the diagram, ST is parallel to PQ.

    a   Prove that triangles SRT and QRP are similar.

    b   Which side corresponds to RT?

    c   Find the length of:

       i   PQ   **ii**   SR

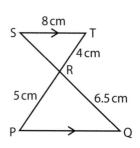

2. Pentagons **F** and **G** are similar.

Calculate the value of:

a x b y

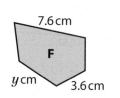
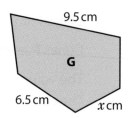

7.6 cm

9.5 cm

F

G

y cm

3.6 cm

6.5 cm

x cm

3. Hexagons **Y** and **Z** are similar.

The area of hexagon **Y** is 30 cm².
The area of hexagon **Z** is 1080 cm².

The perimeter of hexagon **Y** is 25 cm.
Calculate the perimeter of hexagon **Z**.

Y

Z

4. Cylinders **T** and **U** are similar.

The surface area of cylinder **T** is 40 cm².
The surface area of cylinder **U** is 250 cm².

The radius of cylinder **T** is 5 cm.
Calculate the radius of cylinder **U**.

T

U

5. Cuboids **P** and **Q** are similar.

The volume of cuboid **P** is 50 cm³.
Calculate the volume of cuboid **Q**.

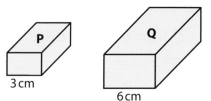

P

Q

3 cm

6 cm

6. Cuboid **A** has a volume of 162 cm³.
Cuboid **B** has a volume of 6 cm³.

What is the length of cuboid B?

A

B

6 cm

l cm

7. Pyramids **P** and **Q** are similar.

The volume of pyramid **P** is 120 cm³.
The volume of pyramid **Q** is 405 cm³.

The surface area of pyramid **Q** is 315 cm².
Calculate the surface area of pyramid **P**.

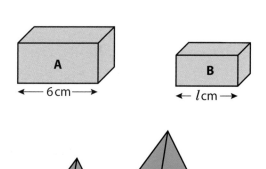

P

Q

8. Cuboids **P** and **Q** are similar.
The surface area of cuboid **Q** is 25 times the surface area of cuboid **P**.
The volume of cuboid **P** is 40 cm³.
Calculate the volume of cuboid **Q**.

(9) Cones **P** and **Q** are similar.

The surface area of cone **P** is 24 cm².
The surface area of cone **Q** is 54 cm².

The volume of cone **P** is 16 cm³.
Calculate the volume of cone **Q**.

 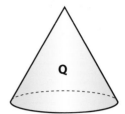

Extension problems

(10) Cylinders **P** and **Q** are similar.

The volume of cylinder **Q** is 216 times
the volume of cylinder P.

The volume of cylinder **P** is 50 cm³.

Calculate the radius of cylinder **P**.
Give your answer to 3 significant figures.

 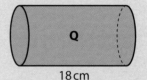

18 cm

(11) The volume of a sphere is $\frac{4}{3}\pi r^3$, where r is the radius.

The surface area of sphere **Q** is 49 times the surface
area of sphere **P**.

The volume of sphere **P** is 50 cm³.

Calculate the radius of sphere **Q**.
Give your answer to 3 significant figures.

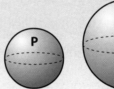 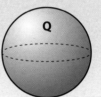

⊙ Points to remember

⊙ In similar shapes, the lengths of corresponding sides are in the same ratio.

⊙ Regular polygons with the same number of sides are similar.

⊙ For similar shapes or solids, when lengths are multiplied by k:

– area is multiplied by k^2;

– volume is multiplied by k^3.

How well are you doing?

Geometrical reasoning (no calculator)

1 *GCSE 1387 November 2007*

a O is the centre of the circle.

A, B and C are points on the circle.

Angle COA = 130°

  i Find the size of angle CBA.

  ii Give a reason for your answer.

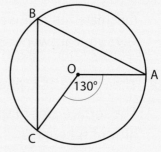

Diagram NOT drawn accurately

b O is the centre of the circle.

P, Q, R and S are points on the circle.

Angle ROP = 110°

Calculate the size of angle RSP.

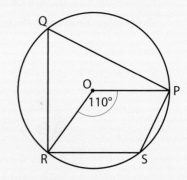

Diagram NOT drawn accurately

2 *2003 level 8*

The diagram shows three points, A, B and C, on a circle, centre O.

AC is a diameter of the circle.

a Angle BAO is x and angle BCO is y.

Explain why angle ABO must be x and angle CBO must be y.

b Use algebra to show that angle ABC must be 90°.

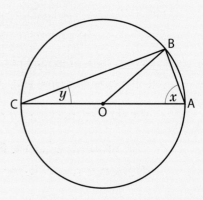

Diagram NOT drawn accurately

3 *2000 Exceptional performance*

AD is a tangent to the circle, centre O.

Angle ABC is 63° and AC is a chord.

Write down the size of:

a angle AOC

b angle OCA

c angle CAD

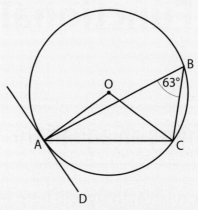

Diagram NOT drawn accurately

4 ABCD is a parallelogram.

The two diagonals of the parallelogram intersect at X.

a Prove that triangle BCX is congruent to triangle DAX.

b Prove that triangle ABX is congruent to triangle CDX.

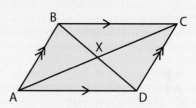

Diagram NOT drawn accurately

5 *GCSE 1387 June 2006*

ABCD is a square.

BEC and DCF are equilateral triangles.

a Prove that triangle BEC is congruent to triangle DCF.

b G is a point such that BEGF is a parallelogram.

Prove that ED = EG.

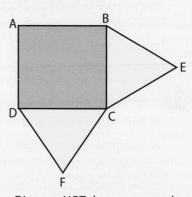

Diagram NOT drawn accurately

6 *GCSE 1387 June 2007*

Two cones, **P** and **Q**, are mathematically similar.
The total surface area of cone **P** is 24 cm².
The total surface area of cone **Q** is 96 cm².
The height of cone **P** is 4 cm.

a Work out the height of cone **Q**.

b The volume of cone **P** is 12 cm³.
Work out the volume of cone **Q**.

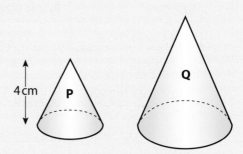

Diagram NOT drawn accurately

Functional skills 4

Designing an aquarium

This group activity will help you to:

- identify the mathematics in a situation;
- decide on the information, methods and tools to use;
- find and interpret results and draw conclusions.

Background

Aquariums are designed in different shapes to fit different spaces. The world's largest aquarium is in a hotel in Berlin. It is cylindrical and has a lift inside it.

The Berlin aquarium, 25 m tall, and 11 m wide, is the largest acrylic glass cylinder in the world. It contains 900 000 litres of sea water and 56 different species of fish. Two divers do the daily cleaning and fish feeding.

Here is some information about some of the small fish kept in an aquarium.

Species	Adult size (cm)
Gambusia male	2–2.5
Black tetra	4
Gambusia female	4–5
Black Molly	5
Guppy	5–6
Angel fish	5–8

Species	Adult size (cm)
Fighting fish	6
Goldfish	6
Zebra fish	6
Golden Gourami	8.5
Kissing Gourami	10

Typically, gravel, plants and decorations take up 10–15% of the volume of an aquarium.

Stocking an aquarium

A 'rule of thumb' for stocking an aquarium in the shape of a cuboid is that you need 1.8 litres of water for every 1 cm length of fish.

If your tank is not a cuboid a better rule of thumb to use is that you need 75 cm² of surface area for 1 cm length of fish.

Larger-bodied fish generally need more space in an aquarium.

1 litre of water has a volume of 1000 cm³ and a mass of 1 kg.

Problems

Work in a small group.

1. A fish tank in the shape of a cuboid is 60 cm wide, 30 cm long and 30 cm high.
   a. Calculate the volume of the tank and the weight of that volume of water.
   b. What is the maximum and minimum number of fish that you would put in a tank of this size? Explain your reasoning.
   c. What other factors could affect how many fish you can fit in a particular tank?

2. An aquarium is in the shape of a prism.

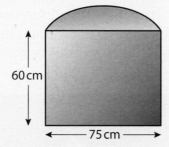

   It is 60 cm tall and has a semi-circular cross-section of diameter 75 cm.

   Choose some suitable fish for this aquarium.

3. Design your own aquarium, considering its size, shape and volume, the weight of the water and the number and size of the fish it will contain.

4. What other factors might affect someone's choice of an aquarium and what fish to buy?

Be ready to discuss your designs and the factors you have considered with other groups.

Probability 1

This unit will help you to:

- ⊙ use tree diagrams to work out probabilities involving events that are independent or not independent;
- ⊙ work out probabilities of combined events;
- ⊙ work out experimental probability from relative frequency;
- ⊙ use the 'and' and 'or' rules to solve probability problems;
- ⊙ use probability to investigate simple games.

1 Using tree diagrams

This lesson will further your understanding of the use of tree diagrams to work out probabilities.

Did you know that...?

The scientific study of probability is a relatively modern development.

Aside from some elementary considerations made by the Italian **Girolamo Cardano** in the 16th century, the mathematics of probability dates to the correspondence which began in 1654 between the French lawyer and mathematician **Pierre de Fermat** and the scientist **Blaise Pascal** (1623–1662). Their work strongly influenced the later development of modern economics and social science.

Blaise Pascal (1623–1662)

Pierre de Fermat (1601–1665)

Two events are **independent** when the outcomes of one event do not affect the outcomes of the other event. For example, Tara has two boxes of counters – box A and box B.

Box A contains
3 red counters
1 blue counter

Box B contains
2 red counters
1 blue counter

Tara picks a counter at random from box A. She then picks a counter at random from box B.

The colour that Tara picks from box A does not affect the probability of the colour she picks from box B. So picking a counter from box A and picking a counter from box B are **independent** events.

You can use a **tree diagram** to help you to work out the probabilities of combined outcomes.

This tree diagram shows the combined outcomes when Tara picks the counters.

On a tree diagram it is usual to:

☺ write the outcomes of each event (**R** and **B**) at the end of the branches;

☺ write the probabilities of each outcome on the branches.

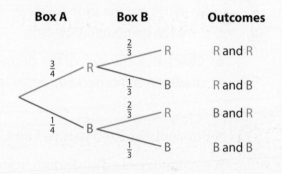

Notice that:

☺ for Box A $P(\mathbf{R}) + P(\mathbf{B}) = \frac{3}{4} + \frac{1}{4} = 1$ for Box B $P(\mathbf{R}) + P(\mathbf{B}) = \frac{2}{3} + \frac{1}{3} = 1$

☺ the sum of the probabilities on each set of branches of a tree diagram is 1;

☺ each route through the branches of the tree gives a combined outcome.

The probability of each combined outcome is worked out by multiplying the probabilities on the appropriate branches of the tree.

$P(\mathbf{R} \text{ and } \mathbf{R}) = P(\mathbf{R}) \times P(\mathbf{R}) = \frac{3}{4} \times \frac{2}{3} = \frac{6}{12} = \frac{1}{2}$

$P(\mathbf{R} \text{ and } \mathbf{B}) = P(\mathbf{R}) \times P(\mathbf{B}) = \frac{3}{4} \times \frac{1}{3} = \frac{3}{12} = \frac{1}{4}$

$P(\mathbf{B} \text{ and } \mathbf{R}) = P(\mathbf{B}) \times P(\mathbf{R}) = \frac{1}{4} \times \frac{2}{3} = \frac{2}{12} = \frac{1}{6}$

$P(\mathbf{B} \text{ and } \mathbf{B}) = P(\mathbf{B}) \times P(\mathbf{B}) = \frac{1}{4} \times \frac{1}{3} = \frac{1}{12}$

Because the combined outcomes **R** and **R**, **R** and **B**, **B** and **R** and **B** and **B** include **all** possible mutually exclusive outcomes:

$P(\mathbf{R} \text{ and } \mathbf{R}) + P(\mathbf{R} \text{ and } \mathbf{B}) + P(\mathbf{B} \text{ and } \mathbf{R}) + P(\mathbf{B} \text{ and } \mathbf{B}) = \frac{6}{12} + \frac{3}{12} + \frac{2}{12} + \frac{1}{12} = \frac{12}{12} = 1$

1. An experiment is carried out using two boxes of counters.

Box A contains
2 red counters and
1 blue counter.

Box B contains
1 red counter and
1 blue counter.

A counter is picked at random from box A.
A counter is picked at random from box B.

a Explain why picking a counter from box A and picking a counter from box B are independent events.

b i Copy and complete the tree diagram.

ii Show all the possible combined outcomes.

iii Work out the probability of each combined outcome.

c Check that the sum of the probabilities of **all** the combined outcomes is 1.

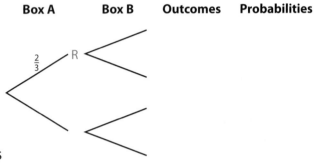

2. A box contains 3 red counters and 7 blue counters

A counter is picked at random from the box.
The counter is replaced and a second counter is picked at random from the box.

a Explain why the first pick from the box and the second pick from the box are independent events.

b Copy and complete the tree diagram to show all the possible combined outcomes.

c Use the tree diagram to work out:

i P(**R** and **R**)

ii P(**R** and **B**)

iii P(**B** and **R**)

iv P(**B** and **B**)

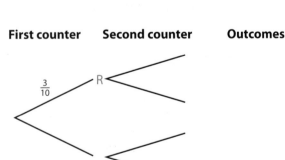

d Show that P(**R** and **R**) + P(**R** and **B**) + P(**B** and **R**) + P(**B** and **B**) = 1.

3 A box of counters contains 3 red counters, 4 green counters and 1 blue counter.

A counter is picked at random from the box.
The counter is replaced and a second counter is picked at random from the box.

a Copy and complete this tree diagram to show all the outcomes of the trial.

b Use the tree diagram to work out:

   i P(**R** and **R**)

  ii P(**G** and **G**)

 iii P(**B** and **B**)

First counter   **Second counter**   **Outcomes**

4 An experiment is carried out on three boxes of counters.

Box A contains
1 red counter
and 1 blue counter.

Box B contains
1 red counter
and 1 blue counter.

Box C contains
2 red counters
and 1 blue counter.

       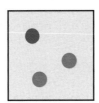

A counter is picked at random from box A.
Another counter is picked at random from box B.
Another counter is picked at random from box C.

a Draw a tree diagram to show all the possible outcomes.

b Use the tree diagram to work out:

   i P(**R** and **R** and **R**)   **ii** P(**R** and **B** and **R**)   **iii** P(**B** and **R** and **B**)

  iv P(**R** and **R** and **B**)   **v** P(**B** and **B** and **B**)

⊙ Points to remember

- ⊙ **Mutually exclusive outcomes** are outcomes that cannot occur at the same time.
- ⊙ Two events are **independent** when the outcomes of one event do not affect the outcomes of the other event.
- ⊙ You can use **tree diagrams** to represent outcomes of combined independent events.
- ⊙ When A and B are outcomes of independent events:
  P(A and B) = P(A) × P(B).

2 The probability of combined events

This lesson will help you to appreciate when to multiply and when to add probabilities when working out the probability of combinations of outcomes of combined events.

Exercise 2

Mutually exclusive outcomes are outcomes that cannot occur at the same time.

Example

In the example on p. 181, Tara picks red (**R**) and blue (**B**) counters at random from two boxes.

The probabilities of the combined outcomes are:

$$P(\mathbf{R} \text{ and } \mathbf{R}) = \frac{3}{4} \times \frac{2}{3} = \frac{6}{12} = \frac{1}{2}$$

$$P(\mathbf{R} \text{ and } \mathbf{B}) = \frac{3}{4} \times \frac{1}{3} = \frac{3}{12} = \frac{1}{4}$$

$$P(\mathbf{B} \text{ and } \mathbf{R}) = \frac{1}{4} \times \frac{2}{3} = \frac{2}{12} = \frac{1}{6}$$

$$P(\mathbf{B} \text{ and } \mathbf{B}) = \frac{1}{4} \times \frac{1}{3} = \frac{1}{12}$$

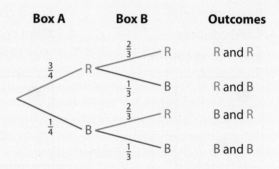

a   What is the probability of **picking two counters with the same colour**?

Because the two outcomes **R** and **R** and **B** and **B** are mutually exclusive:

$$P(\mathbf{R} \text{ and } \mathbf{R} \text{ or } \mathbf{B} \text{ and } \mathbf{B}) = P(\mathbf{R} \text{ and } \mathbf{R}) + P(\mathbf{B} \text{ and } \mathbf{B})$$
$$= \frac{1}{2} + \frac{1}{12} = \frac{7}{12}$$

b   What is the probability of **picking two counters with different colours**?

Because picking the same colour and picking different colours include all mutually exclusive outcomes:

$$P(\text{different colour}) = 1 - P(\text{same colour})$$
$$= 1 - \frac{7}{12} = \frac{5}{12}$$

c   What is the probability of **picking exactly one red counter**?

The two outcomes **R** and **B** and **B** and **R** include exactly one red counter and are mutually exclusive:

$$P(\mathbf{R} \text{ and } \mathbf{B} \text{ or } \mathbf{B} \text{ and } \mathbf{R}) = P(\mathbf{R} \text{ and } \mathbf{B}) + P(\mathbf{B} \text{ and } \mathbf{R})$$
$$= \frac{1}{4} + \frac{1}{6} = \frac{10}{24} = \frac{5}{12}$$

1 Tom throws two darts at this target. Each dart hits the target.

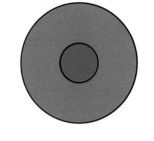

If Tom hits the blue circle he scores 5 points.
If Tom hits the red outer section he scores 2 points.

On each throw the probability that Tom scores 5 points is $\frac{1}{5}$.

a Copy and complete this tree diagram to show the points Tom scores on his first and second throws.

b Use the tree diagram to work out the probability that Tom scores a total of at least 7 points with two darts.

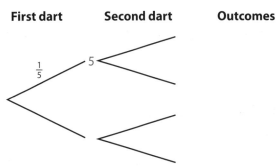

2 A box contains 2 red counters, 3 yellow counters and 5 blue counters.
A counter is picked at random from the box.
The counter is replaced and a second counter is picked at random from the box.

a Copy and complete this tree diagram to show all the outcomes of the trial.

b Work out the probability that the two counters are the same colour.

c Work out the probability that the two counters include exactly one yellow counter.

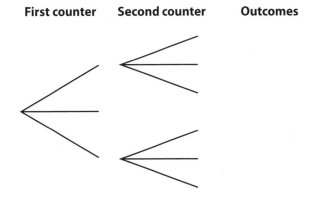

3 Sadiq has these two sets of cards.

Sadiq picks an orange card at random and a green card at random.

a Copy and complete this tree diagram to show all possible outcomes.

b Work out the probability that at least one of the letters on the two cards is a vowel.

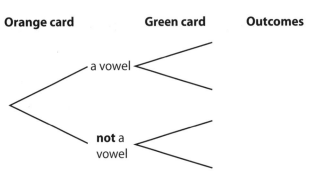

4 Three fair 1–6 dice are rolled. For each dice, whether or not a 6 is rolled is recorded.

Calculate these probabilities:

a exactly two sixes are rolled **b** one or two sixes are rolled.

Points to remember

⊙ When outcomes A and B of an event are mutually exclusive:
P(A or B) = P(A) + P(B).

⊙ For two combined independent events each with mutually exclusive outcomes
A and **B**:

– The probability that the outcomes are the same is:
P(**A** and **A** or **B** and **B**) = P(**A**) × P(**A**) + P(**B**) × P(**B**)

– The probability that the outcomes are different is:
P(**A** and **B** or **B** and **A**) = P(**A**) × P(**B**) + P(**B**) × P(**A**)

– The probability of at least one A is:
P(**A** and **A** or **A** and **B** or **B** and **A**) = P(**A**) × P(**A**) + P(**A**) × P(**B**) + P(**B**) × P(**A**)
or 1 − P(**B** and **B**) = 1 − P(**B**) × P(**B**)

3 Investigating a game of chance

Did you know that...?

Rock, paper, scissors (**RPS**) is a game for two people using hand signals. It is
played all over the world although different names are used.

⊙ The Japanese call the game Jankenpon.

⊙ In France it is known as Rochambeau.

⊙ In South Africa it is called Ching-Chong-Cha.

Here are the World Rock Paper Scissors Society's rules.

Rock (R)

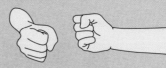

Paper (P)

Rules

1 Players use hand signals to represent rock, paper
and scissors.

2 Players must show their hand signals at the same time.

3 Rock wins against scissors.
Scissors wins against paper.
Paper wins against rock.
If players show the same hand signal the game is tied.

Scissors (S)

This lesson will help you to use probability to investigate strategies for playing a game of chance.

There is a large element of luck in Rock, paper, scissors but players can analyse their opponent's choices and use them to advantage.

For example, in a game, a player notices that their opponent is starting to favour, say, paper. Should the player choose scissors more often?

Answers to questions like this can be investigated using tree diagrams.

Example

Player 1 chooses rock, paper and scissors at random.
Player 2 chooses rock, paper and scissors in the ratio $2:1:1$.

Work out the probability of each player winning and of a tie.

The probabilities of each choice for each player are shown in this table.

	P(**R**)	P(**P**)	P(**S**)
Player 1	$\frac{1}{3}$	$\frac{1}{3}$	$\frac{1}{3}$
Player 2	$\frac{1}{2}$	$\frac{1}{4}$	$\frac{1}{4}$

Player 1	Player 2	Outcomes	Probabilities	Result
	R $\frac{1}{2}$	**R** and **R**	$\frac{1}{3} \times \frac{1}{2} = \frac{1}{6}$	Tie
R	P $\frac{1}{4}$	**R** and **P**	$\frac{1}{3} \times \frac{1}{4} = \frac{1}{12}$	Player 2
$\frac{1}{3}$	S $\frac{1}{4}$	**R** and **S**	$\frac{1}{3} \times \frac{1}{4} = \frac{1}{12}$	Player 1
	R $\frac{1}{2}$	**P** and **R**	$\frac{1}{3} \times \frac{1}{2} = \frac{1}{6}$	Player 1
$\frac{1}{3}$ P	P $\frac{1}{4}$	**P** and **P**	$\frac{1}{3} \times \frac{1}{4} = \frac{1}{12}$	Tie
	S $\frac{1}{4}$	**P** and **S**	$\frac{1}{3} \times \frac{1}{4} = \frac{1}{12}$	Player 2
$\frac{1}{3}$	R $\frac{1}{2}$	**S** and **R**	$\frac{1}{3} \times \frac{1}{2} = \frac{1}{6}$	Player 2
S	P $\frac{1}{4}$	**S** and **P**	$\frac{1}{3} \times \frac{1}{4} = \frac{1}{12}$	Player 1
	S $\frac{1}{4}$	**S** and **S**	$\frac{1}{3} \times \frac{1}{4} = \frac{1}{12}$	Tie

P(tie) = P(**R** and **R**) + P(**P** and **P**) + P(**S** and **S**) = $\frac{1}{6} + \frac{1}{12} + \frac{1}{12} = \frac{1}{3}$

P(Player 1 wins) = P(**R** and **S**) + P(**P** and **R**) + P(**S** and **P**) = $\frac{1}{12} + \frac{1}{6} + \frac{1}{12} = \frac{1}{3}$

P(Player 2 wins) = P(**R** and **P**) + P(**P** and **S**) + P(**S** and **R**) = $\frac{1}{12} + \frac{1}{12} + \frac{1}{6} = \frac{1}{3}$

It is equally likely that a game will end with a win for Player 1 or Player 2 or end in a tie.

1. Alex and Kirsty play Rock, paper, scissors.
Both players make their choice of hand signals at random.

   a Copy and complete this tree diagram to show all the possible outcomes.

   b Write the probability of making each choice on the branches of your tree diagram.

   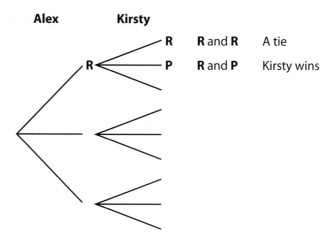

   Work out the probability that:

   i Alex wins

   ii Kirsty wins

   iii there is a tie.

   c Estimate the number of times that Alex wins in a match of 300 games.

2. Sean and Asif play Rock, paper, scissors.
Sean chooses rock, paper and scissors at random. Asif does not.

   Each of the three possible results is equally likely.

   Investigate whether the results are **always** equally likely when Sean chooses rock, paper and scissors at random and Asif does not.

3. Ella and Jade play Rock, paper, scissors.
Ella chooses rock, paper and scissors in the ratio $2:1:1$.

   a Show that Jade is most likely to win if she chooses rock, paper and scissors in the ratio $1:2:1$.

   b Investigate other ways that Jade is more likely to win.

4. David and Sally play Rock, paper, scissors.

   David is equally likely to choose paper or scissors but chooses rock 40% of the time.
Sally is equally likely to choose rock or scissors but chooses paper 20% of the time.

   a Work out the probability that:

   i David wins

   ii Sally wins

   iii the game is a tie.

   b David and Sally play a match of five 'best out of three' games.

   Explain why the probabilities you calculated in part **a** are unlikely to predict the outcome of the game.

Extension problem

 a Generalise the result for a game of Rock, paper, scissors when Player 1 chooses rock, paper and scissors at random and Player 2 does not.
Show your working.

> ### Hint
> Let Player 1 choose at random and Player 2 choose rock, paper and scissors in the ratio $a:b:c$.

b Player 1 chooses rock, paper and scissors in the ratio $a:b:c$.
Player 2 chooses rock, paper and scissors in the ratio $c:b:a$.

Show that, if $a \neq c$, Player 1 and Player 2 are equally likely to win if $2b = a + c$.

c Two players choose rock, paper and scissors in the **same** ratio.

Prove that they are equally likely to win.

 Points to remember

⊙ Relative frequency and theoretical probability can be compared to investigate whether or not a simple game is a game of chance.

⊙ You can use probability theory to investigate strategies for playing a game of chance.

4 Conditional probability

This lesson will help you to use tree diagrams to solve probability problems involving two or more events that are **not** independent.

Exercise 4

When the outcomes of an event depend on the outcomes of a previous event, the events are **not independent**.

The probability of an outcome of an event that is dependent on the outcome of a previous event is called **conditional probability**.

For example, if you choose two pieces of fruit from a bowl without replacing the first one, the probabilities for the second choice of fruit are affected by your first choice.

Example

There are 3 chocolate (C) and 4 ginger (G) biscuits on a plate. A biscuit is chosen at random and eaten. A second biscuit is then chosen at random.

a Work out the probability that both the biscuits chosen will be chocolate.

1st choice: $P(C) = \frac{3}{7}$ — To start with, there are 7 biscuits, 3 of which are chocolate.

2nd choice: $P(C \text{ given } C) = \frac{2}{6} = \frac{1}{3}$ — Since the first choice was chocolate, there are now 6 biscuits, only 2 of which are chocolate.

$P(C \text{ and } C) = P(C) \times P(C \text{ given } C) = \frac{3}{7} \times \frac{1}{3} = \frac{1}{7}$ — Multiply the probabilities.

b Work out the probability that the first biscuit will be chocolate and the second ginger.

1st choice: $P(C) = \frac{3}{7}$ — To start with, there are 7 biscuits, 3 chocolate and 4 ginger.

2nd choice: $P(G \text{ given } C) = \frac{4}{6} = \frac{2}{3}$ — Since the first choice was chocolate, there are now 6 biscuits, 2 chocolate and 4 ginger.

$P(C \text{ and } G) = P(C) \times P(G \text{ given } C) = \frac{3}{7} \times \frac{2}{3} = \frac{2}{7}$ — Multiply the probabilities.

c Work out the probability that at least one chocolate biscuit will be chosen.

$P(\text{at least one chocolate}) = 1 - P(G \text{ and } G)$ — There are four possible outcomes: C and C, C and G, G and C and G and G. So: $P(\text{at least one chocolate}) + P(G \text{ and } G) = 1$

1st choice: $P(G) = \frac{4}{7}$ — Find the probability that the first choice will be ginger. To start with there are 3 chocolate and 4 ginger biscuits.

2nd choice: $P(G \text{ given } G) = \frac{3}{6} = \frac{1}{2}$ — Find the probability that the second choice will be ginger. Since the first choice was ginger, there are now 6 biscuits, 3 chocolate and 3 ginger.

$P(G \text{ and } G) = P(G) \times P(G \text{ given } G) = \frac{4}{7} \times \frac{1}{2} = \frac{2}{7}$ — Multiply the probabilities.

$P(\text{at least one chocolate}) = 1 - P(G \text{ and } G)$

$= 1 - \frac{2}{7} = \frac{5}{7}$

1. A bag contains 7 blue (**B**) counters and 3 red (**R**) counters.

Jo takes a counter from the bag at random and puts it in his pocket.
Shelley then takes a counter from the bag at random and puts it in her pocket.

a Jo picks a blue counter. How many blue and how many red counters are now in the bag?

b Jo picks a red counter. How many blue and how many red counters are now in the bag?

c Copy and complete this tree diagram to show all the possible outcomes.

Write the probabilities of each outcome on the branches of the tree diagram.

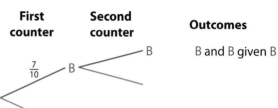

d Explain how the tree diagram shows that picking the first counter and picking the second counter are events that are **not** independent.

e Calculate the probability that Jo and Shelley pick:

   i two blue counters

   ii two counters the same colour

   iii two counters of different colours

   iv at least one blue counter

2. Ben rolls a fair dice.

If the dice shows a square number Ben picks a blue card at random.

If the dice does **not** show a square number Ben picks a red card at random.

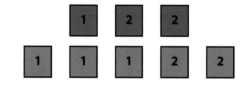

a Explain why rolling the dice and picking the card are **not** independent events.

b Copy and complete this tree diagram to show all the possible outcomes.
Write the probabilities of each outcome on the branches of the tree diagram.

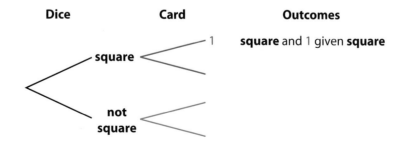

c Work out the probability that the number on the card is 2.

3 A bag contains 7 blue (**B**) counters and 13 red (**R**) counters.

Mary-Lou takes a counter from the bag at random and puts it in her pocket.
Winston then takes a counter from the bag at random and puts in his pocket.

a Draw a tree diagram to show all the possible outcomes.
Write the probabilities of each outcome on the branches of the tree diagram.

b Calculate the probability that Mary-Lou and Winston pick:

   i two blue counters

   ii two counters the same colour

   iii two counters of different colours

   iv at least one blue counter

4 Each tree diagram represents the outcomes of a pair of events.

a For each diagram, state whether the events are independent or not independent.
Explain your answers.

i
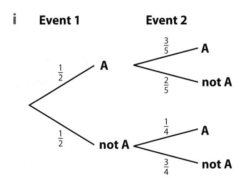

ii
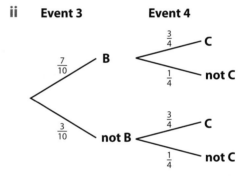

iii
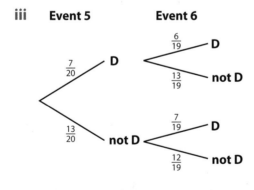

iv
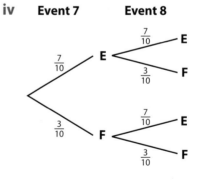

b The tree diagrams show the outcomes A and not A, B and not B, C and not C, D and not D, and E and F. Calculate these probabilities:

   i P(**A** and **A**)

   ii P(at least one **B**)

   iii P(**not D** and **D** or **D** and **not D**)

   iv P(exactly one **E**)

Extension problem

 5 Box A contains 3 red (**R**) counters and 1 blue (**B**) counter.
Box B contains 1 red (**R**) counter and 3 blue (**B**) counters.

A counter is taken at random from box A and put in box B.
A counter is then taken at random from box B and put in box A.

a Draw a tree diagram to represent this situation.

b Work out the probability that both boxes then contain an equal number of red and blue counters.

c Work out the probability that both boxes then contain counters of the same colour.

d Work out the probability that the boxes contain the same number of red and blue counters as they started with.

 Points to remember

⊙ When the outcomes of an event depend on the outcomes of a previous event, the events are not independent.

⊙ The probability of an outcome of an event that depends on the outcome of a previous event is called **conditional probability**.

⊙ You can use tree diagrams to help work out conditional probabilities.

5 The 'and' and 'or' rules

This lesson will help you to solve probability problems without using a tree diagram.

Exercise 5

The 'and' rule for combined events A and B, independent or not independent

P(**A** and **B**) = P(**A**) × P(**B**)

This rule can be extended to any number of independent events. For example:

P(**A** and **B** and **C**) = P(**A**) × P(**B**) × P(**C**)

The 'or' rule for two mutually exclusive outcomes X and Y

P(**X** or **Y**) = P(**X**) + P(**Y**)

This rule can be extended to any number of mutually exclusive outcomes. For example:

P(**X** or **Y** or **Z**) = P(**X**) + P(**Y**) + P(**Z**)

Using both rules together

Outcomes of combined events are also mutually exclusive. For example:

P(**A** and **A** or **B** and **B**) = P(**A**) × P(**A**) + P(**B**) × P(**B**)

Example 1

A fair 1–6 dice is rolled twice.

Work out the probability of rolling two sixes.

The events are independent.

P(6 **and** 6) = P(6) × P(6) = $\frac{1}{6}$ × $\frac{1}{6}$ = $\frac{1}{36}$

Example 2

A bag contains 10 counters, 7 of which are red.

3 counters are taken from the bag at random and put in a box.
Work out the probability that all the counters in the box are red.

The events are **not** independent.

P(**R** and **R** and **R**) = P(**R**) × P(**R** *given* **R**) × P(**R** *given* **R** and **R**)

$= \frac{7}{10} × \frac{6}{9} × \frac{5}{8} = \frac{7}{24}$

Example 3

The arrow of this spinner is spun twice.

What is the probability that the numbers the arrow lands on
add up to 4?

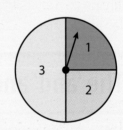

The events are independent.

P(**1**) = $\frac{1}{4}$, P(**2**) = $\frac{1}{4}$ and P(**3**) = $\frac{1}{2}$

Outcomes for a total score of 4 are **1** and **3** or **2** and **2** or **3** and **1**

P(**1** and **3** or **2** and **2** or **3** and **1**) = P(**1**) × P(**3**) + P(**2**) × P(**2**) + P(**3**) × P(**1**)

$= \frac{1}{4} × \frac{1}{2} + \frac{1}{4} × \frac{1}{4} + \frac{1}{2} × \frac{1}{4}$

$= \frac{1}{8} + \frac{1}{16} + \frac{1}{8}$

$= \frac{5}{16}$

---

(1) A dice is biased. The probability of rolling a 6 is 0.3 and the probability of rolling a 5 is 0.2.

The dice is rolled twice.

a   Work out the probability of rolling two fives.

b   Work out the probability of rolling two fives or two sixes.

2 A fair dice has three red faces, two blue faces and one green face.
The dice is rolled twice and the colour is recorded.

   a Work out the probability that on both rolls the dice lands on a blue face.

   b Work out the probability that on both rolls the dice lands on a face of the same colour.

3 The probability that Ben is late for school is 0.2.
The probability that Julie is late for school is 0.15.
Assume that these are independent events.

   What is the probability that either Ben or Julie is late for school?

4 A bag contains 2 red counters, 5 blue counters and 3 green counters.

   A counter is picked from the bag at random.
Its colour is recorded and the counter is then replaced.

   Another counter is then picked from the bag at random and its colour recorded.

   Calculate the probability that both counters are the same colour.

5 Repeat question 4 with the counters being **not** replaced after the first pick.

6 Billy has 6 red socks and 9 blue socks in a drawer.
He takes two socks out of the drawer at random and puts them on.

   What is the probability that Billy picks two socks of the same colour?

7 In a box of chocolates there are 10 milk chocolates and 12 plain chocolates.

   Zola takes two chocolates at random and eats them.

   Work out the probability that:

   a Zola takes two milk chocolates;

   b at least one chocolate that Zola takes is a milk chocolate.

8 A bag contains 11 black beads, 6 red beads and 3 green beads.

   Dan takes a bead at random from the bag, records its colour and replaces it.
He does this two more times.

   Work out the probability that of the three beads Dan takes, exactly two are the same colour.

Extension problems

9 Wendy has 20 pieces of fruit in a bowl.
10 of them are apples, 6 of them are oranges and 4 of them are pears.

Wendy takes two pieces of fruit at random to take on a picnic.

Calculate the probability that the two pieces of fruit that Wendy takes:

a are the same kind;

b include at least one pear.

10 To score points in a game Tom picks two of these cards at random.

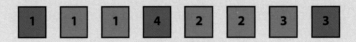

If the cards are both red, he adds the numbers on the cards.
If the cards are both blue, he multiplies the numbers on the cards.
If the cards are a different colour, he subtracts the larger number from the smaller.

Work out the probability that Tom's score is 3.
Show your working.

Points to remember

⊙ You can use the **'and' and 'or' rules** for combined events (independent and not independent) to solve probability problems.

How well are you doing?

Probability 1 (no calculator)

1 *GCSE 1385 June 1998*

Lauren and Yasmina each try to score a goal. They each have one attempt.

The probability that Lauren will score a goal is 0.85.
The probability that Yasmina will score a goal is 0.6.

a Work out the probability that both Lauren and Yasmina will score a goal.

b Work out the probability that Lauren will score a goal and Yasmina will not score a goal.

2 *GCSE 1385 June 2002*

There are n beads in a bag.
6 of the beads are black and all the rest are white.

Heather picks one bead at random from the bag and does not replace it. She picks a second bead at random from the bag.

The probability that she will pick 2 white beads is $\frac{1}{2}$.

Show that $n^2 - 25n + 84 = 0$.

3 *1995 level 8*

Brightlite company makes light bulbs.
The state of the company's machines can be:

Available for use and being used

or   Available for use but not needed

or   Broken down.

a   The table shows the probabilities of the state of the machines in July 1994.

Write down the missing probability.

State of machines: July 1994	Probability
Available for use, being used	
Available for use, not needed	0.09
Broken down	0.03

b   During another month the probability of a machine being available for use was 0.92.
What was the probability of a machine being broken down?

c   Brightlite calculated the probabilities of a bulb failing within 1000 hours and within 2000 hours.

Copy and complete the table to show the probabilities of a bulb still working at 1000 hours and at 2000 hours.

Time	Failed	Still working
At 1000 hours	0.07	
At 2000 hours	0.57	

d   Calculate the probability of two bulbs both failing within 1000 hours.

e   Calculate the probability of two bulbs **both** still working at 2000 hours.

4 *1996 level 8*

A company makes computer disks.
It tested a random sample of the disks from a large batch.
The company calculated the probability of any disk being defective as 0.025.

Glenda buys two disks.

a   Calculate the probability that both disks are defective.

b   Calculate the probability that only one of the disks is defective.

c   The company found 3 defective disks in the sample they tested.
How many disks were likely to have been in the sample?

5 A box contains 5 red counters, 3 blue counters and 2 white counters.
Two counters are taken at random from the box and put in a bag.

a Explain why picking the first counter and picking the second counter are **not** independent events.

b Draw a tree diagram to show all the possible outcomes from the trial.
Write the probabilities of each outcome on the branches of the tree diagram.

c The trial is carried out 300 times.
Estimate the number of times that the two counters have the same colour.

6 *2000 Exceptional performance*

A computer game has nine circles arranged in a square.
The computer chooses circles at random and shades them black.

a At the start of the game, two circles are to be shaded black.

Show that the probability that both circles J and K will be shaded black is $\frac{1}{36}$.

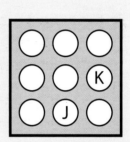

b Halfway through the game, three circles are to be shaded black.

Here is one example of the three circles shaded black in a straight line.

Show that the probability that the three circles shaded black will be in a straight line is $\frac{8}{84}$.

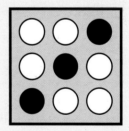

c At the end of the game, four circles are to be shaded black.

Here is one example of the four circles shaded black forming a square.

What is the probability that the four circles shaded black form a square?

Show your working.

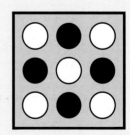

Solving equations

This unit will help you to:

⊙ solve linear and quadratic equations;

⊙ solve simultaneous equations where one is linear and the other non-linear.

1 Linear equations

This lesson will help you to solve linear equations.

Exercise 1

There are often several different approaches to solving a linear equation but where there are fractions it is best to begin by multiplying through by the lowest common denominator.

Example

Solve $\frac{2x}{3} + \frac{x}{9} = 42$.

Multiply both sides by 9	$6x + x = 378$	The lowest common denominator of 3 and
Simplify	$7x = 378$	9 is 9, so multiply both sides of the equation
Divide by 7	$x = \mathbf{54}$	by 9.

① Solve the equations.

a $3(2x + 4) + 2(4x + 7) = 7x$

b $(x + 1)^2 = x^2 + 3x - 3$

c $\frac{2x}{5} + \frac{7x}{3} = 82$

d $\frac{3x}{16} - \frac{9x}{4} = 132$

e $\frac{5x}{12} + \frac{7x}{6} = \frac{19}{4}$

f $\frac{7}{x} + \frac{9}{x} = 64$

g $\frac{3}{x} + \frac{5}{2x} = 11$

h $\frac{3x}{8} - \frac{5x}{16} - \frac{9x}{12} = \frac{11}{8}$

② Solve the equations.

a $\frac{4x + 1}{3} + \frac{6x - 2}{7} = 11$

b $\frac{5x - 4}{9} - \frac{2x + 1}{5} = 2$

c $\frac{x}{5} - 3 = \frac{x}{10} + 4$

d $\frac{4x}{7} - 5 = 6 - \frac{3x}{14}$

e $\frac{3x + 2}{5x + 8} = 2$

f $\frac{3x + 4}{5x + 2} = \frac{2}{3}$

g $\frac{2x + 1}{7} - \frac{3x + 2}{16} = 1$

h $\frac{x^2 - 1}{3x - 3} = 3$

3 The same number is added to the numerator and the denominator of the fraction $\frac{15}{31}$. The resulting fraction is $\frac{5}{6}$. Find the number.

4 Tina and Karl cycle towards each other along an 8 mile stretch of a cycle track.

They meet after a quarter of an hour.

Tina's average speed was 4 mph less than Karl's. What was Tina's average speed?

5 Alex and Janet live 195 miles apart along a motorway. They set off at the same time to meet each other.

Alex travels at an average speed of 60 mph.
Janet travels at an average speed of 70 mph.

After how many hours will they meet?

Extension problem

6 Petra takes part in a triathlon.

She swims 2 km, cycles 50 km ten times faster than her average swimming speed, and runs 10 km at a quarter of her average cycling speed.

Her total time is $2\frac{3}{4}$ hours.

At what speed does Petra cycle?

🎯 Points to remember

⊙ Before you solve a **linear equation**, simplify expressions on both sides.

⊙ If there are algebraic fractions in the equation, multiply through by the lowest common denominator.

⊙ Rearrange the equation to get the unknown on one side and numbers on the other.

⊙ There are often different ways of approaching solutions to equations. Look carefully at the equation and try to find the most efficient method.

2 Solving quadratic equations graphically

This lesson will help you to use graphs to solve quadratic equations, including by using ICT.

Exercise 2

You can solve the equation of $ax^2 + bx + c = 0$ by drawing the graph of $y = ax^2 + bx + c$ and looking at the points where the graph intersects the x-axis.

The values of x at these points are called the **roots** of the equation.
If the graph does not intersect the x-axis the equation does not have any real solutions.

This method is best used for quadratic equations with integer solutions.

Example

Solve $x^2 - x - 6 = 0$.

Draw the graph of $y = x^2 - x - 6$.

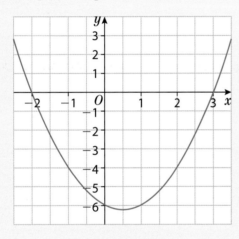

The graph cuts the x-axis at $x = 3$ and $x = -2$.

The two solutions to the equation are $x = \mathbf{3}$ and $x = \mathbf{-2}$.

You will need either a computer with a graph plotter or a graphics calculator.

1 Solve these equations.

    a $x^2 = 196$ **b** $x^2 = 0.25$ **c** $x^2 = 0.0009$ **d** $x^2 = 3600$

    e $x^2 = 0.64$ **f** $x^2 = 225$ **g** $x^2 = 1024$ **h** $x^2 = 1681$

2 Write the equation of the graph you would draw to solve these equations.

    a $x^2 + 3x - 10 = 0$ **b** $x^2 + 7x + 12 = 0$ **c** $2x^2 - 12x - 54 = 0$

    d $6x^2 - 29x + 35 = 0$ **e** $10x^2 + 13x = 3$ **f** $12x^2 + 23x + 6 = 15$

3 Use ICT to draw graphs to solve these equations.
Check your answers by substituting each value for x back into the original equation.

 a $x^2 + 3x - 4 = 0$ **b** $x^2 + 5x + 6 = 0$ **c** $x^2 - 8x - 9 = 0$

 d $2x^2 + 7x - 4 = 0$ **e** $5x^2 - x - 6 = 0$ **f** $x^2 - 5x = 6$

 g $4x^2 + x - 5 = -2$ **h** $4x^2 + 12 = 7 - 9x$

4 Use ICT to help you to say whether these
equations have no real solution, two
different solutions or two equal solutions.

 a $x^2 - 3x + 4 = 0$

 b $x^2 - 4x + 4 = 0$

 c $x^2 - 9 = 0$

 d $x^2 + x + 1 = 0$

 e $x^2 - 5x = 0$

 f $5x^2 + 3 = 23$

5 Use ICT to draw graphs to estimate the solution of these equations to 1 decimal place.
Use trial and improvement to find the solutions to 3 decimal places.

 a $x^2 + 5x - 3 = 0$ **b** $x^2 - 2x = 7$ **c** $3x^2 - 2x + 2 = 4$

Extension problem

6   **a** Solve the equation $x^2 - 3x - 10 = 0$ by drawing an appropriate graph.

 b Factorise the expression $x^2 - 3x - 10$.

 c Describe what you notice.

◉ Points to remember

⊙ A **quadratic graph** may cut the x-axis at two points, touch it at one point
or not touch it at all.

⊙ At any point (x, y) where the graph of $y = ax^2 + bx + c$ meets the x-axis:
 – the value of y is 0;
 – the value of x is a solution of the equation $ax^2 + bx + c = 0$.

⊙ A **quadratic equation** has two real solutions, one real solution or no
real solution.

3 Solving quadratic equations by factorisation 1

This lesson will help you to solve quadratic equations by factorisation.

Exercise 3

You can solve quadratic equations with integer solutions using the **method of factorisation**.

Example

Solve $x^2 + x - 6 = 0$.

$x^2 + x - 6 = (x + 3)(x - 2)$ First factorise the left-hand side.

When $(x + 3)(x - 2) = 0$,   Make each factor equal to zero.
either $(x + 3) = 0$
or $(x - 2) = 0$.

If $(x + 3) = 0$, then $x = -3$.   Solve each equation.
If $(x - 2) = 0$, then $x = 2$.

The solutions of $x^2 + x - 6 = 0$ are   Write the answer.
$x = -3$ **and** $x = 2$.

When $x = -3$, $(-3)^2 - 3 - 6 = 0$ Check by substituting each value back into the
When $x = 2$, $(2)^2 + 2 - 6 = 0$ original equation.

---

①   Solve these equations.

    a $52a = 0$ **b** $8pq = 0$ **c** $b(c + 8) = 0$

②   Solve these equations.

    a $(n + 6)(n - 7) = 0$ **b** $(p + 15)(p - 8) = 0$ **c** $(q + 12)(q - 21) = 0$

    d $(a + 9)(a - 14) = 0$ **e** $(x + 16)(x - 17) = 0$ **f** $(y + 23)(y - 39) = 0$

③   Use factorisation to solve these quadratic equations.
    Check your answers by substituting each value for x back into the original equation.

    a $x^2 + 5x + 6 = 0$ **b** $x^2 + 7x + 6 = 0$ **c** $x^2 - x - 6 = 0$

    d $x^2 - 5x + 6 = 0$ **e** $x^2 + x - 6 = 0$ **f** $x^2 - 5x - 6 = 0$

    g $x^2 + 5x - 6 = 0$ **h** $x^2 - 7x + 6 = 0$ **i** $x^2 - 3x - 10 = 0$

    j $x^2 + 5x + 4 = 0$ **k** $x^2 + 7x + 10 = 0$ **l** $x^2 - 4x + 3 = 0$

    m $x^2 - 9x + 20 = 0$ **n** $x^2 - 6x + 8 = 0$ **o** $x^2 - 2x - 6 = 2x + 6$

4 The diagram shows a trapezium.
All the measurements are in centimetres.

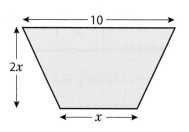

a Write an expression in x for the area of the trapezium.

b The area of the trapezium is 75 cm².
Show that $x^2 + 10x - 75 = 0$.

c Solve the equation $x^2 + 10x - 75 = 0$.

d Write the height of the trapezium.

5 The diagram shows a path around a rectangular lawn.
All the measurements are in metres.
The width of the path is 1 m.

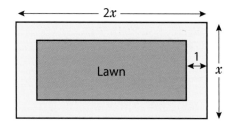

a The area of the lawn is 220 m².
Show that $x^2 - 3x - 108 = 0$.

b Solve this equation.

c Find the length of the longest side of the path.

6 This cuboid has length $(x + 4)$ cm, width $(x + 3)$ cm
and height $(x + 5)$ cm.

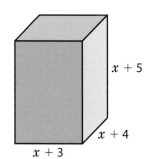

a Write and simplify an expression in x for the surface
area of the cuboid.

b The surface area of the cuboid is 292 cm².
Write an equation and solve it to find the value of x.

Extension problem

7 **a** Look at the equation $x^2 + 2x - 9 = 0$.
Explain why the expression on the left-hand side of the equation cannot be factorised.

b Add 10 to both sides of the equation.

c Factorise the expression that is now on the left-hand side of the equation.

d Take the square root of both sides of the equation and find two values of x.

Points to remember

⊙ To solve a quadratic equation by **factorisation**:

– factorise the quadratic expression;

– in turn, make each bracket equal to zero and find the value of x;

– check the solutions by substituting the values into the original equation.

4 Solving quadratic equations by factorisation 2

This lesson will help you to solve quadratic equations by factorisation.

Exercise 4

When the coefficient of x^2 is not one, you may still be able to use factorisation to solve a quadratic equation.

Example

Solve $10x^2 + 3x - 1 = 0$.

$10x^2 + 3x - 1 \equiv (2x + 1)(5x - 1)$	First factorise the left-hand side.
When $(2x + 1)(5x - 1) = 0$, then either $(2x + 1) = 0$ or $(5x - 1) = 0$.	Make each factor equal to zero.
If $(2x + 1) = 0$, then $x = -\frac{1}{2}$. If $(5x - 1) = 0$, then $x = \frac{1}{5}$.	Solve each equation.
When $x = -\frac{1}{2}$ or -0.5, $10 \times 0.25 - 1.5 - 1 = 0$ When $x = \frac{1}{5}$ or 0.2, $10 \times 0.04 + 0.6 - 1 = 0$	Check by substituting each value back into the original equation. When the values are fractions, it is often easier to change them to decimals before substituting.
The solutions of $10x^2 + 3x - 1 = 0$ are $x = -\frac{1}{2}$ and $x = \frac{1}{5}$.	Write the answer.

1. Use the method of factorisation to solve these quadratic equations. Check your answers by drawing graphs.

   a $8x^2 + 10x + 3 = 0$ b $2x^2 + 11x + 15 = 0$ c $4x^2 - 9 = 0$

   d $9x^2 - 24x + 16 = 0$ e $35x^2 + 8x - 3 = 0$ f $16x^2 + 2x - 3 = 0$

   g $12x^2 + 7x - 10 = 0$ h $6x^2 + 17x - 14 = 0$

2. a The sum of the squares of three consecutive positive integers is 110. Find the numbers.

   b The sum of the squares of three consecutive even numbers is 596. Find the numbers.

3. The opposite parallel sides of a trapezium are $(3x + 2)$ cm and $(5x + 4)$ cm.
   The perpendicular distance between these two sides is x cm.
   The area of the trapezium is 115 cm².
   Find the perpendicular distance between the two parallel sides.

4 A rectangular swimming pool has length $(2x + 1)$ m and width $(x − 3)$ m.
Its area is 60 m².

  a Show that $2x^2 − 5x − 63 = 0$.

  b Find the length of each side of the rectangle.

5 The hypotenuse of a right-angled triangle is $(4x − 3)$ cm.
The other two sides are x cm and $(2x + 10)$ cm.
Find the length of each side of the triangle.

6 The prism in the diagram has length 16 cm.
The base of the triangle is $(3x + 2)$ cm and its
height is $(x + 4)$ cm.

  a Write an expression in x for the volume of
  the prism.

  b The volume of the prism is 384 cm³.
  Write an equation and solve it to find the
  value of x.

  c Work out the total surface area of the prism.

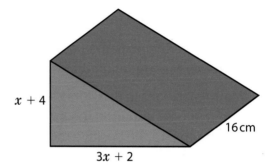

$x + 4$

$3x + 2$

16 cm

Extension problems

7 The difference between a number and its reciprocal is 9.9.
Find both the possible values of the number.

8 **a** Write as an expression in x the area of the
shaded part of the diagram.

  b If the area of the shaded part is 35π, find x.

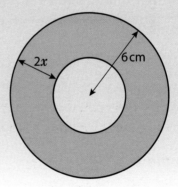

$2x$

6 cm

Points to remember

⊙ To solve a quadratic equation by **factorisation**:
  – factorise the quadratic expression;
  – in turn, make each bracket equal to zero and find the value of x;
  – check the solutions by substituting the values back into the
  original equation.

5 Completing the square

This lesson will help you to solve quadratic equations by another method: completing the square.

Did you know that...?

The word *quadratic* is derived from the Latin *quadratus*, which means square.

In India in about the 8th century BC, quadratic equations were explored **geometrically**.

Euclid, the Greek mathematician, produced a geometrical method for completing the square in about 300 BC.

Mathematicians in Babylonia about 400 BC and in China about 200 BC also used the method of **completing the square** to find the positive roots of quadratic equations but they did not have a general formula.

Euclid (325–265 BC)

Exercise 5

Another way to solve quadratic equations is called **completing the square**. The aim is to make the left-hand side (LHS) of the equation equal to the square of a linear expression and the right-hand side (RHS) equal to a number.

Example 1

Solve $(x + 3)^2 = 25$.

Take the square root of each side	$x + 3 = \pm 5$
Subtract 3	$x = -3 \pm 5$
	$x = 2 \text{ or } -8$

Example 2

Solve $x^2 + 4x - 3 = 0$.

Add 3	$x^2 + 4x = 3$
Make the LHS the square of a linear expression	$(x + 2)^2 - 4 = 3$
Add 4	$(x + 2)^2 = 7$
Take the square root of each side	$x + 2 = \pm 2.646$
Subtract 2	$x = 0.646 \text{ or } -4.65$ (to 3 s.f.)

① Find two values of x that satisfy these equations.

    a $(x + 7)^2 = 64$ **b** $(x - 3)^2 = 81$ **c** $(x - 6)^2 = 49$

2 Find two values of x that satisfy these equations.
Give your answers **i** in surd form and **ii** to three significant figures.

    a $(x - 5)^2 = 50$ **b** $(x + 1)^2 = 88$ **c** $(x + 4)^2 = 42$

    d $(x + 3)^2 = 55$ **e** $(x - 8)^2 = 76$ **f** $(x - 6)^2 = 23$

3 Find two values of x that satisfy these equations.
Give answers to three significant figures.

    a $(x - 1)^2 - 16 = 54$ **b** $(x - 7)^2 + 6 = 92$ **c** $(x + 5)^2 + 7 = 48$

    d $(x - 9)^2 - 1 = 44$ **e** $(x + 3)^2 - 4 = 76$ **f** $(x + 4)^2 - 5 = 150$

4   **a** Write an expression for the area of the trapezium.

    b The area of the trapezium is $34\,cm^2$.
       Write an equation and solve it to find the value of x.
       Give your answer to three significant figures.

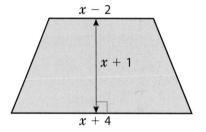

5 Solve these quadratic equations by completing the square.
Give your answers to three significant figures.

    a $x^2 - 2x - 11 = 0$ **b** $x^2 + 4x - 3 = 0$ **c** $x^2 - 8x - 7 = 0$

    d $x^2 + 10x + 11 = 0$ **e** $x^2 + 6x + 4 = 0$ **f** $x^2 - 12x + 9 = 0$

    g $x^2 - 4x + 1 = 0$ **h** $x^2 - 6x + 3 = 0$

Extension problem

6 Look at the quadratic equation $x^2 + bx + c = 0$.
Follow the steps for solving a quadratic equation by completing the square to find a formula for the solution.

⦿ Points to remember

⊙ The solutions of $x^2 = p$ are $x = \pm\sqrt{p}$.

⊙ The solutions of $(x + a)^2 = q$ are:
$$x + a = \pm\sqrt{q}$$
giving $\qquad x = -a \pm\sqrt{q}$

⊙ You can rearrange a quadratic equation in the form $(x + a)^2 = q$ to solve it by **completing the square**.

6 Using the quadratic formula

This lesson will help you to use a formula to solve quadratic equations.

Did you know that...?

In 628, the Indian mathematician **Brahmagupta** gave the first explicit solution of the positive root of a quadratic equation. He described a formula which is very similar to the quadratic formula that we use today.

It was not until 500 years later that his fellow countryman, **Bhaskara II** (1114–1185), a mathematician and astronomer, gave the first general solution to the quadratic equation with two roots.

Brahmagupta (598–668)

Exercise 6

The formula for solving any quadratic equation $ax^2 + bx + c = 0$ is:

$$x = \frac{-b \pm \sqrt{b^2 - 4ac}}{2a}$$

The equation has two real roots when $b^2 \geq 4ac$, one real root when $b^2 = 4ac$, and no real roots when $b^2 < 4ac$.

Example

Solve the equation $x^2 - 5x + 1 = 0$.

Comparing with the general quadratic equation $ax^2 + bx + c = 0$, $a = 1$, $b = -5$ and $c = 1$.

Substituting these values into the formula gives $x = \dfrac{5 \pm \sqrt{25 - 4}}{2} = \dfrac{5 \pm \sqrt{21}}{2}$.

This gives the solutions $x = 4.79$ and $x = 0.209$ (to 3 significant figures).

① Solve these quadratic equations by using the formula.
Give answers to three significant figures.

- **a** $x^2 - 7x + 3 = 0$
- **b** $x^2 + 4x - 9 = 0$
- **c** $x^2 + 8x - 14 = 0$
- **d** $x^2 + 6x + 2 = 0$
- **e** $x^2 + 6x + 4 = 0$
- **f** $x^2 - 5x + 5 = 0$
- **g** $x^2 + 2x - 1 = 0$
- **h** $x^2 - 10x + 11 = 0$

(2) Solve these quadratic equations by using the formula.
Give answers to three significant figures.

a $2x^2 - 4x - 9 = 0$ b $3x^2 + 6x - 8 = 0$ c $5x^2 - 3x - 6 = 0$

d $4x^2 + 7x - 11 = 0$ e $2x^2 + 3x - 4 = 0$ f $3x^2 - 2x - 9 = 0$

g $6x^2 - 5x + 1 = 0$ h $5x^2 - 11x - 8 = 0$

(3) Write the number of real roots in each of these quadratic equations.

a $x^2 + 10x + 8 = 0$ b $x^2 - 10x + 25 = 0$ c $5x^2 + 3x + 6 = 0$

d $4x^2 + 12x + 9 = 0$ e $6x^2 + 5x + 1 = 0$ f $-2x^2 + 3x - 4 = 0$

(4) The length of a room is 4 metres longer than its width.
The height of the room is 3 m.
Its volume is 1000 m³.

Find the length and width of the room.
Give your answers to the nearest cm.

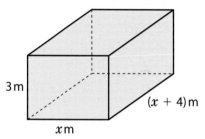

(5) One edge of a cube is increased in length by 3 cm.
Another edge is decreased in length by 2 cm.
The third edge stays the same.

The volume of the new cuboid formed is 55 cm³ more
than the volume of the original cube.

Find the length of each edge of the original cube.

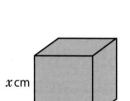

(6) A rectangular lawn measures 8 m by 5 m.
It has a border x m wide all around it.

The area of the lawn is equal to the area of the border.

Find the width of the border to the nearest cm.

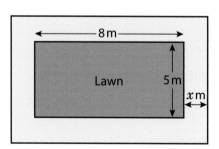

(7) A cylinder has a surface area of 300π cm² and
a height of 8 cm.

What is the radius of its base to the nearest mm?

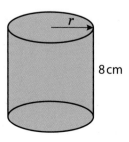

Extension problems

8 Solve these quadratic equations by using the formula.
Give answers to three significant figures.

  a $2t^2 - 5t = 4$ **b** $4s^2 = 9 - 8s$ **c** $1 = 3r^2 - 7r$ **d** $h^2 + 2h = 5$

9 A family drives 180 km to visit grandparents.
On their return journey their average speed is reduced by 10 km/h and they take 15 minutes longer.

Find their average speed on the outward journey.

⊙ Points to remember

- The **formula for solving any quadratic equation** $ax^2 + bx + c = 0$ is

$$x = \frac{-b \pm \sqrt{b^2 - 4ac}}{2a}.$$

- Memorise the formula by saying 'minus b plus or minus the square root of b squared minus four ac all over two a'.

7 Simultaneous linear and quadratic equations

This lesson will help you to solve simultaneous equations, one linear and the other quadratic.

Exercise 7

To solve a pair of simultaneous linear and quadratic equations you need to find the values of the two variables that satisfy both equations. The solution can be seen at the points of intersection of their graphs.

You can also solve the equations algebraically by subtracting one equation from the other.

Example

Solve

$$y = x^2 - 2 \ \dots\dots\dots \ (1)$$
$$y = x + 4 \ \dots\dots\dots \ (2)$$

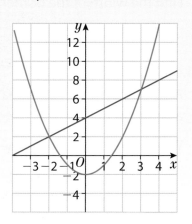

(1) − (2) $0 = x^2 - x - 6$
Factorise $0 = (x - 3)(x + 2)$
          $x = 3$ or $x = -2$
Substitute for x in (2) $y = 7$ or $y = 2$

The two solutions are $x = 3$, $y = 7$ and $x = -2$, $y = 2$.

You will need either a computer with a graph plotter or a graphics calculator.

1 Use an algebraic method to solve these pairs of simultaneous equations.
Check your answers by drawing graphs.

a $y = x^2 + 3x + 2$
$y = x + 1$

b $y = x^2 - 2x + 1$
$y = -x + 3$

c $y = x^2 - 3x - 1$
$y = -x - 1$

d $y = x^2 - 4x + 5$
$y = 2x - 3$

e $y = 2x^2 - 3x + 2$
$y = x + 2$

f $y = 2x^2 - 7x + 2$
$y = 3x - 6$

g $y = 3x^2 + 8x - 4$
$y = 2x + 5$

h $y = -x^2 + 3x + 2$
$y = 3x - 2$

i $y = -2x^2 - 4x + 6$
$y = 6x + 14$

2 Use an algebraic method to solve these pairs of simultaneous equations.
Check your answers by drawing graphs.

a $y - 2x - 1 = x^2$
$y + x = 1$

b $y + x - 2x^2 + 4 = 0$
$y + 5x + 4 = 0$

c $2y = x^2 + 4x - 3$
$3 + 2x - y = 0$

3 Use ICT to check whether these pairs of equations
have two, one or no simultaneous solutions.

a $y = x^2 + 2x - 3$
$y = 6x - 2$

b $y = x^2 - 4x - 2$
$x = 2$

c $y = x^2 + 3x - 1$
$y = x - 4$

d $y = x^2 + 5x - 3$
$y = x - 7$

e $y = x^2 + 8x + 8$
$y = 2x - 2$

f $y = x^2 - 5$
$y = 5 - x$

g $y = 2x^2 - 4x - 1$
$y = 2x - 2$

h $y = 2x^2 - x - 3$
$y = x - 5$

Points to remember

⊙ The simultaneous solutions to **one linear and one quadratic equation**
  are where their graphs intersect.

⊙ To solve a pair of **simultaneous equations, one linear and one
  quadratic**, using an algebraic method:
  – make one variable the subject of the linear equation;
  – substitute for this variable into the quadratic equation, and solve it
    using factorisation or the formula;
  – in turn, substitute each value back into the linear equation and find
    the corresponding value of the other variable.

8 Simultaneous linear and non-linear equations

This lesson will help you to solve simultaneous equations, one linear and the other non-linear.

Exercise 8

To solve a pair of simultaneous linear and non-linear equations you need to find the values of the two variables that satisfy both equations. The solution can be seen at the points of intersection of their graphs.

For an accurate solution, use an algebraic method.

Example

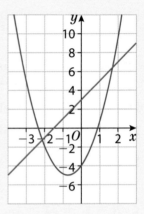

Solve
$$y = 2x^2 + 3x - 4 \quad \cdots\cdots\cdots \text{ (1)}$$
$$y = 2x + 3 \quad \cdots\cdots\cdots\cdots \text{ (2)}$$

(1) − (2)
$$0 = 2x^2 + x - 7$$

use the formula
$$x = \frac{-1 \pm \sqrt{1 + 56}}{4}$$

$$x = 1.637 \text{ or } x = -2.137 \text{ (to 3 d.p.)}$$

substitute for x in (2) $y = 6.274$ or $y = -1.274$ (to 3 d.p.)

The two solutions are $x = \mathbf{1.637}, y = \mathbf{6.274}$

and $x = \mathbf{-2.137}, y = \mathbf{-1.274}$

You will need either a computer with a graph plotter or a graphics calculator.

1   Use an algebraic method to solve these pairs of simultaneous equations.
Give your answers to 3 significant figures.
Check your answers by drawing graphs.

     a $y = x^2 + 2x - 1$ **b** $y = 2x^2 - 3x - 2$ **c** $y = -3x^2 - 4x + 5$
        $y = x + 3$ $y = 2x + 4$ $y = -x + 2$

     d $y = x^2 + 6x - 7$ **e** $y = -2x^2 + 5x + 5$ **f** $y = 2x^2 + 9x - 5$
        $y = -2x - 4$ $y = -x + 2$ $y = 6x + 1$

     g $y = 3x^2 + 4x - 3$ **h** $y = -x^2 + x + 7$
        $y = -x + 1$ $y = 3$

2   For each pair of equations, use ICT to draw the graphs.
Use an algebraic method to find the points of intersection of the graphs.
Give your answers to 3 significant figures.

     a $x^2 + y^2 = 9$ **b** $x^2 + y^2 = 16$
        $y = x + 1$ $y = 2x + 2$

Extension problem

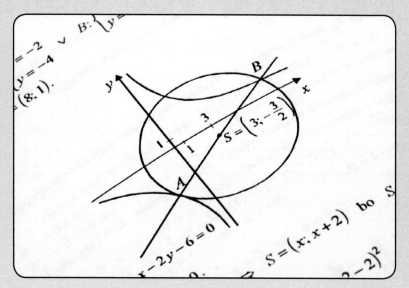

3 For each pair of equations, use ICT to draw the graphs.
Use an algebraic method to find the points of intersection of the graphs.
Give your answers to 3 significant figures.

a $(x - 2)^2 + (y + 3)^2 = 25$

$y = 2x$

b $y = \dfrac{9}{x}$

$y = x - 2$

  Points to remember

⊙ To solve a pair of **simultaneous equations, one linear and one non-linear**, using an algebraic method:

– make one variable the subject of the linear equation;

– substitute for this variable into the non-linear equation, and solve it;

– in turn, substitute each value back into the linear equation and find the corresponding value of the other variable.

⊙ When you find the solution to a linear and non-linear equation it is useful to sketch a graph first. This helps you to check solutions.

How well are you doing?

Equations (no calculator)

1 *2004 level 8*

Solve this equation: $\dfrac{5(2y - 3)}{3y} = 3$

Show your working.

2 *2007 level 8*

I am thinking of a number.

What is my number?
Show an algebraic method.

> When I subtract 25 from my number,
> then square the answer,
> I get the **same result as**
> when I square my number, then
> subtract 25 from the answer.

3 *GCSE 1387 June 2006*

a Factorise $x^2 + 6x + 8$.

b Solve $x^2 + 6x + 8 = 0$.

4 *GCSE 1387 November 2007*

The diagram shows a 6-sided shape.
All the corners are right angles.
All the measurements are given in centimetres.

The area of the shape is 85 cm².

a Show that $9x^2 - 17x - 85 = 0$.

b i Solve $9x^2 - 17x - 85 = 0$.
Give your solutions correct to 3 significant figures.

ii Hence, work out the length of the shortest side of the 6-sided shape.

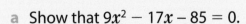

Diagram NOT drawn accurately

5 *GCSE 1387 November 2005*

The diagram shows a circle of radius 5 cm, centre the origin.

Copy the diagram on graph paper.

Draw a suitable straight line on your diagram to find estimates of the solutions to the pair of equations

$$x^2 + y^2 = 25$$
$$y = 2x + 1$$

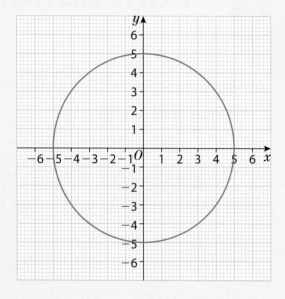

6 *GCSE 1387 November 2006*

By eliminating y, find the solutions to the simultaneous equations.

$$x^2 + y^2 = 25$$
$$y = 2x + 1$$

Functional skills 5

Being a scientist

This group activity will help you to:

- solve routine and non-routine problems in familiar and unfamiliar contexts;
- choose and combine representations from a range of perspectives;
- select and apply a range of methods, operations and tools, including ICT;
- examine patterns and relationships;
- recognise limitations in the accuracy of results and conclusions;
- interpret and communicate results and solutions.

Background

Scientists carry out experiments to collect data. They analyse the data they collect to look for patterns and relationships that explain the world around us.

Work on the problems with a partner.
You will need a computer with Excel to create your spreadsheets.

The relationship between pressure and volume is called **Boyle's Law**. Boyle was a 17th-century scientist who is regarded as one of the founders of modern chemistry.

Problem 1

In an experiment to find the relationship between pressure and volume, pressure is measured in kilopascals (kPa) and volume is measured in cm^3.

The table shows a set of results.

Volume (cm³)	75	70	65	60	55	50	45	40	35	30
Pressure (kPa)	32	35	37	40	44	48	52	60	70	80

Look for patterns in the table. It might help to use a spreadsheet or draw a graph.

Can you find a formula connecting pressure and volume?

Can you find a simple way to express the relationship?

Have you noticed the headlights of oncoming cars at night? The light starts as a dim glow in the distance, but as the car gets closer, the brightness of the headlights increases rapidly.

Problem 2

The data in the table below is about light intensity and distance from a lightsource. The light intensity is measured in lux using a light probe and distance is measured in centimetres.

Distance (cm)	Light intensity (lux)
10	50.0
20	12.5
30	5.6
40	3.1
50	2.0
60	1.4
70	1.0

What patterns can you find in the table?

Try to find a formula connecting light intensity and distance.

Can you find a simple way to express the relationship?

Be prepared to discuss your findings with other pairs.

Transformations and vectors

This unit will help you to:

- ☉ explore symmetry patterns;

- ☉ use vector notation to describe combinations of translations;

- ☉ calculate and represent the sum or difference of two vectors and a scalar multiple of a vector;

- ☉ calculate the resultant of two vectors;

- ☉ use vectors to solve two-dimensional geometrical problems.

1 Symmetry patterns

This **double lesson** will help you to explore combinations of transformations and symmetry patterns.

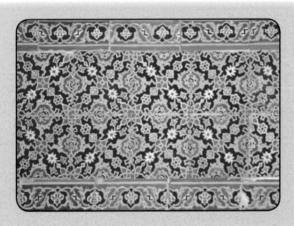
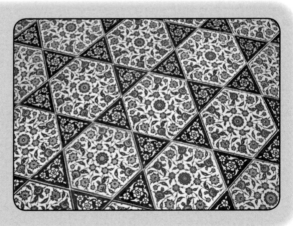

Exercise 1

A **glide reflection** is a combination of a reflection and a translation.

Triangle A is mapped onto triangle B by a glide reflection.

This combines a translation of 5 squares to the right and reflection in a horizontal mirror line.

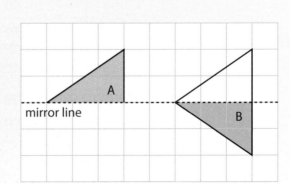

1. A magazine for secondary pupils is going to publish some articles about symmetry patterns. There will also be a presentation at an after-school club.

Do some Internet research to find out more about symmetry patterns. Make notes while you do this. Present your findings either in Word in the form of an illustrated magazine article or as a PowerPoint presentation.

Here are some useful websites.

> nrich.maths.org/public/viewer.php?obj_id=1349
>
> www.scienceu.com/geometry/articles/tiling/
>
> mathforum.org/geometry/rugs/symmetry/fp.html
>
> www2.spsu.edu/math/tile/
>
> britton.disted.camosun.bc.ca/alhambra/index.html

2. Here are some points to take into account as you do your research.

   a Who was Leonardo da Vinci? What is his theorem about rosette patterns? Describe and illustrate each type of rosette pattern.

   b Describe and illustrate as many as possible of the different types of frieze patterns.

   c How many different types of wallpaper patterns are there? Describe and illustrate three different examples of wallpaper patterns.

Extension problem

3. What are Penrose tilings? Who are they named after?

 Points to remember

- An **isometry** of the plane is a transformation in the plane that preserves length and therefore shape. The four isometries are translations, reflections, rotations and **glide reflections**.
- There are three categories of symmetry patterns: **rosette patterns** (two types), **frieze patterns** (seven types) and **wallpaper patterns** (17 types).
- Geometrical patterns play an important part in architecture and art.
- Every culture has a preference for certain types of symmetry patterns. The important thing is not the motif in the patterns, but the types of symmetry. This can be used to date objects and identify connections between different cultures.

3 Vectors and vector notation

This lesson will help you to understand the meaning of a vector and use vector notation.

Did you know that...?

The word **vector**, like the word *vehicle*, is derived from the Latin *vehere*, to carry.

Before it was used in mathematics, a vector was a technical term in astronomy.

The earliest entry in the Oxford English Dictionary that refers to a vector is from 1704:

> 'A Line supposed to be drawn from any Planet moving round a Center, to that Center, is by some Writers of the New Astronomy, called the Vector; because 'tis that Line by which the Planet seems to be carried round its Center.'

Exercise 3

When you hit a tennis ball, the direction of the stroke is as important as its strength. How a body moves when it is pushed or pulled by a **force** depends on the direction of the push or pull and also its size or magnitude.

When a car driver stops and asks the way to the tennis courts, she needs to be told which way to go and also how far to go. To describe a change in position or **displacement**, the direction of the movement must be given and the distance moved.

Forces and displacements that need a size and a direction to describe them are examples of **vectors**. A **vector** needs a **magnitude** and a **direction** to describe it completely.

For example, the displacement from A to B is 5 cm on a bearing of 080°.

This displacement is written $\overrightarrow{AB}$ to show that it is a vector and it has a direction from A to B.

In the diagram the line from A to B is drawn 5 cm long in a direction of 080°. The line is marked with an arrow to show that the direction is from A to B.

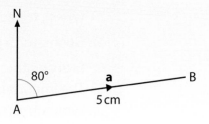

Vectors are also written as single bold letters such as **a**, **b** or **c**.

The vector **b** has been drawn on a centimetre grid.

The displacement represented by **b** is described as 4 to the right and 2 up.

Like a translation, it is written as the column vector $\binom{4}{2}$.

So $\mathbf{b} = \binom{4}{2}$.

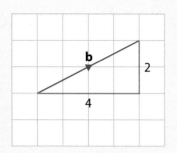

Example 1

A vector **a** has magnitude 4 cm and direction 030°. Draw the vector **a**.

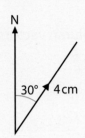

Draw a line 4 cm long on a bearing of 030°.

Mark the direction with an arrow.

Example 2

Point A is (1, 3) and point B is (5, 1). Write AB as a column vector.

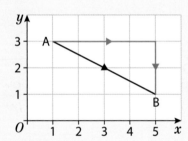

Mark the points A and B on a grid.

$$\overrightarrow{AB} = \binom{4}{-2}$$

You need plain and squared paper, a ruler and protractor.

(1) Write each of these as a column vector.

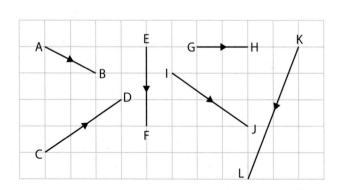

2 On plain paper, draw and label these vectors.

Vector	**a**	**b**	$\overrightarrow{MN}$	$\overrightarrow{XY}$	$\overrightarrow{CD}$
Magnitude	5 cm	6 cm	4 cm	3 cm	4.5 cm
Direction	south	bearing 045°	bearing 225°	bearing 120°	bearing 300°

3 On squared paper, draw and label these vectors.

a $\begin{pmatrix} 2 \\ 1 \end{pmatrix}$ **b** $\begin{pmatrix} 0 \\ 3 \end{pmatrix}$ **c** $\begin{pmatrix} -3 \\ 4 \end{pmatrix}$ **d** $\begin{pmatrix} -4 \\ -2 \end{pmatrix}$ **e** $\begin{pmatrix} 5 \\ 0 \end{pmatrix}$ **f** $\begin{pmatrix} 4 \\ -1 \end{pmatrix}$

4 Point X is (0, 2), point Y is (5, 8) and point Z is (4, −4). Write as column vectors:

a $\overrightarrow{XY}$ **b** $\overrightarrow{YX}$ **c** $\overrightarrow{YZ}$ **d** $\overrightarrow{ZY}$ **e** $\overrightarrow{XZ}$ **f** $\overrightarrow{ZX}$

What do you notice about your answers?

5 Point A is (2, 2). $\overrightarrow{AB} = \begin{pmatrix} 2 \\ 4 \end{pmatrix}$, $\overrightarrow{BC} = \begin{pmatrix} 3 \\ 1 \end{pmatrix}$ and $\overrightarrow{CD} = \begin{pmatrix} 1 \\ -3 \end{pmatrix}$.

  a On squared paper, draw quadrilateral ABCD. What kind of quadrilateral is it? Explain how you know.

  b Write as column vectors:

    i $\overrightarrow{AD}$ **ii** $\overrightarrow{AC}$ **iii** $\overrightarrow{BD}$

6 ABCD is a rhombus. Point A is (3, 1). $\overrightarrow{AB} = \begin{pmatrix} -2 \\ 3 \end{pmatrix}$ and $\overrightarrow{AD} = \begin{pmatrix} 2 \\ 3 \end{pmatrix}$.

  a On squared paper, draw the rhombus ABCD.

  b Write as column vectors:

    i $\overrightarrow{BC}$ **ii** $\overrightarrow{DC}$ **iii** $\overrightarrow{BD}$ **iv** $\overrightarrow{CA}$

  c What do you notice about these pairs of vectors?

    i $\overrightarrow{AB}$ and $\overrightarrow{DC}$ **ii** $\overrightarrow{AD}$ and $\overrightarrow{BC}$ **iii** $\overrightarrow{BD}$ and $\overrightarrow{CA}$

⦿ Points to remember

- ⦿ A **vector** has magnitude and direction.
- ⦿ This vector can be written as $\overrightarrow{AB}$ or **a** or as $\begin{pmatrix} 3 \\ 4 \end{pmatrix}$.
- ⦿ A **displacement** is a change in position.

4 The magnitude of a vector

This lesson will help you to work out the magnitude of a vector.

Exercise 4

Vectors are **equal** only when they have equal magnitudes **and** the same direction.

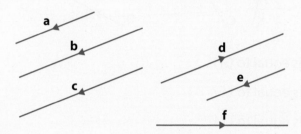

Vectors **b** and **c** are equal, that is **b** = **c**. They have the same magnitude and direction.

Vectors **a** and **c** are not equal. They have the same direction but not the same magnitude.

Vectors **b** and **d** are not equal. They have the same magnitude and are parallel but they are in opposite directions, not the same direction.

Vectors **d** and **f** are not equal. They have the same magnitude but not the same direction.

The **magnitude** of a vector is its size.

The magnitude of the vector **c** is written as c or $|c|$.

The magnitude of the vector $\overrightarrow{AB}$ is AB, which is the length of the line segment AB.

The magnitude of the vector $\begin{pmatrix} a \\ b \end{pmatrix}$ is the positive value of $\sqrt{a^2 + b^2}$.

A quantity with magnitude but no direction is called a **scalar**.

Example

Find the magnitude of the vector $\mathbf{c} = \begin{pmatrix} 6 \\ -2 \end{pmatrix}$.
Give your answer as a surd.

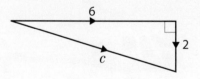

Draw a right-angled triangle to show the vector.

Using Pythagoras, $c^2 = 6^2 + 2^2 = 36 + 4 = 40$

$c = \sqrt{40} = 2\sqrt{10}$

① The diagram shows eight vectors.

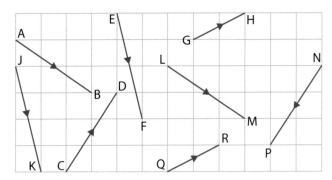

a Which vector is equal to $\overrightarrow{GH}$?

b Which vector is equal to $\overrightarrow{EF}$?

c Which vector is equal to $\overrightarrow{LM}$?

d Which two vectors are parallel but not equal?

e Which three vectors have the same magnitude as $\overrightarrow{NP}$?

② Work out the magnitude of these vectors. Where necessary, leave your answer as a surd.

a $\begin{pmatrix} 10 \\ 24 \end{pmatrix}$ b $\begin{pmatrix} 6 \\ -18 \end{pmatrix}$ c $\begin{pmatrix} -3 \\ 4 \end{pmatrix}$ d $\begin{pmatrix} -10 \\ -25 \end{pmatrix}$ e $\begin{pmatrix} -7 \\ 14 \end{pmatrix}$ f $\begin{pmatrix} 8 \\ 15 \end{pmatrix}$

③ WXYZ is a quadrilateral. $\overrightarrow{WX} = \begin{pmatrix} 5 \\ 12 \end{pmatrix}$, $\overrightarrow{XY} = \begin{pmatrix} 10 \\ 0 \end{pmatrix}$ and $\overrightarrow{YZ} = \begin{pmatrix} 16 \\ -12 \end{pmatrix}$.

What type of quadrilateral is WXYZ? Work out its area.

④ $\overrightarrow{AB}$ is the vector $\begin{pmatrix} 10 \\ 3 \end{pmatrix}$. $\overrightarrow{AC}$ is the vector $\begin{pmatrix} 5 \\ -9 \end{pmatrix}$. Find the length of BC.

⑤ In triangle PQR, $\overrightarrow{PQ} = \begin{pmatrix} -16 \\ 63 \end{pmatrix}$ and $\overrightarrow{PR} = \begin{pmatrix} 33 \\ 56 \end{pmatrix}$. Show that triangle PQR is isosceles.

⑥ A helicopter flies 2.5 km north, then 6 km east.

a How far is it from its starting point?

b Write the vector that represents its displacement.

c Work out its bearing from its starting point.

Points to remember

- The magnitude of the vector $\overrightarrow{AB}$ is AB, which is the distance from A to B.
- The magnitude of the vector **p** is written as p.
- The magnitude of the vector $\begin{pmatrix} a \\ b \end{pmatrix}$ is the positive value of $\sqrt{a^2 + b^2}$.
- The magnitudes of $\begin{pmatrix} a \\ b \end{pmatrix}$ and $\begin{pmatrix} -a \\ -b \end{pmatrix}$ are equal.
- $-\overrightarrow{AB} = \overrightarrow{BA}$.
- Two vectors are equal if they have the same magnitude and the same direction; vectors with the same magnitude are not necessarily equal.
- Lines with the same direction are parallel; lines that are parallel can have opposite directions.

5 Vector addition

This lesson will help you to add vectors.

Did you know that...?

Trinity College, Dublin

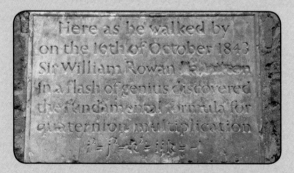

Plaque on Broom Bridge, near Dublin

The terms *vector* and *scalar* were introduced by the Irish mathematician **Sir William Hamilton** (1805–1865), who studied at Trinity College, Dublin. In 1843, he described *quaternions*. Today we largely use vectors, but quaternions are still used in calculations involving 3D rotations, for example, in computer graphics and video games.

Sir William envisaged how to multiply quaternions when he was out walking along the Royal Canal, near Dublin. A plaque on Broome Bridge commemorates his discovery:

'Here as he walked by on 16th of October 1843 Sir William Rowan Hamilton in a flash of genius discovered the fundamental formula for quaternion multiplication.'

Adding vectors

To add two vectors, think of them as displacements.

Carry out the first displacement, then the second. So the second displacement must start where the first one ends.

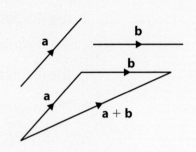

The vector sum **a** + **b** is called the **resultant**.
This is the vector you get when you join up the triangle.

This is called the **triangle law** for adding vectors.

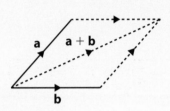

Here is another way to add two vectors. Instead of making the second vector start where the first one finishes, make them both start at the same place and complete a parallelogram.

Because opposite sides of a parallelogram are equal and in the same direction, **b** is repeated at the top of the parallelogram.

This is called the **parallelogram law** for adding vectors. It gives the same result as the triangle law.

Subtracting vectors

−**b** is a vector equal in magnitude to **b**, but in the opposite direction.

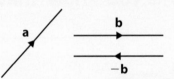

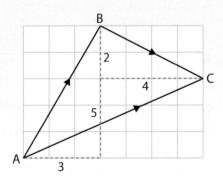

Subtracting **b** from **a**, or **a** − **b**, is the same as adding −**b** to **a**, or **a** + (−**b**).

Example 1

$\overrightarrow{AB}$ is the vector $\binom{3}{5}$. $\overrightarrow{BC}$ is the vector $\binom{4}{-2}$. Find $\overrightarrow{AC}$.

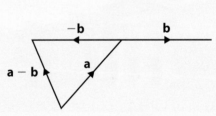

$\overrightarrow{AB} + \overrightarrow{BC} = \overrightarrow{AC}$

From A to C is 3 + 4 = 7 to the right.
From A to C is 5 + (−2) = 3 up.

So $\overrightarrow{AC}$ is the vector $\binom{7}{3}$.

Example 2

ABCD is a trapezium.

$\overrightarrow{AB} = \mathbf{a}$, $\overrightarrow{AB} = \mathbf{b}$ and $\overrightarrow{CD} = \mathbf{c}$.

Find vector $\overrightarrow{AD}$.

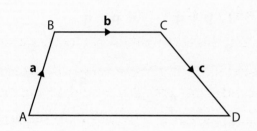

$\overrightarrow{AD} = \overrightarrow{AC} + \overrightarrow{CD}$, using the triangle law.

But $\overrightarrow{AC} = \overrightarrow{AB} + \overrightarrow{BC}$, using the triangle law.

So $\overrightarrow{AD} = \overrightarrow{AB} + \overrightarrow{BC} + \overrightarrow{CD}$

$\phantom{So \overrightarrow{AD}} = \mathbf{a} + \mathbf{b} + \mathbf{c}$

You need plain paper, squared paper, a ruler and a protractor.

1 Find these vector sums.

a $\begin{pmatrix} 1 \\ -4 \end{pmatrix} + \begin{pmatrix} 0 \\ 7 \end{pmatrix}$ b $\begin{pmatrix} -3 \\ 4 \end{pmatrix} + \begin{pmatrix} -2 \\ -6 \end{pmatrix}$ c $\begin{pmatrix} 5 \\ -1 \end{pmatrix} + \begin{pmatrix} -7 \\ 3 \end{pmatrix}$ d $\begin{pmatrix} 0 \\ 4 \end{pmatrix} + \begin{pmatrix} -3 \\ -4 \end{pmatrix}$ e $\begin{pmatrix} -2 \\ -3 \end{pmatrix} + \begin{pmatrix} -5 \\ 9 \end{pmatrix}$

2 Express these as the sum or difference of two vectors.

a $\overrightarrow{AC}$

b $\overrightarrow{XZ}$

c $\overrightarrow{PR}$

d $\overrightarrow{ML}$

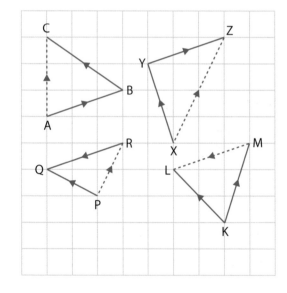

3 A vector $\mathbf{a}$ has magnitude 4 cm and direction 060°.
A vector $\mathbf{b}$ has magnitude 7 cm and direction 150°.
Draw the vectors:

a $\mathbf{a}$ b $\mathbf{b}$ c $-\mathbf{b}$ d $\mathbf{a} + \mathbf{b}$ e $\mathbf{a} - \mathbf{b}$

4 $\mathbf{a}$ is the vector $\begin{pmatrix} 3 \\ 5 \end{pmatrix}$. $\mathbf{b}$ is the vector $\begin{pmatrix} 2 \\ -4 \end{pmatrix}$. $\mathbf{c}$ is the vector $\begin{pmatrix} -1 \\ 6 \end{pmatrix}$.

a Work out $\mathbf{a} + \mathbf{b}$ and $\mathbf{b} + \mathbf{a}$. What do you notice?

b Work out $\mathbf{a} - \mathbf{b}$ and $\mathbf{b} - \mathbf{a}$. What do you notice?

c Work out $(\mathbf{a} + \mathbf{b}) + \mathbf{c}$ and $\mathbf{a} + (\mathbf{b} + \mathbf{c})$. What do you notice?

5 For each pair of vectors **p** and **q** shown below, draw vectors on squared paper to represent:

  i p + q   ii p − q

  a 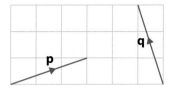 **b** 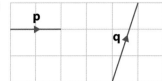 **c**

6 Make scale drawings to find the magnitude and direction of the resultant of each pair of vectors:

  a a force of 10 newtons horizontally and a force of 10 newtons inclined at 20° to the horizontal

  b an aircraft's speed of 20 m/s at a bearing of 115° and a wind speed of 15 m/s at a bearing of 077°

Extension problem

7 X is the point (3, 3) and Y is the point (−1, 0).
O is the origin (0, 0).

Z is the point such that $\overrightarrow{YZ}$ is parallel to $\begin{pmatrix} 0 \\ 1 \end{pmatrix}$.

The length of $\overrightarrow{YZ}$ equals the length of $\overrightarrow{XY}$.

  a Write $\overrightarrow{XY}$ as a column vector.

  b Find the length of the vector $\overrightarrow{XY}$.

  c Write $\overrightarrow{OZ}$ as a column vector.

  d W is the point such that XYZW is a rhombus. XZ is a diagonal of the rhombus.

    Write $\overrightarrow{YW}$ as a column vector.

Points to remember

⊙ $\overrightarrow{AB} + \overrightarrow{BC} = \overrightarrow{AC}$ refers to vectors, such as displacements, not to distances.

⊙ $\overrightarrow{AC}$ is the **resultant** of $\overrightarrow{AB} + \overrightarrow{BC}$.

⊙ $\begin{pmatrix} a \\ b \end{pmatrix} + \begin{pmatrix} c \\ d \end{pmatrix} = \begin{pmatrix} a + c \\ b + d \end{pmatrix}$

⊙ $\mathbf{a} - \mathbf{b} = \mathbf{a} + (-\mathbf{b})$

⊙ The vector $\overrightarrow{AB}$ can be expressed as the sum of several vectors if the end of one vector is the start of the next, so $\overrightarrow{AB} = \overrightarrow{AC} + \overrightarrow{CD} + \overrightarrow{DE} + \overrightarrow{EB}$.

6 Parallel vectors and problem solving

This lesson will help you to use parallel vectors to solve geometric problems.

Exercise 6A

The diagram shows that $\mathbf{a} + \mathbf{a} + \mathbf{a} = 3\mathbf{a}$.

3$\mathbf{a}$ is a vector in the same direction as $\mathbf{a}$ and with three times the magnitude.

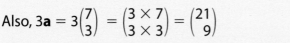

If $\mathbf{a} = \begin{pmatrix} 7 \\ 3 \end{pmatrix}$, then $3\mathbf{a} = \begin{pmatrix} 7 \\ 3 \end{pmatrix} + \begin{pmatrix} 7 \\ 3 \end{pmatrix} + \begin{pmatrix} 7 \\ 3 \end{pmatrix} = \begin{pmatrix} 7+7+7 \\ 3+3+3 \end{pmatrix} = \begin{pmatrix} 21 \\ 9 \end{pmatrix}$

Also, $3\mathbf{a} = 3\begin{pmatrix} 7 \\ 3 \end{pmatrix} = \begin{pmatrix} 3 \times 7 \\ 3 \times 3 \end{pmatrix} = \begin{pmatrix} 21 \\ 9 \end{pmatrix}$

In general, if $\mathbf{a} = \begin{pmatrix} p \\ q \end{pmatrix}$, then $k\mathbf{a} = k\begin{pmatrix} p \\ q \end{pmatrix} = \begin{pmatrix} kp \\ kq \end{pmatrix}$

Example

$\mathbf{p} = \begin{pmatrix} 2 \\ 6 \end{pmatrix}$ and $\mathbf{q} = \begin{pmatrix} -2 \\ 2 \end{pmatrix}$. Find $2\mathbf{p} + 3\mathbf{q}$.

$2\mathbf{p} + 3\mathbf{q} = 2\begin{pmatrix} 2 \\ 6 \end{pmatrix} + 3\begin{pmatrix} -2 \\ 2 \end{pmatrix} = \begin{pmatrix} 4 \\ 12 \end{pmatrix} + \begin{pmatrix} -6 \\ 6 \end{pmatrix} = \begin{pmatrix} 4-6 \\ 12+6 \end{pmatrix} = \begin{pmatrix} -2 \\ 18 \end{pmatrix} = 2\begin{pmatrix} -1 \\ 9 \end{pmatrix}$

You need a ruler and protractor.

1 The diagram shows vectors $\mathbf{p}$ and $\mathbf{q}$.

Express in terms of $\mathbf{p}$ or $\mathbf{q}$:

a $\mathbf{a}$	**b** $\mathbf{b}$
c $\mathbf{c}$	**d** $\mathbf{d}$
e $\mathbf{e}$	**f** $\mathbf{f}$
g $4\mathbf{a}$	**h** $3\mathbf{b}$
i $4\mathbf{e} + \mathbf{a}$	**j** $2\mathbf{c} + 3\mathbf{d}$
k $\mathbf{a} - \mathbf{b}$	**l** $\mathbf{f} - \mathbf{c}$

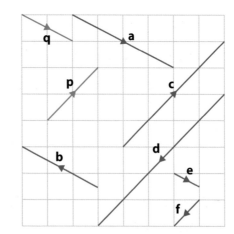

2 Vector $\mathbf{p}$ has magnitude 3 cm and direction 40°.
Vector $\mathbf{q}$ has magnitude 4 cm and direction 130°.
Draw these vectors.

a $3\mathbf{p}$ **b** $-\mathbf{q}$ **c** $2\mathbf{p} + \mathbf{q}$ **d** $2\mathbf{q} - \mathbf{p}$

(3) Point A is at $(2, 4)$, point B is at $(5, 6)$, and point C is at $(-1, -3)$.
Find the coordinates of the point D where $\overrightarrow{CD} = 4\overrightarrow{AB}$.

(4) In triangle OAB, point M is the midpoint of OA and point N is the midpoint of OB.

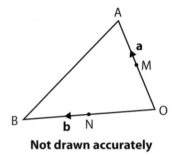

Not drawn accurately

  a Write $\overrightarrow{AB}$ in terms of **a** and **b**.

  b Write $\overrightarrow{MN}$ in terms of **a** and **b**.

  c What do your answers in parts **a** and **b** show about AB and MN?

Exercise 6B

The **position vector** of the point P is the vector $\overrightarrow{OP}$, where O is the origin.

The triangle law is useful when you solve geometric problems.
Here are three more useful results.

⊙ A negative sign in front of a vector reverses its direction, so −**a** is in the opposite direction to **a**, and $\overrightarrow{AB} = -\overrightarrow{BA}$.

⊙ When $\overrightarrow{AB} = k\overrightarrow{CD}$, where k is a scalar, the lines AB and CD are parallel and the length of AB is k times the length of CD.

⊙ When $\overrightarrow{AB} = k\overrightarrow{AE}$, then the lines AB and AE are parallel. But as these lines have point A in common they are part of the same straight line. So points A, B and E lie on the same straight line.

Example 1

In triangle OAB, OA = **a** and OB = **b**.

P is the midpoint of AB.

Find these vectors in terms of **a** and **b**.

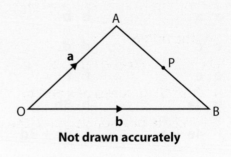

Not drawn accurately

  a $\overrightarrow{AB}$ b $\overrightarrow{AP}$ c $\overrightarrow{OP}$

  a $\overrightarrow{AB} = \overrightarrow{AO} + \overrightarrow{OB} = -\mathbf{a} + \mathbf{b} = \mathbf{b} - \mathbf{a}$

  b $\overrightarrow{AP} = \frac{1}{2}\overrightarrow{AB} = \frac{1}{2}(\mathbf{b} - \mathbf{a})$

  c $\overrightarrow{OP} = \overrightarrow{OA} + \overrightarrow{AP} = \mathbf{a} + \frac{1}{2}(\mathbf{b} - \mathbf{a}) = \frac{1}{2}(\mathbf{a} + \mathbf{b})$

Example 2

OABC is a quadrilateral.

$\overrightarrow{OA} = 2\mathbf{a}$, $\overrightarrow{OB} = 2\mathbf{a} + 2\mathbf{b}$ and $\overrightarrow{OC} = 4\mathbf{b}$

P is the midpoint of BC.
D is the point such that $\overrightarrow{BD} = \overrightarrow{OC}$.

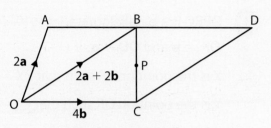

Not drawn accurately

a Find $\overrightarrow{AB}$ in terms of **a** and **b**. $\overrightarrow{AB} = \overrightarrow{AO} + \overrightarrow{OB} = -2\mathbf{a} + 2\mathbf{a} + 2\mathbf{b} = 2\mathbf{b}$

So AB and OC are parallel and AB is half the length of OC.

b Find $\overrightarrow{BC}$ in terms of **a** and **b**. $\overrightarrow{BC} = \overrightarrow{BO} + \overrightarrow{OC} = -2\mathbf{a} - 2\mathbf{b} + 4\mathbf{b} = 2\mathbf{b} - 2\mathbf{a}$

c Find $\overrightarrow{OP}$ in terms of **a** and **b**. $\overrightarrow{OP} = \overrightarrow{OB} + \overrightarrow{BP}$

$\overrightarrow{OB} = 2\mathbf{a} + 2\mathbf{b}$

P is the midpoint of BC, so

$\overrightarrow{BP} = \frac{1}{2}\overrightarrow{BC} = \frac{1}{2}(2\mathbf{b} - 2\mathbf{a}) = \mathbf{b} - \mathbf{a}$

So $\overrightarrow{OP} = 2\mathbf{a} + 2\mathbf{b} + \mathbf{b} - \mathbf{a} = \mathbf{a} + 3\mathbf{b}$

d Show that the points O, P and D lie in the same straight line.

Given that $\overrightarrow{BD} = \overrightarrow{OC}$, $\overrightarrow{BD} = 4\mathbf{b}$

So $\overrightarrow{OD} = \overrightarrow{OB} + \overrightarrow{BD}$

$= 2\mathbf{a} + 2\mathbf{b} + 4\mathbf{b}$

$= 2\mathbf{a} + 6\mathbf{b}$

$= 2(\mathbf{a} + 3\mathbf{b})$

$= 2\overrightarrow{OP}$

So O, P and D lie in the same straight line.

---

(1) O is the origin.

$\overrightarrow{OS} = 2\mathbf{a} + 3\mathbf{b}$ and $\overrightarrow{OT} = \mathbf{b} - \mathbf{a}$.

a Find $\overrightarrow{ST}$ in terms of **a** and **b**.

b Find the position vector of the midpoint of ST.

(2) A is the point $(4, -5)$ and B is the point $(3, 10)$.

a Write the position vector of A as a column vector.

b Write $\overrightarrow{AB}$ as a column vector.

c Find the length of AB.

3 OPRQ is a parallelogram.

$\overrightarrow{OP} = \mathbf{p}$ and $\overrightarrow{OQ} = \mathbf{q}$.

X is the point on PR such that $PX = \frac{1}{4}PR$.

Y is the point on QR such that $QY = \frac{1}{4}QR$.

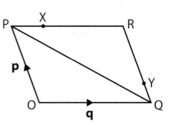

Not drawn accurately

a Find these vectors in terms of **p** and **q**.

     i $\overrightarrow{PQ}$ **ii** $\overrightarrow{PX}$ **iii** $\overrightarrow{OX}$

     iv $\overrightarrow{OY}$ **v** $\overrightarrow{XY}$

b Show that XY is parallel to PQ.

4 Five squares **P**, **Q**, **R**, **S** and **T** have these vectors as one of their sides.

P $\begin{pmatrix} 2 \\ 3 \end{pmatrix}$ Q $\begin{pmatrix} 4 \\ 0 \end{pmatrix}$ R $\begin{pmatrix} 2 \\ 2 \end{pmatrix}$ S $\begin{pmatrix} -4 \\ 1 \end{pmatrix}$ T $\begin{pmatrix} 5 \\ 0 \end{pmatrix}$

a Write the five squares in order of size, starting with the smallest.

b For each of the five squares, write the two vectors that represent the diagonals.

c One of the diagonals of a sixth square is the vector $\begin{pmatrix} 7 \\ 3 \end{pmatrix}$.

     Write a vector for one side of the square.

5 Here are five vectors: **p**, **q**, **r**, **s** and **t**.

p $\begin{pmatrix} 3 \\ 4 \end{pmatrix}$ q $\begin{pmatrix} 5 \\ 0 \end{pmatrix}$ r $\begin{pmatrix} 4 \\ -3 \end{pmatrix}$ s $\begin{pmatrix} -8 \\ 6 \end{pmatrix}$ t $\begin{pmatrix} 3 \\ -4 \end{pmatrix}$

a Which two of the vectors could be two sides of a square?

b Which two of the vectors could be two sides of a rhombus?

c Which two of the vectors could be two sides of a rectangle?

d Which three of the vectors could be three sides of an isosceles trapezium?

6 The diagram shows a point P dividing AB in the ratio 1 : 5.

Find $\overrightarrow{AP}$ in terms of **a** and **b**.

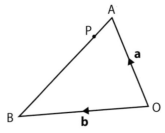

Not drawn accurately

Extension problem

 7 ABCD is a parallelogram. M is the midpoint of AB.
T divides DM in the ratio $2:1$.

a If $\mathbf{p} = \overrightarrow{AD}$ and $\mathbf{q} = \overrightarrow{AB}$, write $\overrightarrow{AT}$ in terms of $\mathbf{p}$ and $\mathbf{q}$.

b Show that A, T and C lie on a straight line.

c Find AT : TC.

 Points to remember

⊙ A **scalar** is quantity with magnitude but no direction.

⊙ When $\overrightarrow{AD} = k\overrightarrow{CD}$, where k is a positive scalar, the lines AB and CD are parallel and the length of AB is k times the length of CD.

⊙ When $\overrightarrow{AB} = k\overrightarrow{AE}$, the points A, B and E lie on the same straight line.

⊙ $k\begin{pmatrix} a \\ b \end{pmatrix} = \begin{pmatrix} ka \\ kb \end{pmatrix}$, where k is a scalar.

⊙ The **position vector** of the point P is the vector $\overrightarrow{OP}$, where O is the origin.

⊙ You can use vectors to solve geometric problems.

How well are you doing?

Vectors (no calculator)

1 O is the origin. The point P is (6, 2).

    a Write the vector $\vec{OP}$ as a column vector.

    b Calculate the magnitude of $\vec{OP}$.

2 PQRS is a parallelogram.
P is the point (1, 4) and R is the point (4, 4).
$\vec{PQ} = \begin{pmatrix} 3 \\ 2 \end{pmatrix}$ and T is the point such that $\vec{RT} = \begin{pmatrix} 1 \\ -3 \end{pmatrix}$.

    a Find the coordinates of Q.

    b Express $\vec{QS}$ as a column vector.

    c Calculate the length of PT.

3 ABCO is a parallelogram.

The midpoint of CB is Q.

P is the point on AC such that $AP = \frac{2}{3}AC$.

$\vec{OA} = 6\mathbf{a}$ and $\vec{OC} = 6\mathbf{c}$.

    a Find $\vec{OP}$ in terms of **a** and **c**.

    b Prove that OPQ is a straight line.

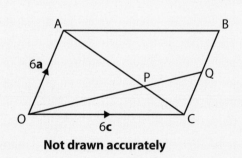

Not drawn accurately

4 OACB is a parallelogram.

M is the midpoint of BC.

OB is extended to X so that OB = BX.

$\overrightarrow{OA} = \mathbf{a}$ and $\overrightarrow{OB} = \mathbf{b}$.

a Find in terms of **a** and **b**:

   i $\overrightarrow{BC}$ **ii** $\overrightarrow{BM}$ **iii** $\overrightarrow{OM}$

b Prove that AMX is a straight line.

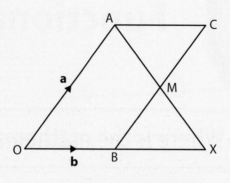

Not drawn accurately

5 *GCSE 1387 June 2006*

ABCDEF is a regular hexagon.

$\overrightarrow{OB} = \mathbf{a}$ $\overrightarrow{BC} = \mathbf{b}$ $\overrightarrow{AD} = 2\mathbf{b}$

a Find vector $\overrightarrow{AC}$ in terms of **a** and **b**.

b $\overrightarrow{AC} = \overrightarrow{CX}$

   Prove that AB is parallel to DX.

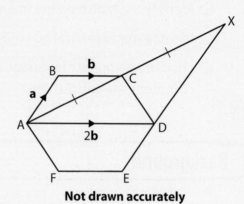

Not drawn accurately

6 *GCSE 1387 November 2007*

PQRS is a kite.

The diagonals PR and QS intersect at M.

$\overrightarrow{PM} = 4\mathbf{p}$ $\overrightarrow{QM} = \mathbf{q}$ $\overrightarrow{MR} = \mathbf{p}$

$\overrightarrow{QM} = \overrightarrow{MS}$

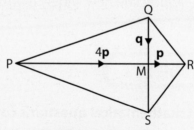

Not drawn accurately

a Find expressions, in terms of **p** and/or **q** for:

   i $\overrightarrow{PR}$ **ii** $\overrightarrow{QS}$ **iii** $\overrightarrow{PQ}$

b SR and PQ are extended to meet at T.

   Find $\overrightarrow{RT}$ in terms of **p** and **q**.

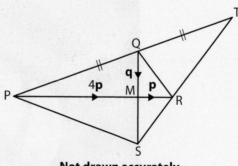

Not drawn accurately

Functional skills 6

Where is the mathematics?

This group activity will help you to:

- identify the mathematics in a situation;
- identify mathematical questions to ask;
- choose appropriate language and forms of presentation to communicate conclusions.

Background

Maths is all around us.

Looking for the maths in a situation or in information will help you to appreciate how widely maths is used.

Problem 1

What mathematical questions could you ask about this picture?

What answers to your questions would you give?

What mathematical questions could you ask about this picture?

What answers to your questions would you give?

What mathematical questions could you ask about this picture?

What answers to your questions would you give?

Be prepared to discuss your questions and answers with other groups.

Enquiry 2

This unit will help you to:

- ⊙ carry out a statistical enquiry;

- ⊙ consider how the choice of samples affects the reliability of results;

- ⊙ construct and interpret histograms, cumulative frequency tables and graphs, and box plots;

- ⊙ compare distributions using five-figure summary statistics;

- ⊙ calculate moving averages and use a trend line to make predictions.

1 Sampling and statistics

This lesson will help you understand how sample size affects the reliability of results.

Did you know that...?

A **census** is a survey of all the people and households in a country. It provides key information from national to local level for government, business and the community.

The most recent UK census was on 29 April 2001 and the next census will be in 2011.

In a census, each householder is required to complete a form giving the address of the household, and the names, ages, gender, occupations and places of birth of each individual living there.

People called census enumerators copy the data on each householder's form into books.

Details provided by the households are kept for 100 years before the census information is released to the public.

Nowadays census information is stored on computers. You can find out more about the UK census and search for information on the website www.ukcensusonline.com/index.php.

The mode, median and mean are different ways of finding the average of a set of numbers. The range shows how spread out the numbers are.

- The mode is the number that occurs most often in the set.

- The mean is the sum of all the numbers divided by the number of numbers.

- The median is the middle number, or the mean of the middle two numbers, when all the numbers are arranged in order.

- The range is the difference between the highest and lowest numbers.

Example

Here are the scores of 10 pupils in a spelling test: 3, 8, 5, 9, 10, 4, 7, 8, 4, 8

Calculate the mode, mean, median and range of the data.

The scores in order are: 3, 4, 4, 5, 7, 8, 8, 8, 9, 10.

The mode is 8.

The mean = $(3 + 8 + 5 + 9 + 10 + 4 + 7 + 8 + 4 + 8) \div 10 = 66 \div 10 = 6.6$

The middle pair of scores are 7 and 8 so the median is 7.5.

The range is $10 - 3 = 7$.

You will need to work in a group of three or four with a copy of **S7.3 Resource sheet 1.1**.

All the data is height data in centimetres from www.censusatschool.org and has been generated using their random sampler asking for samples of certain sizes from a single large set of data. Your teacher will tell you which samples to use.

1. For each of your samples, find:

    a the minimum value

    b the median

    c the mean

    d the maximum value

    For the larger samples you will need to use a scientific calculator or a computer to help you.

2. Share your results with another group so that you have the values for a number of samples of different sizes.

    a How much do the values for the different samples vary?

    b Look at the values for some samples of the same size.
    Do they vary or are they the same?

    c Is there anything you notice as the sample size gets larger?

1 Calculate the mean, median and range for each set of data.

a Foot lengths in centimetres of 30 pupils

25	25	30	27	24	21	23	21	25.5	24
23	21	22	34	22.5	20	27	34	30	22
25	22	29	24	28	23	26	22	20	34

b Height in centimetres from the floor of the belly button of 30 pupils

93	95	115	106	96	94	100	102	93	50
97	93	105	107	91	98	102	105	110	95
105	102	107	85	115	93	96	99	100	105

c Angle in degrees between first and second finger of 30 pupils

70	60	60	65	30	28	55	55	50	40
40	67	50	45	45	47	48	80	20	29
50	36	61	30.2	50	65	45	44	25	48

◉ Points to remember

- ⊙ Each sample from a population is different and will produce different results.
- ⊙ Smaller samples tend to be more variable.
- ⊙ Larger samples are more similar to each other and to the whole population.

2 Five-figure summaries

This lesson will help you to use five statistical measures to describe a data set.

Did you know that...?

Sir Francis Galton (1822–1911), the inventor of fingerprint identification, is described, among other things, as a Victorian polymath: geographer, meteorologist, tropical explorer, pioneer of statistical correlation and regression, convinced hereditarian, half-cousin of Charles Darwin and best-selling author (galton.org).

In one of Francis Galton's papers is the earliest known use of the term *interquartile range*.

The range is limited as a measure of spread of a data set as it is heavily influenced by any very large or small values. The **interquartile range** is another way to describe the spread.

To calculate the interquartile range, you first need to find the quartiles for a data set:

- the **lower quartile** is the value of the midpoint of the lower half of the data set, so 25 per cent of the values of the data set are less than the lower quartile;

- the **upper quartile** is the value of the midpoint of the upper half of the data set, so 25 per cent of the values of the data set are greater than the upper quartile.

The **interquartile range** is the upper quartile − the lower quartile.

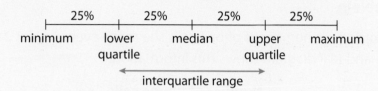

The **five-figure summary** is a set of five statistics describing a data set: the minimum, lower quartile, median, upper quartile and maximum.

Example

Find the interquartile range and five-figure summary for this set of 12 numbers.

67, 46, 68, 56, 51, 69, 59, 56, 43, 73, 63, 53

The numbers in ascending order are: First order the numbers.
43, 46, 51, 53, 56, 56, 59, 63, 67, 68, 69, 73

The middle pair of numbers is 56 and 59 so the **median** is: Next find the median.
$(56 + 59) \div 2 = 57.5$

The lower half of the set is: 43, 46, 51, 53, 56, 56   Now find the median for the
lower half of the set.
The middle pair is 51 and 53 so the **lower quartile** is 52.

The upper half of the set is: 59, 63, 67, 68, 69, 73   Now find the median for the
upper half of the set.
The middle pair is 67 and 68 so the **upper quartile** is 67.5.

43 46 51 | 53 56 56 | 59 63 67 | 68 69 73
    lower quartile   median   upper quartile
       52   57.5   67.5

The **five-figure summary** is 43, 52, 57.5, 67.5, 73.

The **interquartile range** is $67.5 − 52 = 15.5$.

You will need your copy of **S7.3 Resource sheet 1.1** from the last lesson.

① For the five samples of size 7 on the resource sheet:

    a Calculate the five-figure summary and the interquartile range for each of the samples.

    b Compare the samples of size 7. Write down what you notice about their variation.

    c Are there any data sets of size 7 on the resource sheet where the range would be an unhelpful measure of spread? Give your reasons.

② Repeat question 1 for the five samples of size 10 on the resource sheet.

Extension problem

③ Jenni recorded the number of phone calls she made every day for 21 days.
The stem-and-leaf diagram shows this information.

Number of phone calls

0	4 5 5 6 7 7 8 9
1	0 1 2 3 3 4 6 7 8
2	0 1 3 6

Key 1 | 8 means 18 phone calls

    a Find the median number of phone calls that Jenni made in the 21 days.

    b Work out the range of the number of phone calls that Jenni made in the 21 days.

    c Find the interquartile range of the number of phone calls that Jenni made in the 21 days.

⊙ Points to remember

⊙ When all the values in a data set are arranged in ascending order:

    – the **lower quartile** is the value one quarter of the way through the data;

    – the **upper quartile** is the value three-quarters of the way through the data.

⊙ The **five-figure summary** for a set of data is given by the minimum, lower quartile, median, upper quartile and maximum.

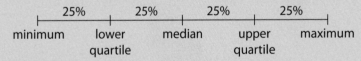

⊙ The **interquartile range** is a measure of the spread over the middle 50% of the data, so:

interquartile range = upper quartile − lower quartile

3 Cumulative frequency 1

This lesson will help you to construct cumulative frequency tables and graphs.

Exercise 3

The grouped frequency table shows the time that 160 people spent exercising one Saturday morning.

The information in the table can be used to find, for example, the total number of people who spent up to and including 20 minutes exercising: $4 + 12 = 16$.

16 is the cumulative frequency, or running total, for the interval $0 < x \leqslant 20$.

The second table on the right is the completed cumulative frequency table.

The last number in the cumulative frequency column is 160, the total number of people.

Time (minutes)	Frequency
$0 < x \leqslant 10$	4
$10 < x \leqslant 20$	12
$20 < x \leqslant 30$	46
$30 < x \leqslant 40$	68
$40 < x \leqslant 50$	20
$50 < x \leqslant 60$	10

Time (minutes)	Cumulative frequency
$0 < x \leqslant 10$	4
$0 < x \leqslant 20$	$4 + 12 = 16$
$0 < x \leqslant 30$	$16 + 46 = 62$
$0 < x \leqslant 40$	$62 + 68 = 130$
$0 < x \leqslant 50$	$130 + 20 = 150$
$0 < x \leqslant 60$	$150 + 10 = 160$

The cumulative frequency table can be used to draw a cumulative frequency graph.

The cumulative frequency 4 for the interval $0 < x \leqslant 10$ is plotted at (10, 4), that is, at the upper end of the interval to ensure that all 4 people have been included.

The points can be joined with a smooth curve.

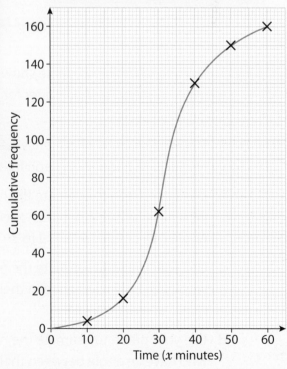

All data in this exercise is from www.censusatschool.org.

You need some graph paper.

① This grouped frequency table shows the heights above the floor of the belly buttons of 200 secondary pupils.

a Draw a cumulative frequency table and a cumulative frequency graph for this set of data.

b Use your graph to estimate the number of pupils who have a belly button height of 110 cm or less.

c Use your graph to estimate the number of pupils who have a belly button height of 95 cm or less.

Height (cm)	Frequency
$50 < x \leqslant 60$	8
$60 < x \leqslant 70$	3
$70 < x \leqslant 80$	9
$80 < x \leqslant 90$	30
$90 < x \leqslant 100$	45
$100 < x \leqslant 110$	93
$110 < x \leqslant 120$	8
$120 < x \leqslant 130$	2
$130 < x \leqslant 140$	2

Length (cm)	Frequency
$10 < x \leqslant 15$	3
$15 < x \leqslant 20$	14
$20 < x \leqslant 25$	125
$25 < x \leqslant 30$	38
$30 < x \leqslant 35$	20

② This grouped frequency table shows the foot lengths in centimetres of 200 secondary pupils.

a Draw a cumulative frequency table and a cumulative frequency graph for this set of data.

b Use your graph to estimate the number of pupils who have a foot length of 22 cm or less.

c Use your graph to estimate the number of pupils who have a foot length of more than 22 cm.

③ This grouped frequency table shows the angle between first and second finger for each of 200 secondary pupils.

a Draw a cumulative frequency table and a cumulative frequency graph for this set of data.

b Use your graph to estimate the number of pupils who have an angle between their first and second finger of less than or equal to 35°.

c Use your graph to estimate the number of pupils who have an angle between their first and second finger of more than 65°.

d Use your graph to estimate the number of pupils who have an angle between their first and second finger of between 25° and 75°.

Angle (°)	Frequency
$0 < x \leqslant 10$	6
$10 < x \leqslant 20$	13
$20 < x \leqslant 30$	27
$30 < x \leqslant 40$	43
$40 < x \leqslant 50$	49
$50 < x \leqslant 60$	28
$60 < x \leqslant 70$	11
$70 < x \leqslant 80$	13
$80 < x \leqslant 90$	5
$90 < x \leqslant 100$	5

4 This grouped frequency table shows the angle between thumb and first finger for each of 200 pupils.

Angle (°)	Frequency
$0 < x \leqslant 20$	9
$20 < x \leqslant 40$	13
$40 < x \leqslant 60$	44
$60 < x \leqslant 80$	47
$80 < x \leqslant 100$	72
$100 < x \leqslant 120$	10
$120 < x \leqslant 160$	5

a Draw a cumulative frequency table and a cumulative frequency graph for this set of data.

b Use the graph to estimate the number of pupils who have an angle between their first and second finger of between 45° and 90°.

 Points to remember

- **Cumulative frequency** at a particular point is the 'running total' of all the frequencies up to that point.
- You can represent cumulative frequencies in a **cumulative frequency table** and plot them on a **cumulative frequency graph**.

4 Cumulative frequency 2

This lesson will help you to estimate quartiles from a cumulative frequency graph.

Exercise 4

Cumulative frequency tables and graphs can also be drawn for **discrete data**. Note the labelling of the intervals in the tables below and how the graph is plotted.

Example 1

This cumulative frequency table below shows the number of lengths swum by 30 members of a swimming club in a Saturday morning session.

The points to plot are (4, 4), (9, 11), (14, 22), (19, 27) and (24, 30).

Number of lengths swum	Frequency	Cumulative frequency
0–4	4	4
5–9	7	11
10–14	11	22
15–19	5	27
20–24	3	30

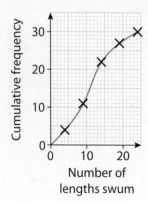

Draw a cumulative frequency graph for this set of data.

You can use a cumulative frequency graph to **estimate** the median and the upper and lower quartiles of a large data set. Mark the graph with lines to show how you read off the values.

For a large data set of n values:

- ◉ use the value at $\frac{1}{2}n$ for an estimate of the **median**;
- ◉ use the value at $\frac{1}{4}n$ for an estimate of the **lower quartile**;
- ◉ use the value at $\frac{3}{4}n$ for an estimate of the **upper quartile**.

Use your estimates of the quartiles to work out an estimate for the interquartile range.

Example 2

The cumulative frequency graph shows the times of 160 people on a cross-country run.

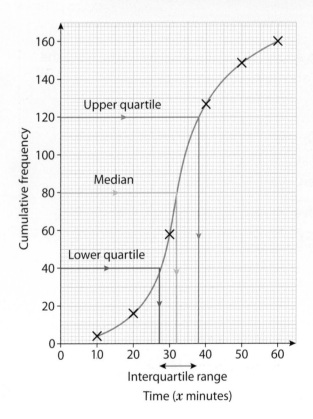

Use the graph to estimate:

a the median: $\frac{1}{2}$ of 160 = 80

Read off from the graph a cumulative frequency of 80, giving **32 minutes**.

b the lower quartile: $\frac{1}{4}$ of 160 = 40

Read off from the graph a cumulative frequency of 40, giving **27 minutes**.

c the upper quartile: $\frac{3}{4}$ of 160 = 120

Read off from the graph a cumulative frequency of 120, giving **38 minutes**.

d the interquartile range

Find the difference between the upper and lower quartiles:

38 − 27 = **11 minutes**

You need some graph paper and your graphs from Exercise 3 or **S7.3 Resource sheet 4.1**.

① The grouped frequency table gives information about the number of people catching a train from Alderley Edge to Manchester for 50 consecutive days.

Number of passengers	Frequency
0–9	2
10–19	5
20–29	10
30–39	16
40–49	15
50–59	0
60–69	2

a Draw a cumulative frequency table for the data.

b Use the table to draw a cumulative frequency graph.

② The grouped frequency table shows the number of meals served in a school for 190 days.

Number of meals	Frequency
40–49	3
50–59	10
60–69	45
70–79	53
80–89	31
90–99	48

a Draw a cumulative frequency table for the data.

b Use the table to draw a cumulative frequency graph.

③ Use your graphs from Exercise 3, questions 1 to 4.

Using each graph in turn, estimate:

a the median

b the lower quartile

c the upper quartile

d the interquartile range

Remember to include the units in your answers.

5 Estimating statistics for grouped data

This lesson will help you to estimate statistical measures for large sets of grouped data.

Exercise 5

When data is grouped the actual items of data are not known.

It is not possible to work out the actual mean but an estimate can be made.

For example, this table shows the population of the United Kingdom in 2008 broken down by age group.

To estimate the mean, assume that the mean of all the values in each class is the midpoint of the class interval.

Estimated total of ages:
  2424.45 million

Number of people:
  60.5 million

Estimated mean age:
  2431.25 ÷ 60.5
  = **40.2 years** (to 3 s.f.)

The modal class is the class interval with the highest frequency, which is **40–44 year olds**.

Age range	Midpoint of interval	Frequency (millions)	Midpoint × frequency
0–4	2.5	3.2	8
5–9	7.5	3.4	25.5
10–14	12.5	3.7	46.25
15–19	17.5	4.0	70
20–24	22.5	4.0	90
25–29	27.5	3.9	107.25
30–34	32.5	3.8	123.5
35–39	37.5	4.4	165
40–44	42.5	4.8	204
45–49	47.5	4.6	218.5
50–54	52.5	3.9	204.75
55–59	57.5	3.6	207
60–64	62.5	3.7	231.25
65–69	67.5	2.7	182.25
70–74	72.5	2.3	166.75
75–79	77.5	1.9	147.25
80+	90.0	2.6	234
TOTAL		60.5	2431.25

Population distribution enquiry

Work in a group of four for this activity.

Use either the country data that you printed out from the International Database on the US Census website (www.census.gov/ipc/www/idb/) or **S7.3 Resource sheet 5.1**.

Choose a question to investigate about the age distribution of the populations in different countries over time. For example, you could choose one of the following questions:

- What differences are there between the population distributions in developed countries compared with developing countries?

- Are there differences between countries on the same continent, for example, in Africa?

- How does the population distribution for a country change over time?

- What predictions are being made about the population distribution for a particular country for the future?

① Estimate the modal group and calculate an estimate of the mean for your data sets.

② What evidence do you have to support your statistical enquiry?

③ If time allows, start to draw a cumulative frequency graph for each of your data sets. You will need these for the next lesson.

◉ Points to remember

⊙ When data is grouped, you cannot calculate accurate values of average and spread but you can estimate them.

⊙ You can calculate an estimate of the mean from a grouped frequency table using the formula:

$$\frac{\Sigma(f \times x)}{\Sigma f}$$

where: the symbol Σ means 'the sum of'
x represents the midpoint of the class interval
f represents the frequency of the class.

This lesson will help you to display five-figure summaries graphically to compare sets of data.

Did you know that...?

Box plots were invented in 1977 by the American statistician **John Tukey** (1915–2000). Among his many other achievements, he helped to develop the U2 spy plane.

When he gave a lecture in London in 1977, Tukey was described as 'a great bear of a man dressed in baggy pants and a black knitted shirt'.

He is quoted as saying: 'Far better an approximate answer to the right question, than the exact answer to the wrong question.'

Exercise 6

Box plots (sometimes called box-and-whisker diagrams) are diagrams that indicate the spread of the data. They show the five-figure summary statistics: the median, lower and upper quartiles along with the minimum and maximum values.

Box plots should always be drawn to scale.

Box plots are particularly useful for comparing distributions. When you draw two box plots, draw them with one above the other using the same scale or a common scale.

Example

The table shows the time in minutes that some people waited at an airport to check in for a flight. Draw a box plot to show this data.

	Time (min)
Minimum	8
Lower quartile	26
Median	32
Upper quartile	38
Maximum	57

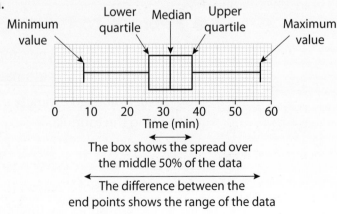

You need some graph paper and your data and results from the previous lesson.

1 The diagram shows the times taken by some pupils to find the answer to a mental maths question.

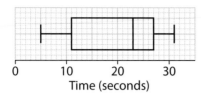

	Time (s)
Minimum	
Lower quartile	
Median	
Upper quartile	
Maximum	

Use the box plot to copy and complete the table.

2 The table shows some information about the time taken in minutes for some students to complete a questionnaire.

Draw a box plot to show this information.

	Time (min)
Minimum	8
Lower quartile	13
Median	16
Upper quartile	19
Maximum	23

3 The table shows some information about the height in centimetres from the belly button to the floor for a group of teenagers.

Draw a box plot to show this information.

	Height (cm)
Minimum	50
Lower quartile	90
Median	100
Upper quartile	106
Maximum	135

4 Pupils in two groups did a maths test. Their results were used to draw the box plots on the right.

In which group did the students do better in the test? Explain your answer.

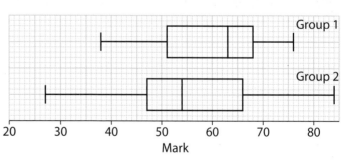

5 The box plots show the heights of girls and boys in Year 5 in New Zealand.

a Write down the five-figure summaries for the boys and girls.

b Write some sentences comparing the heights of boys and girls.

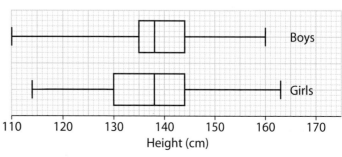

Data source: www.censusatschool.org

6 Population distribution enquiry

You need your work from the previous lesson for this activity.

a Complete drawing cumulative frequency graphs for your data sets.
Use them to estimate the median and quartiles for each data set.

b Draw a box plot for each of your data sets.
Use a common scale so that you can compare the data sets.

c What further evidence do you have to support your statistical enquiry?

Points to remember

⊙ A **box plot** should always be drawn to scale.

⊙ You can use box plots to compare distributions. Draw one box plot above the other using the same scale or a shared scale.

7 Histograms and frequency density

This lesson will help you to draw and interpret histograms with equal and unequal class intervals.

Exercise 7

A **histogram** represents continuous data so there are no gaps between the bars. There is a scale on the horizontal axis.

When the class widths for a data set are **equal**, the heights of the bars on the histogram represent the frequency.

When the class intervals are **unequal**, the histogram is drawn so that the area of each bar is proportional to the frequency.

The height of each rectangle is called the **frequency density** of the class and the vertical axis is labelled 'frequency density'.

So frequency
= area of rectangle
= height of rectangle × class width
= frequency density × class width

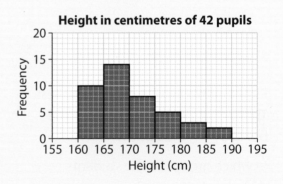

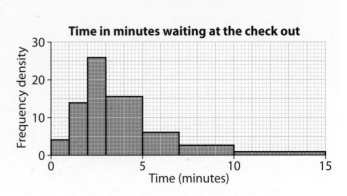

$$\text{frequency density} = \frac{\text{frequency}}{\text{class width}}$$

Example

The table shows the ages of spectators at a basketball match.
Draw a histogram to illustrate the data.

Age (years)	Frequency
$0 < x \leqslant 15$	12
$15 < x \leqslant 25$	66
$25 < x \leqslant 35$	90
$35 < x \leqslant 40$	45
$40 < x \leqslant 70$	60

First work out the class widths then calculate the frequency density.

Age (years)	Frequency (f)	Class width (w)	Frequency density ($f \div w$)
$0 < x \leqslant 15$	12	$15 - 0 = 15$	$12 \div 15 = 0.8$
$15 < x \leqslant 25$	66	$25 - 15 = 10$	$66 \div 10 = 6.6$
$25 < x \leqslant 35$	90	$35 - 25 = 10$	$90 \div 10 = 9$
$35 < x \leqslant 40$	45	$40 - 35 = 5$	$45 \div 5 = 9$
$40 < x \leqslant 70$	60	$70 - 40 = 30$	$60 \div 30 = 2$

To draw the histogram, label the
horizontal axis 'Age (years)' and mark
off the class intervals as in the table.

Label the vertical axis 'Frequency
density'. Make the heights of the bars
the values you have calculated for
frequency density for each interval.

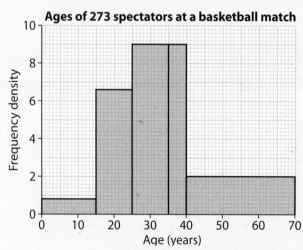

Ages of 273 spectators at a basketball match

You need some graph paper and your data and results from the previous two lessons.

1 **Population distribution enquiry**

    a Write down the question you have been investigating. For example:

> • *How does the population distribution for a country change over time?*

    b Draw a histogram for each of your sets of data.

    c Use all your diagrams and statistics to write a conclusion for your enquiry. Refer back to
your original question and explain in detail how the data informs you about this question.

2 The table shows the angles between first and second finger for a large group of pupils.

a Copy the table adding two more columns, one for class width and one for frequency density.

Calculate the class width and frequency density to complete the table.

b Draw a histogram to represent the data, with frequency density on the vertical axis.

Angle (°)	Frequency
$0 < x \leqslant 20$	21
$20 < x \leqslant 30$	13
$30 < x \leqslant 35$	16
$35 < x \leqslant 40$	27
$40 < x \leqslant 45$	25
$45 < x \leqslant 50$	23
$50 < x \leqslant 60$	28
$60 < x \leqslant 70$	11
$70 < x \leqslant 100$	23

3 The table shows information about foot length for a large group of pupils.

a Copy and complete the table, adding two more columns, one for class width and one for frequency density.

b Draw a histogram to represent the data, with frequency density on the vertical axis.

Foot length (cm)	Frequency
$10 < x \leqslant 15$	3
$15 < x \leqslant 20$	14
$20 < x \leqslant 22$	33
$22 < x \leqslant 24$	61
$24 < x \leqslant 26$	51
$26 < x \leqslant 30$	29
$30 < x \leqslant 35$	9

Extension problems

4 The histogram shows the time in minutes some teenagers spent watching TV in one evening.

a How many of the teenagers spent 1 hour or less watching TV?

b How many of the teenagers spent more than 3 hours watching TV?

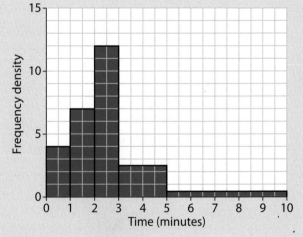

5 The histogram shows the heights in centimetres of some plants.

a Calculate the percentage of the plants with a height between 2 cm and 4 cm.

b Find the median height of the plants.

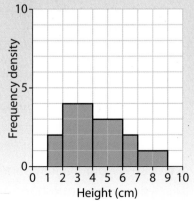

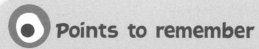

Points to remember

⊙ When a **histogram** has unequal class intervals, the area of each rectangle is proportional to the frequency.

⊙ The vertical axis is labelled '**frequency density**'.

⊙ The height of each rectangle is the frequency density of the class, where:

$$\text{frequency density} = \frac{\text{frequency}}{\text{class width}}$$

8 Moving averages

This lesson will help you to calculate and use moving averages for time series data.

Exercise 8

A **time series graph** shows a set of readings taken over a period of time. Time is plotted on the horizontal axis and the values of the readings on the vertical axis. The data sometimes shows **seasonality**, peaking at certain points in the year on a regular cycle.

To see whether the values are generally increasing, decreasing or staying the same, you can calculate the **moving averages** and plot those on the graph. This provides a more stable measure of the variable against time.

A set of **4-point moving averages** is the mean of the 1st to 4th values, then the mean of the 2nd to 5th values, then the mean of the 3rd to 6th values, and so on. They are called 4-point moving averages because four consecutive values are used in each case.

The **trend line** is the line of best fit through the moving averages. It can be used to make predictions for the future based on past performance.

Example

The table shows the quarterly sales in thousands for a manufacturing company.

Have the sales increased or decreased over the three years?

Quarter	Year 1	Year 2	Year 3
1	31	32	34
2	42	46	43
3	58	60	62
4	46	47	49

a Calculate the 4-point moving averages.

The mean of the first four values is (31 + 42 + 58 + 46) ÷ 4 = **44.25 thousands** of sales.

The mean of the next four values is (42 + 58 + 46 + 32) ÷ 4 = **44.5 thousands** of sales.

The mean of the next four values is (58 + 46 + 32 + 46) ÷ 4 = **45.5 thousands** of sales, etc.

b Are the sales increasing or decreasing?

Plot the moving averages on a time series graph.

The point representing the first moving average is plotted against the median time for the relevant period of time, which is half way between Q2 and Q3 of year 1 at a height of 44.25, and so on.

Draw the trend line: the line of best fit through the moving averages. It is clear from the trend line that sales are **increasing**.

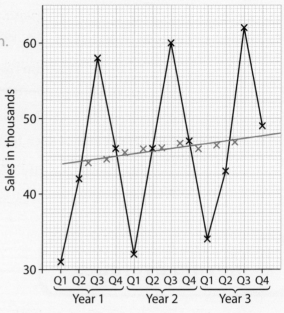

c Predict the sales for the first quarter of year 4.

Q1 for year 4 cuts the trend line at 48 thousands. As first quarter sales are about 13 thousands below the trend line, an estimate of Q1 for year 4 is 48 − 13 = **35 thousands**.

You need some graph paper.

1 The table shows the weekly sales in a school tuck shop rounded to the nearest £10.

Week	Sales (£)
1	310
2	200
3	190
4	460

Week	Sales (£)
5	290
6	190
7	170
8	440

Week	Sales (£)
9	260
10	170
11	160
12	410

a Draw a time series graph to represent the data.

b Calculate the 4-point moving averages for the data.

c Plot the moving averages on the graph and draw a line of best fit.

d What is the trend in the tuck shop sales?

e Suggest some possible reasons for the shape of the graph and the trend in sales.

f Predict the tuck shop sales for weeks 13 and 14.

2 The table shows the number of copies of a magazine sold every day for three weeks. Sales are in thousands of copies.

Week 1	
Monday	6
Tuesday	4
Wednesday	27
Thursday	16
Friday	12
Saturday	21
Sunday	7

Week 2	
Monday	7
Tuesday	4
Wednesday	28
Thursday	16
Friday	13
Saturday	22
Sunday	6

Week 3	
Monday	7
Tuesday	5
Wednesday	31
Thursday	18
Friday	13
Saturday	23
Sunday	7

a Draw a time series graph to represent the data.

b Calculate the 7-point moving averages for the data.

c Plot the moving averages on the graph and draw a line of best fit.

d What is the trend in the magazine sales?

e How frequently is the magazine published? On which day of the week is it published? Explain how you know.

f Predict the sales for Monday and Tuesday of week 4.

3 The table shows the quarterly gas production of Australia between December 1989 and September 1994 in millions of megajoules.

Quarter	1989	1990	1991	1992	1993	1994
March		113 000	111 000	117 000	106 000	127 000
June		138 000	141 000	151 000	149 000	159 000
September		151 000	160 000	175 000	163 000	184 000
December	128 000	123 000	125 000	129 000	138 000	

Data source: www-personal.buseco.monash.edu.au/~hyndman/TSDL/

a Draw a time series graph to represent the data.

b Calculate the 4-point moving averages for the data.

c Plot the moving averages on the graph and draw a line of best fit.

d What is the trend in gas production?

e Explain the seasonal pattern of gas use.

f Predict the gas production for December 1994 and March 1995.

Extension problem

 4 The graph shows the time series, moving averages and line of best fit for those averages for some data on car sales in thousands in Quebec in 1960 and 1961.

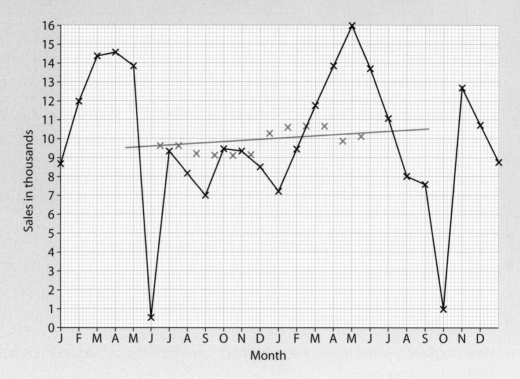

a What trend is shown by the moving averages?

b Describe the shape of the graph.
Give some possible explanations for the peaks and troughs.

⊙ Points to remember

- ⊙ Some time series data sets show regular patterns called **seasonality**, peaking at certain points in the year on a regular cycle.

- ⊙ To look for trends and patterns in the data over time, plot the **moving averages**.

- ⊙ Draw a **trend line** as the line of best fit and use it to make predictions for the future based on past performance.

How well are you doing?

(1) *2007 level 8*

5000 pupils took part in a test. Pupils took two papers, paper 1 and paper 2. The graph shows the cumulative frequencies of their marks for each paper.

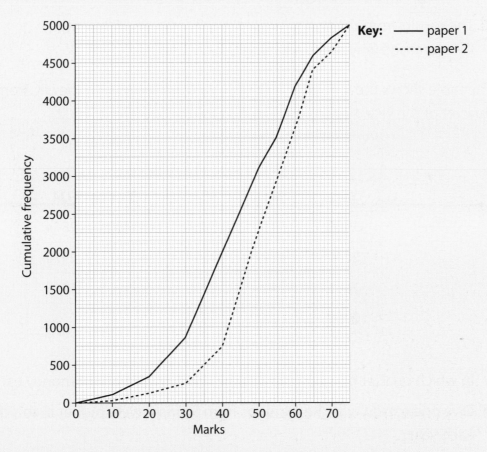

Use the graph to answer these questions.

For each question answer **True**, or **False**, or **Not enough information**.

a The median mark for paper 1 was about 38. Explain your answer.

b The interquartile range of the marks for paper 1 was about 23. Explain your answer.

c Paper 1 was easier than paper 2. Explain your answer.

Two groups of pupils collected a sample of acorns from the same oak tree.
The box plots summarise the two sets of results.

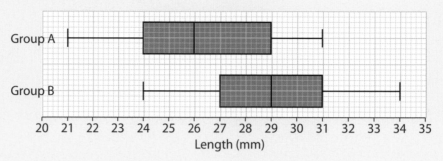

Length (mm)

a Explain how the box plots show the median of group B is 3 mm more than the median of group A.

b Which group has the bigger interquartile range?

c The results from the two groups of pupils are very different.
Give a reason why the results might have been different.

③ The table shows the earnings each quarter from tourism to the UK, from the first quarter of the year 1999 to the second quarter of the year 2002.

Year	Earnings from tourism to the UK (in £ millions)			
	Q1	Q2	Q3	Q4
1999	2413	3064	4148	2874
2000	2315	3297	4284	2910
2001	2406	2815	3819	2265
2002	1901	2815		

Data source: National Statistics

a In which quarter of each year was the greatest amount of money earned?

b Give one reason why the earnings from tourism were higher in this quarter of each year.

c The first 9 four-quarterly moving averages, in £ millions, to two significant figures are:

3100 3100 3200 3200 3200 3200 3100 3000 2800

Calculate the last two moving averages.

d Describe the trend in the earnings from tourism over the years 1999 to 2002.

A triathlon is a competition in which people compete in three events.

304 people took part in a triathlon.

They swam 1.5 km, then cycled for 40 km, then ran for 10 km.

The histograms show the distributions of their times for each of the three events.

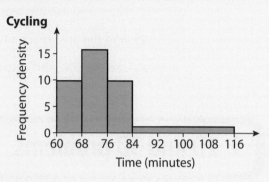

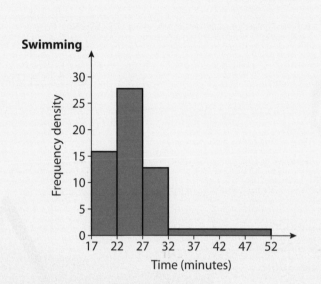

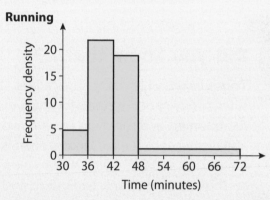

a   The histograms are constructed using frequency densities. The table shows the frequency densities for swimming.

Copy and complete the table to show the frequencies.

Time t (minutes)	Frequency density	Frequency
$17 \leqslant t < 22$	16.0	80
$22 \leqslant t < 27$	28.0	
$27 \leqslant t < 32$	12.4	
$32 \leqslant t < 52$	1.1	

b   304 people took part in the triathlon.
Calculate an estimate of the mean time for swimming. Show your working.

c   Explain why the median time for swimming must be between 22 and 27 minutes.

d   Calculate an estimate of the median time for swimming. Show your working.

e   Each of the three distributions is skewed. Explain what this means.

f   Data that relate to human beings are often normally distributed, but the data in this question are skewed. Give a reason why this might be the case.

Trigonometry 2

This unit will help you to:

- use Pythagoras' theorem and trigonometry to solve 2D and 3D problems;
- draw and use the graphs of trigonometric functions for angles of any size;
- find the area of a triangle using the formula $\frac{1}{2}ab \sin C$;
- use the sine and cosine rules to solve problems involving triangles.

1 2D and 3D problems

Did you know that...?

Trigonometry has many applications. It is used in satellite navigation systems for ships, aircraft and cars. Astronomers and surveyors use it to work out angles and distances to stars or landmarks. It is used in ultrasound and CAT scans, in seismology to predict earthquakes or volcanic explosions and in computer graphics and game development. Robotic arms on the International Space Station are operated by controlling the angles of their joints. This requires repeated use of the sine, cosine and tangent of the angles.

This lesson will help you to apply Pythagoras' theorem and trigonometry to 2D and 3D problems.

Exercise 1

To find lengths and angles in 2D and 3D shapes you need to identify right-angled triangles and apply **Pythagoras' theorem** and the **trigonometric ratios** to them.

Pythagoras' theorem shows that in a right-angled triangle:

$$a^2 + b^2 = c^2$$

The **trigonometric ratios** are:

$$\sin x = \frac{\text{opp}}{\text{hyp}} \qquad \cos x = \frac{\text{adj}}{\text{hyp}} \qquad \tan x = \frac{\text{opp}}{\text{adj}}$$

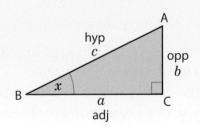

Example

ABCDO is a pyramid.

The base ABCD is a horizontal rectangle in which AB = 11 cm and AD = 7 cm. The vertex, O, is vertically above the midpoint of the base and OB = 16 cm.

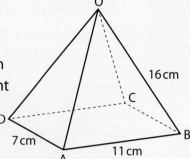

Find the angle that OB makes with ABCD.
Give your answer correct to one decimal place.

The midpoint M of the base is directly below O.

Join O to M and M to B.

As OM is perpendicular to the base of the pyramid the angle OBM is the angle between OB and the base ABCD.

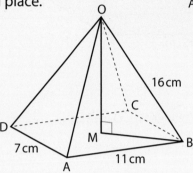

Draw triangle OBM marking OB = 16 cm.

To find the size of angle OBM, find the length of either MB or OM.

MB is the diagonal of the rectangular base. As M is the midpoint of the base, MB = ½DB.

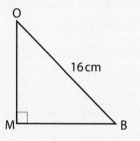

Calculate the length of DB.

Draw the right-angled triangle ABD marking the known lengths.

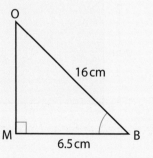

Using Pythagoras' theorem:

$$DB^2 = 7^2 + 11^2 = 49 + 121 = 170$$

$$DB = \sqrt{170} = 13.0 \text{ cm}$$

$$MB = \tfrac{1}{2}DB = 6.5 \text{ cm}$$

In triangle OBM, mark MB = 6.5 cm.

In relation to angle OBM, 16 cm is the hypotenuse, 6.5 cm is the adjacent side, so use the cosine ratio,

$$\cos(\text{angle OBM}) = \frac{6.5}{16}$$

$$\text{angle OBM} = \cos^{-1}\frac{6.5}{16} = 66.0° \text{ (to 1 d.p.)}$$

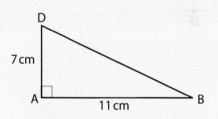

The angle between OB and the horizontal plane is **66.0°** (to 1 d.p.).

You need a scientific calculator.
Show your working clearly and round only the final answer.
Give your answers to 3 significant figures for lengths or 1 decimal place for angles.

1. Calculate the angles in the cuboids.

   a The angle between the line TZ and the plane WXYZ

   b The angle between the line EC and the plane EFGH

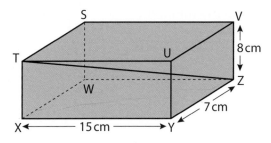
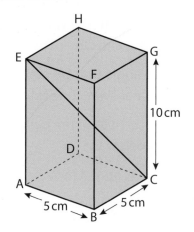

2. The diagram shows a right-angled triangular prism.

   Calculate the size of the angle between:

   a BD and the plane ADEF

   b BD and the plane BCEF

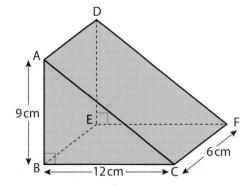

3. The diagram shows a right-angled triangular prism.

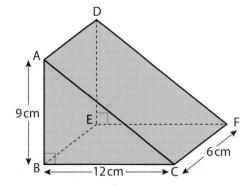

   Calculate the size of the angle between:

   a AE and the plane BCFE

   b AF and the plane BCFE

4. Pyramid VWXYZ has a square base. The apex V is 12 cm vertically above O, which is the centre of the base.

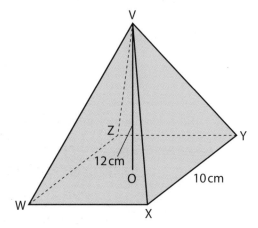

   Calculate the size of the angle between VW and the plane WXYZ.

5 Pyramid ABCDE has a rectangular base. The apex E is vertically above O, which is the centre of the base.

K is the midpoint of side AB.

Calculate the size of the angle between:

a AE and the plane ABCD

b EK and the plane ABCD

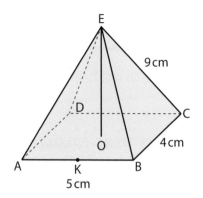

Extension problem

6 The diagram shows a solid cube of side length 8 cm.
The corner of the cube is removed to form a pyramid with triangular base ABC.

DA = DB = DC = 4 cm

a What is the angle between:

  i AC and the plane BCD?

  ii AB and the plane BCD?

b Move A, B and C to divide the sides in a different ratio, for example, so that DA = DB = DC = 3 cm.

Now calculate the size of the angles in part **a**.
What do you notice?

c Move A, B and C again to new positions equidistant from D.
How do the angles in part **a** change?

d What is the volume of the solid formed when the pyramid is removed from the cube?
Calculate the volume for different positions of A, B and C.

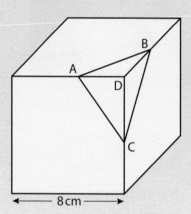

Points to remember

⊙ By identifying right-angled triangles in 2D figures and 3D shapes, you can use **Pythagoras' theorem** and **trigonometry** to find:

– angles and lengths of sides of triangles;

– the angle between a line and a plane.

⊙ Do not round numbers until the final answer.

⊙ In answers give lengths to 3 significant figures and angles to 1 decimal place, unless you are asked to do otherwise.

2 Area of a triangle

This lesson will help you to use a new formula to find the area of a triangle.

Did you know that...?

Heron's formula says that for any triangle with side lengths a, b and c:

$$\text{Area} = \sqrt{s(s-a)(s-b)(s-c)}$$

where s is the semi-perimeter:

$$s = (a+b+c) \div 2$$

Heron of Alexandria (c. AD 10–70) proved his formula in his book, *Metrica*, which was written in about AD 60.

An equivalent formula was also discovered independently by the Chinese.

Exercise 2

The vertices of a triangle are usually labelled with capital letters.

The sides are labelled so that a is the length of the side opposite angle A, b is the length of the side opposite angle B and c is the length of the side opposite angle C.

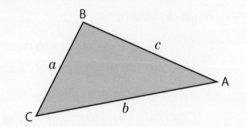

The area of a triangle $= \frac{1}{2} \times$ base $\times$ height, so:

area of triangle ABC $= \frac{1}{2}bh$

In triangle BCN, $\sin C = \dfrac{h}{a}$, so:

$a \times \sin C = h$

Substituting for h gives area of triangle ABC as:

$\frac{1}{2}ab \sin C$

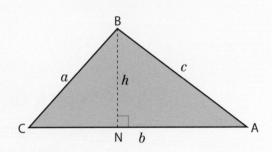

Similarly, the area of the triangle can be expressed as $\frac{1}{2}bc \sin A$ or $\frac{1}{2}ac \sin B$.

The formulae can be expressed in words as.

> **The area of a triangle is half the product of two sides $\times$ the sine of the included angle.**

Example

Find the area of the triangle.

Area $= \frac{1}{2} \times$ product of two sides $\times$ sine of the included angle

$\quad = 0.5 \times 16.2 \times 7.4 \times \sin 118°$

$\quad = \textbf{52.9 m}^2$ (to 3 s.f.)

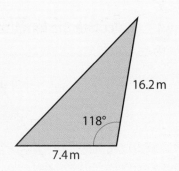

You need a scientific calculator.

1 Given the marked angles and sides, for which of the triangles A to F is it possible to find the area using the formula 'half the product of two sides $\times$ sine of the included angle'?

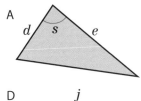

A

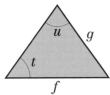

B

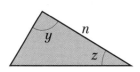

C

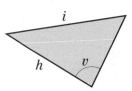

D

E

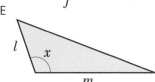

F

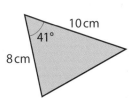

2 Calculate the area of each triangle.

a

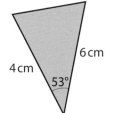

4 cm, 6 cm, 53°

b

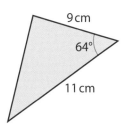

9 cm, 64°, 11 cm

c

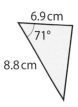

41°, 10 cm, 8 cm

d 4.6 cm, 112°, 8.1 cm

e

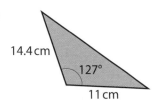

14.4 cm, 127°, 11 cm

f 6.9 cm, 71°, 8.8 cm

3 Calculate the area of each quadrilateral.

a

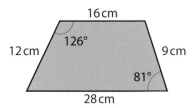

16 cm, 126°, 12 cm, 9 cm, 81°, 28 cm

b

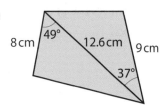

8 cm, 49°, 12.6 cm, 9 cm, 37°

4 Calculate the lengths a and b.

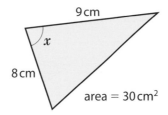

131°

17 cm

area = 25 cm²

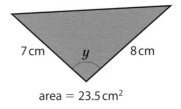

62°

9.2 cm

area = 30 cm²

5 Calculate the size of angles x and y.

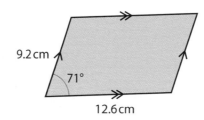

9 cm

x

8 cm

area = 30 cm²

7 cm y 8 cm

area = 23.5 cm²

6 Calculate the area of the parallelogram.

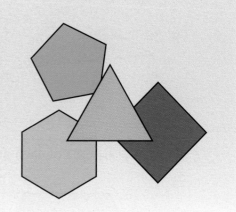

9.2 cm

71°

12.6 cm

Extension problem

7 Amina has a set of regular polygons. For each polygon, the distance from the centre to each vertex is 5 cm.

a Find the areas of Amina's polygons with 5 to 9 sides.

b Find a formula for the area of a polygon with n sides.

c Check that your formula works by finding the areas of Amina's regular polygons with 3 and 4 sides, first by using your formula and then by using a different method.

Points to remember

⊙ The area of triangle ABC is $\frac{1}{2}ab\sin C$

or:

'half the product of two sides times the sine of the included angle'.

3 Angles larger than 90°

This lesson will help you to calculate the values of sine, cosine and tangent for angles greater than 90°.

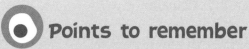

Did you know that...?

The **graphs of trigonometric functions** are some of the most commonly used in science and engineering.

Trigonometric graphs are **periodic**, which means that the shape repeats itself exactly after a certain amount of time.

They are used for modelling many different natural and mechanical phenomena that have a regular cycle such as tides, light waves, sound waves, engine motion, electric current, and so on.

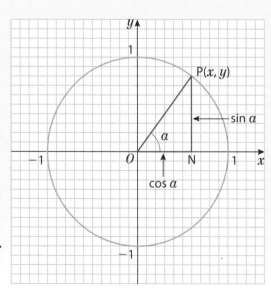

Exercise 3

The diagram shows a circle of radius 1 unit.

In triangle OPN:

$$\sin a = \frac{\text{opposite}}{\text{hypotenuse}} = \frac{\text{PN}}{\text{OP}} = \frac{y}{\text{OP}}$$

Since the hypotenuse OP has length 1 unit:

$$y = \sin a$$

Similarly, ON $= x = \cos a$.

As OP rotates anti-clockwise about O, the angle a increases and the values of $x = \cos a$ and $y = \sin a$ change correspondingly.

You need graph paper and a scientific calculator.

1. Work in pairs in a group of six. Each pair should sketch one of these graphs:

$$y = \sin x \qquad y = \cos x \qquad y = \tan x$$

for values of x from 0° to 540°.

Use a calculator to work out the value of your function every 30°.
Plot the points as accurately as possible and join them with a smooth curve.

In your group of six, compare the three graphs. Write what you notice.

For questions 2–7, work individually and use a copy of **G7.5 Resource sheet 3.1**.

2. Use the sine function graph to estimate:

   a $\sin 30°$ **b** $\sin 120°$ **c** $\sin 200°$ **d** $\sin 300°$ **e** $\sin 450°$

3. Use the cosine function graph to estimate:

   a $\cos 30°$ **b** $\cos 120°$ **c** $\cos 200°$ **d** $\cos 300°$ **e** $\cos 450°$

4. Use the tangent function graph to estimate:

   a $\tan 30°$ **b** $\tan 120°$ **c** $\tan 200°$ **d** $\tan 300°$ **e** $\tan 450°$

5. Use the sine function graph to estimate all the values of x for $0° \leqslant x \leqslant 360°$ for which:

   a $\sin x = 0.5$ **b** $\sin x = -0.5$ **c** $\sin x = 0$

6. Use the cosine function graph to estimate all the values of x for $0° \leqslant x \leqslant 360°$ for which:

   a $\cos x = 0.5$ **b** $\cos x = -0.5$ **c** $\cos x = 0$

7. Use the tangent function graph to estimate all the values of x for $0° \leqslant x \leqslant 360°$ for which:

   a $\tan x = 0.5$ **b** $\tan x = -0.5$ **c** $\tan x = 0$

Extension problems

8. Use a calculator to find the values of the functions in questions 4, 5 and 6.
   What do you notice?

9. Sketch the graphs of $y = \sin x$, $y = \cos x$ and $y = \tan x$ for $-360° \leqslant x \leqslant 360°$.

Points to remember

⊙ Trigonometric ratios can be found for angles of any size.

⊙ Graphs can be drawn for $y = \sin x$, $y = \cos x$ and $y = \tan x$.

4 Graphs of trigonometric functions

This lesson will help you learn more about the graphs of trigonometric functions.

Exercise 4

$y = \sin x$

- cuts the x-axis at
  $\ldots, -180°, 0°, 180°, 360°, \ldots;$

- repeats itself every $360°$;

- has a maximum value of 1 at
  $\ldots, -270°, 90°, 450°, \ldots;$

- has a minimum value of -1 at
  $\ldots, -90°, 270°, \ldots$

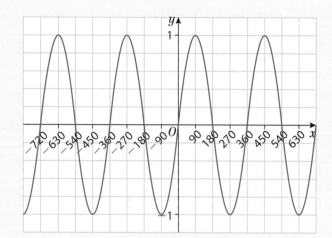

$y = \cos x$

- cuts the x-axis at
  $\ldots, -90°, 90°, 270°, 450°, \ldots;$

- repeats itself every $360°$;

- has a maximum value of 1 at
  $\ldots, 0°, 360°, \ldots;$

- has a minimum value of -1 at
  $\ldots, -180°, 180°, \ldots$

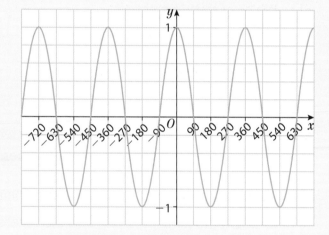

$y = \tan x$

- cuts the x-axis at
  $\ldots, -180°, 0°, 180°, 360°, \ldots;$

- repeats itself every $180°$;

- has no maximum or minimum values;

- has no value at
  $\pm 90°, \pm 270°, \pm 450°, \ldots$

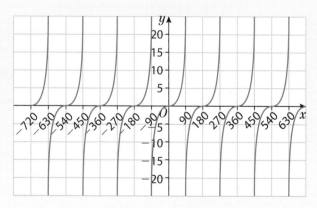

The graphs of $y = \sin x$ and $y = \cos x$ are horizontal translations of each other.

The points where $\tan x = 0$ are the same points for which $\sin x = 0$.

The points where $\tan x$ has no value are the same points for which $\cos x = 0$.

In the first quadrant, for values of a between 0° and 90°, sin a, cos a and tan a are **all positive**.

In the second quadrant, for values of a between 90° and 180°, only **sin a is positive**.

In the third quadrant, for values of a between 180° and 270°, only **tan a is positive**.

In the fourth quadrant, for values of a between 270° and 360°, only **cos a is positive**.

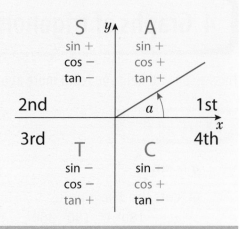

Answer questions 1 and 2 **without using a calculator** and using the quadrants diagram.

1. **a** Use sin 30° = 0.5 to work out the values of sin 150°, sin 210° and sin 390°.

   b Use cos 45° = $\dfrac{\sqrt{2}}{2}$ to work out the values of cos 135°, cos 225° and cos 405°.

   c Use tan 45° = 1 to work out the values of tan 135°, tan 225° and tan 405°.

2. Which of these are equal?

   a sin 50°, sin 130°, sin 310°

   b cos 60°, cos 120°, cos 240°

   c tan 70°, tan 110°, tan 250°

You need a **graphics calculator** or a computer with graphing software for questions 3, 4 and 5. Record what you find out using labelled sketches.

3. **a** Plot and then sketch $y = \sin x$ for several cycles of the function.

   b Using the same axes, plot and then sketch the graph of $y = a \sin x$ for different values of a, including negative values.

   c As a changes, how does the graph change? Write what you notice.

4. **a** Plot and then sketch $y = \cos x$ for several cycles of the function.

   b Using the same axes, plot and then sketch the graph of $y = \cos ax$ for different values of a, including negative values.

   c As a changes, how does the graph change? Write what you notice.

Extension problem

5. Repeat question 3 for some functions of the form $y = \sin x + a$ and $y = \sin(x + a)$ as well as combinations of transformations.

Points to remember

⊙ $\tan x = \dfrac{\sin x}{\cos x}$ for all angles.

⊙ Trigonometric functions are periodic.

⊙ Trigonometric graphs can be transformed using constants.

⊙ Different trigonometric functions are positive in different quadrants.

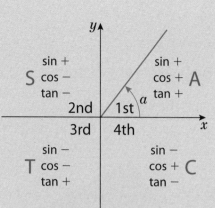

5 The sine rule

This lesson will help you to use the sine rule to find angles and lengths in non-right-angled triangles.

Exercise 5

The area of triangle ABC is

$\frac{1}{2}ab \sin C = \frac{1}{2}bc \sin A = \frac{1}{2}ca \sin B$

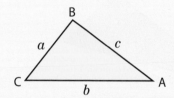

| Starting from: | $\frac{1}{2}ab \sin C = \frac{1}{2}bc \sin A$ | Starting from: | $\frac{1}{2}bc \sin A = \frac{1}{2}ca \sin B$ |

Dividing by $\frac{1}{2}b$ gives: $\quad a \sin C = c \sin A \qquad$ Dividing by $\frac{1}{2}c$ gives: $\quad b \sin A = a \sin B$

Rearranging gives: $\quad \dfrac{a}{\sin A} = \dfrac{c}{\sin C} \qquad$ Rearranging gives: $\quad \dfrac{b}{\sin B} = \dfrac{a}{\sin A}$

Combining the results gives the formula known as the **sine rule**, which holds for any triangle:

$$\dfrac{a}{\sin A} = \dfrac{b}{\sin B} = \dfrac{c}{\sin C}$$

Example 1

Find the length of side a.
Give your answer to 3 significant figures.

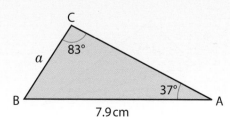

$\dfrac{a}{\sin A} = \dfrac{c}{\sin C}$

$\dfrac{a}{\sin 37°} = \dfrac{7.9}{\sin 83°}$

$a = \dfrac{7.9 \times \sin 37°}{\sin 83°}$

$a = \mathbf{4.79\,cm}$ (to 3 s.f.)

To **calculate an angle**, use a rearrangement of the **sine rule**:

$$\frac{\sin A}{a} = \frac{\sin B}{b} = \frac{\sin C}{c}$$

Example 2

Find the size of angle x.
Give your answer to one decimal place.

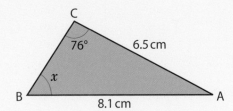

$$\frac{\sin B}{b} = \frac{\sin C}{c}$$

$$\frac{\sin x}{6.5} = \frac{\sin 76°}{8.1}$$

$$\sin x = \frac{6.5 \times \sin 76°}{8.1} = 0.7786...$$

$$x = \mathbf{51.1°} \text{ (to 1 d.p.)}$$

You need a scientific calculator.
Give your answers to 3 significant figures for lengths and 1 decimal place for angles.
Remember to draw a diagram for each question and to show your working clearly.

1. Find the lengths of each side marked with a letter.

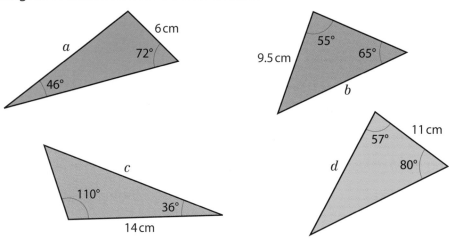

2. Calculate the size of each angle marked with a letter.

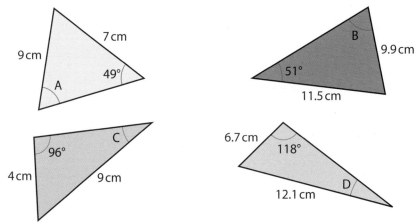

3 The diagram shows a quadrilateral ABCD and its diagonal AC.

    a In triangle ABC work out the length AC.

    b Work out angle ADC.

    c Work out the length AD.

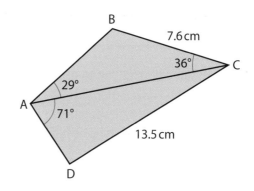

4 In triangle ABC, BC = 7 cm.

Angle ACB = 41° and angle ABC = 59°.

Calculate:

    a length AC

    b length AB

    c the area of the triangle

5 Triangle XYZ is an acute-angled triangle.

XY = 9 cm and XZ = 11.5 cm.

Angle XYZ = 71°

Calculate:

    a angle YXZ

    b length YZ

Extension problem

6 AC is a diagonal of quadrilateral ABCD.
AB is 7.6 cm.

Angle ABC = 116°, angle ACB = 31°, angle CDA = 71°, angle CAD = 57°

Calculate:

    a length AC   **b** length CD   **c** angle BCD

⦿ Points to remember

⦿ You can use the **sine rule** to find lengths
and angles in triangles that are not right-angled:

$$\frac{a}{\sin A} = \frac{b}{\sin B} = \frac{c}{\sin C}$$

or:

$$\frac{\sin A}{a} = \frac{\sin B}{b} = \frac{\sin C}{c}$$

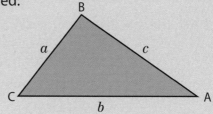

6 The cosine rule

This lesson will help you to use the cosine rule to find angles and lengths in non-right-angled triangles.

Exercise 6

In triangle ABC, BN is perpendicular to AC and meets AC at N. The length of BN is h.

Let AN $= x$ so NC $= (b - x)$.

Using Pythagoras' theorem, in triangle BNA:

$$h^2 = c^2 - x^2$$

Using Pythagoras' theorem, in triangle BNC:

$$h^2 = a^2 - (b - x)^2$$
$$= a^2 - b^2 + 2bx - x^2$$

So: $\quad c^2 - x^2 = a^2 - b^2 + 2bx - x^2$

Rearranging $\quad a^2 = b^2 - 2bx + c^2$

But in triangle BNA, $x = c \cos A$, and substituting for x in the equation above gives:

$$a^2 = b^2 + c^2 - 2bc \cos A$$

Similarly $\quad b^2 = a^2 + c^2 - 2ac \cos B$

and $\quad c^2 = a^2 + b^2 - 2ab \cos C$

The result is known as the **cosine rule**. It can be used in **any** triangle.

Remember that if the angle in the cosine rule is **obtuse**, then its value is **negative**.

Example 1

Find the length of side a. Give your answer to 3 significant figures.

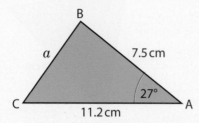

$a^2 = b^2 + c^2 - 2bc \cos A$

$a^2 = 11.2^2 + 7.5^2 - 2 \times 11.2 \times 7.5 \times \cos 27°$

$= 32.001$

$a = \sqrt{32.001} = \mathbf{5.66\,cm}$ (to 3 s.f.)

To **calculate an angle**, use a rearrangement of the cosine rule:

$$\cos A = \frac{b^2 + c^2 - a^2}{2bc} \qquad \cos B = \frac{c^2 + a^2 - b^2}{2ac} \qquad \cos C = \frac{a^2 + b^2 - c^2}{2ab}$$

Remember that if the value of cos A is **negative**, then A must be an **obtuse angle**.

Example 2

Find the size of angle BAC. Give your answer to 1 decimal place.

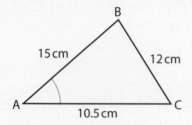

$$\cos A = \frac{b^2 + c^2 - a^2}{2bc}$$

$$\cos A = \frac{10.5^2 + 15^2 - 12^2}{2 \times 10.5 \times 15} = 0.6071$$

So angle BAC is $\cos^{-1} 0.6071 = \mathbf{52.6°}$ (to 1 d.p.)

You need a scientific calculator.

Give your answers to 3 significant figures for lengths and 1 decimal place for angles.

Remember to draw a diagram for each question and to show your working clearly.

(1) Find the length of each side marked with a letter.

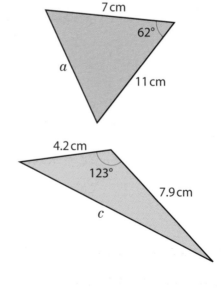

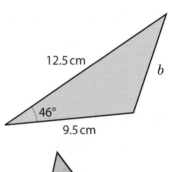

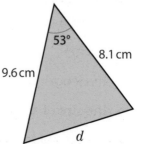

2 Calculate the size of each angle marked with a letter.

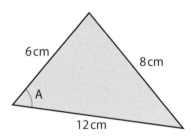

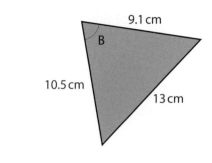

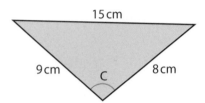

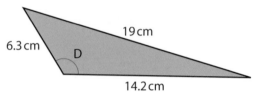

3 AC is a diagonal of quadrilateral ABCD.

Calculate:

a the length of AC

b the length of CD

c the size of angle ADC

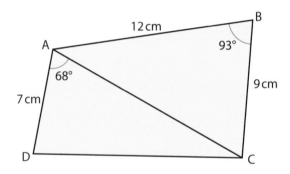

4 The diagram shows a parallelogram.

Calculate the length of each diagonal.

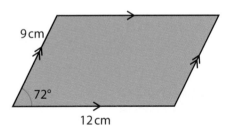

5 In triangle ABC, BC = 9 cm.

AC = 14 cm
Angle ACB = 37°

Calculate:

a the length of AB

b the size of angle BAC

c the area of triangle ABC

6 In triangle XYZ, XY = 8.6 cm.

XZ = 4.7 cm
YZ = 9.5 cm

Calculate:

a the size of angle YXZ

b the size of angle XZY

Extension problem

 AC is a diagonal of quadrilateral ABCD.

AB = 12.6 cm, BC = 9.1 cm, CD = 10.3 cm and AD = 8.6 cm.

Angle ABC = 106°

Calculate:

a the length of AC **b** the size of angle ADC **c** the area of quadrilateral ABCD

◉ Points to remember

- You can use the **cosine rule** to find lengths and angles in triangles that are not right-angled:

$$a^2 = b^2 + c^2 - 2bc \cos A$$

or:

$$\cos A = \frac{b^2 + c^2 - a^2}{2bc}$$

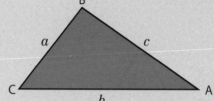

---

7 Using the sine and cosine rules

This lesson will help you to use the sine and cosine rules to solve 2D and 3D problems.

Exercise 7

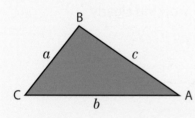

The **sine rule**: $\dfrac{a}{\sin A} = \dfrac{b}{\sin B} = \dfrac{c}{\sin C}$ or: $\dfrac{\sin A}{a} = \dfrac{\sin B}{b} = \dfrac{\sin C}{c}$

The **cosine rule**: $a^2 = b^2 + c^2 - 2bc \cos A$

or: $\cos A = \dfrac{b^2 + c^2 - a^2}{2bc}$

Choose the rule that will help you to find the answer in the most efficient way.

- To **find a side**:
  - if you know two sides and the included angle, use the cosine rule;
  - if you know two angles, and a side opposite one of them, use the sine rule to find the side opposite the other angle.

- To **find an angle**:
  - if you know three sides, use the cosine rule;
  - if you know two sides, and an angle opposite one of them, use the sine rule to find the angle opposite the other side.

It is often useful to sketch the triangles that you use when you solve trigonometric problems.

Example

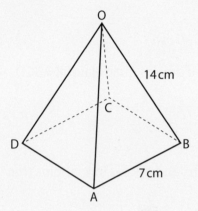

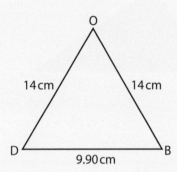

The diagram shows pyramid ABCDO, with apex O. The base ABCD is a square of side 7 cm.

$OA = OB = OC = OD = 14\,cm$

Calculate the size of angle BOD.
Give your answer to 1 decimal place.

$BD^2 = 7^2 + 7^2 = 98$

$BD = \sqrt{98} = 9.90\,cm$

In triangle OBD, you know three sides, so use the cosine rule:

$$\cos A = \frac{b^2 + c^2 - a^2}{2bc}$$

$$\cos BOD = \frac{14^2 + 14^2 - 9.9^2}{2 \times 14 \times 14} = 294 \div 392 = 0.75$$

angle $BOD = \cos^{-1} 0.75 = 41.4°$ (to 1 d.p.)

You need a scientific calculator.
Give your answers to 3 significant figures for lengths and 1 decimal place for angles.
Remember to draw a diagram for each question and to show your working clearly.

① Find the lengths of each side marked with a letter.

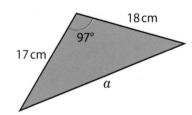

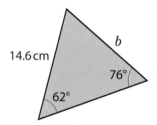

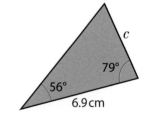

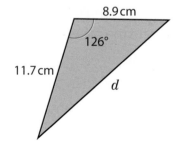

(2) Calculate the size of each angle marked with a letter.

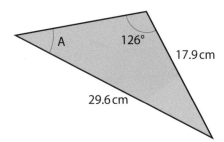

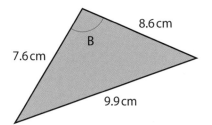

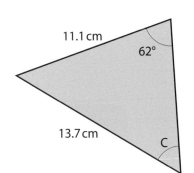

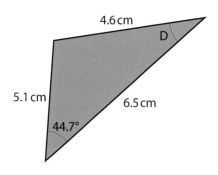

(3) The diagram shows triangle XYZ. Calculate the size of angle XZY.

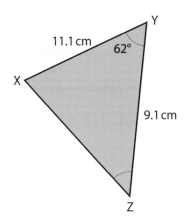

(4) In triangle ABC, P is a point on BC such that AP = x m and PC = y m. Calculate the lengths x and y.

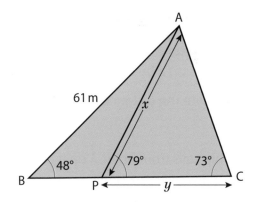

(5) The diagram shows pyramid ABCDE with apex E.

The base ABCD is a rectangle with AB = 11 cm and BC = 6 cm.

EA = EB = EC = ED = 18 cm

Calculate the size of angle BED.

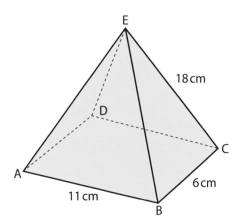

6 The diagram shows a tent in the shape of a triangular prism ABCDEF.

Angle ACB = 120°
AC = BC = 1.6 m

Calculate:

a the length of AB;

b the angle the sloping sides of the tent make with its base;

c the angle FB makes with the base.

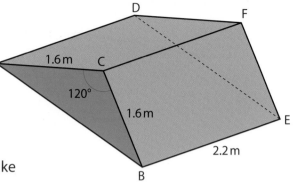

7 A coastguard at X can see two ships out at sea.

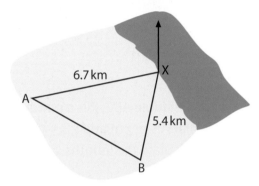

Ship A is on a bearing of 265° at a distance of 6.7 km.
Ship B is on a bearing of 196° at a distance of 5.4 km.

Calculate the distance between the two ships.

8 A ship sails from point A on a bearing of 072° for a distance of 12 km.

It then changes course to a bearing of 169° and sails for a further 17 km.

Find the distance and bearing of the ship's new position at C from its original position at A.

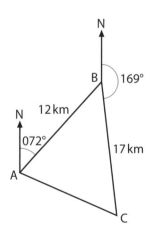

Extension problems

9 The diagram shows tetrahedron ABCD.

AB = 4 cm, AC = 10 cm, AD = 10 cm and BD = 8 cm.
Angle ABC = 75°
Angle CAD = 45°

Calculate:

a angle ACB

b angle ABD

c CD

d BC

e angle DBC

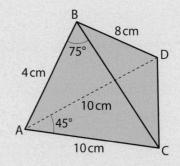

10 Pyramid WXYZO has apex O.

The base WXYZ is a square with side 21 cm.
Each triangular face of the pyramid is at an
angle of 48° to the horizontal.

Calculate:

a the perpendicular height of the pyramid

b the slant height OX

c the angle OX makes with the base

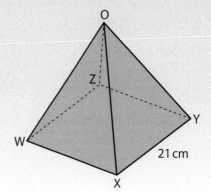

 Points to remember

⊙ You can use the **sine and cosine rules** to find lengths and angles
in triangles.

⊙ Choose the rule that gives you the answer most directly.

⊙ To **find an angle**:
– if you know three sides, use the cosine rule;
– if you know two sides, and an angle opposite one of them, use the
sine rule to find the angle opposite the other side.

⊙ To **find a side**:
– if you know two sides and the included angle, use the cosine rule;
– if you know two angles, and a side opposite one of them, use the sine
rule to find the side opposite the other angle.

How well are you doing?

In any triangle ABC:

- The sine rule is $\dfrac{a}{\sin A} = \dfrac{b}{\sin B} = \dfrac{c}{\sin C}$
- The cosine rule is $a^2 = b^2 + c^2 - 2bc \cos A$
- The area of triangle is $\frac{1}{2}ab \sin C$

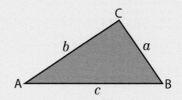

1. The pyramid ABCDE has a square base.

   Point E is vertically above point O, which is the centre of the base.

   K is the midpoint of side AB.

   Calculate the sizes of the angles between:

   a   AE and the plane ABCD

   b   EK and the plane ABCD

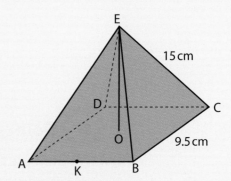

2. *GCSE 1387 June 2007*

   ABC is a triangle.

   AC = 8 cm
   BC = 9 cm
   Angle ACB = 40°

   Calculate the length of AB.
   Give your answer correct to 3 significant figures.

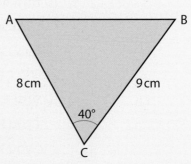

Diagram NOT drawn accurately

(3) *GCSE 1387 November 2007*

The diagram shows a tetrahedron.

AD is perpendicular to both AB and AC.

AB = 10 cm

AC = 8 cm

AD = 5 cm

Angle BAC = 90°

Calculate the size of angle BDC.

Give your answer correct to 1 decimal place.

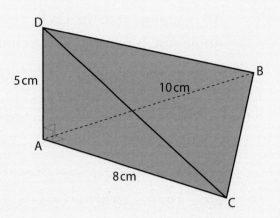

(4) *GCSE 1387 November 2006*

The graph of the curve

$y = \cos x°$ for $0 \leqslant x \leqslant 360$

is drawn on the right.

Use the graph to find estimates of the solutions, in the interval $0 \leqslant x \leqslant 360$, of:

a $\cos x° = -0.4$

b $4 \cos x° = 3$

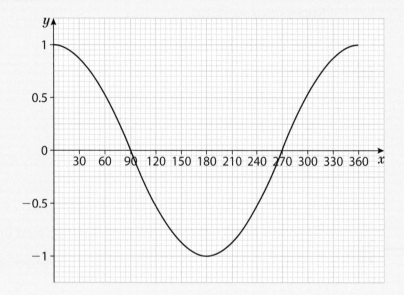

(5) *2001 Exceptional performance*

In triangle ABC:

BC = x

AC = (x − 1)

Angle B = 30°

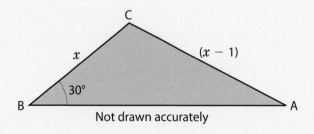

Not drawn accurately

a If $\sin A = \frac{5}{6}$, what is the value of x?
Show your working.

b If $\sin A \leqslant \frac{4}{5}$, what is the least value of x?
Show your working.

6 *2000 Exceptional performance*

AD is a tangent to the circle, centre O.
Angle ABC is 63° and AC is a chord.

a Write the values of:

angle AOC

angle OCA

angle CAD

AB = 18 cm and BC = 3 cm.

b Calculate the area of triangle ABC.
Show your working.

c Calculate the length AC.
Show your working.

d Calculate the radius of the circle.
Show your working.

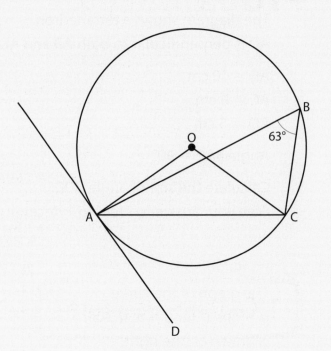

Not drawn accurately

7 *1999 Exceptional performance*

A group of walkers is travelling on a west to east line. At point A they make a detour
to go around a lake. They rejoin the west to east line at point C.

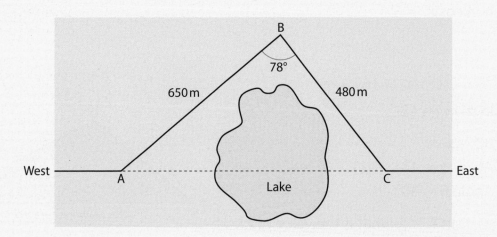

a Calculate the extra distance the walkers travelled in making the detour.
Show your working.

b Calculate the bearing of the route from A to B. Show your working.

c Calculate the bearing of the route from B to C. Show your working.

Probability 2

This unit will help you to:

- apply your knowledge and understanding of probability in a range of contexts including:
  - working out probabilities of combined events, including conditional probabilities;
  - deciding whether to add or to multiply probabilities;
  - estimating the size of a population;
  - determining the best strategy for playing a game of chance.

1 Capture-recapture

This lesson will help you use your knowledge of probability to estimate the size of a population.

Did you know that...?

The basis of **capture-recapture methods** were established in 1812 by the French mathematician **Pierre Laplace** (1749–1827).

In 1896 **Carl George Johannes Peterson**, a Danish fisheries scientist, estimated the size of a fish population using a capture-recapture method and brass tags that he invented.

When capture-recapture methods of estimating the size of a wild-life population are used, the creatures have to be marked in some way for identification.

Biologists often fit leg bands to birds, metal or plastic tags to turtles, and ear tags or radio collars to large animals such as elephants or bears. Fish such as salmon sometimes have tiny microchips embedded under their skin.

To estimate some populations, wildlife biologists take an aerial photograph and then count the number of animals in the photo.

The US Census Bureau has considered using the capture-recapture method to help count the homeless population in large urban areas.

To use the **capture-recapture method** to estimate a population, scientists assume that the proportion of marked animals in the second sample is the same proportion that the initial number of marked animals is of the total number of animals.

$$\frac{\text{marked animals in recapture group}}{\text{total animals in recapture group}} = \frac{\text{marked animals in whole population}}{\text{total animals in whole population}}$$

Example

A scientist wants to estimate how many brown bears live in a forest.

He catches and tags 9 bears. The bears are then set free to continue their usual habits for one month.

The scientist then catches more bears. This time he captures 11 bears, 4 of which are marked.

Estimate how many bears are living in the forest.

Let x be the total population.

The proportion of the population marked is $\frac{9}{x}$.

The proportion marked in the second sample is $\frac{4}{11}$.

These proportions should be the same so $\frac{4}{11} = \frac{9}{x}$.

Rearranging: $x = 9 \times 11 \div 4 = 24.75$

So the bear population in the forest is about 25.

This method of estimating populations is called **capture-recapture**.

Your group needs some beans, a bag or box and a copy of **S7.4 Resource sheet 1.1**.

① Capture-recapture group activity

Investigate how estimates can vary depending on the sampling process.

Choose a number between 85 and 115.
Count out exactly that number of beans and put them in the bag.

Take out and count a handful of beans from the bag. Mark them with a pen.
Replace them and shake the box or bag to mix them up.
You now know the size of the whole population and the proportion that is marked.

Take it in turns to take a handful of beans (maybe 20 to 30). Take at least 12 samples.

- Count the sample size.
- Count the number of marked beans in the sample (number of recaptures).
- Use these two figures and the number that you know you marked initially to make an estimate of the total number of beans.
- Record your results in a row of the table on **Resource sheet 1.1**.

Now answer these questions in your book.

a What is the group's mean estimate of the number of beans (the population)?

b By how much did your samples vary?

c How good were your samples at estimating the population?

(2) A group of marine biology students are working with their tutor to estimate the population of a group of turtles on an island. 85 of the turtles have been tagged and returned to the wild.

Each student then captures a sample of turtles and counts the number in the sample and the number of marked turtles. After each sampling the turtles are returned to the wild.

The table shows the students' results.

a Which student will give the largest estimate for the population?

b Which student will give the smallest estimate for the population?

c Calculate an estimate of the number of turtles living on the island.

Student	Sample size	Number marked
A	64	14
B	135	27
C	122	22
D	142	30
E	107	16
F	107	25

(3) The secondary school in a small town has 500 students.
A random survey of 200 people in the town finds 40 high school students.
What is the estimate for the number of people in the town?

(4) Some scientists estimate that the population of a particular species of bird is about 5500.
They have caught and tagged 460 birds before setting them free again.
Some time later they catch 700 birds.
About how many of these will be tagged if their estimate of the population is a good one?

(5) Some animals in a group are sometimes 'trap happy' – they are easier to capture and easier to recapture than others. So an animal captured for the first time is also likely to be in the second sample.
What do you think this behaviour will do to the estimate of the population size?

(6) In the capture-recapture method, it is assumed that marks will not be removed or wear off before recapture. If some animals lose their marks during the study, how will this affect the estimate of the population size?

(7) Suppose the time between the capture and the recapture is too long and some marked animals die. Will the deaths tend to make the estimate of the population size too large or too small? Explain your answer.

Extension problems

 8 A slightly better estimate of population size can be obtained with a modified version of the method above.

This modified formula reduces bias in the population estimate. The formula is:

$$N = \frac{(a + 1)(b + 1)}{c + 1} - 1$$

where N is the estimate of the population size

a is the total number of animals captured on the first visit

b is the total number captured on the second visit

c is the number of marked animals captured on the second visit.

a Use this formula to estimate the population of bears in the example for this exercise.

b Do you think this might be a better estimate? Why?

 9 To use this capture-recapture method, scientists and statisticians must be convinced that three basic assumptions are satisfied reasonably well.

What do you think those assumptions are, based on questions 5, 6 and 7?

Points to remember

- **Capture-recapture** sampling methods are used to estimate the size of a population when it is impossible count the size exactly.

- When you choose samples, it is important to consider the assumptions that you make.

2 The birthday problem

This lesson will help you to use tree diagrams to calculate probabilities with and without replacement.

 ## Did you know that...?

'How many people must be in a room before the probability that some share a birthday, ignoring the year and ignoring leap days, becomes at least 50 percent?'

The **birthday problem** was first suggested in 1939 by the Austrian scientist and mathematician **Richard von Mises** (1883–1953), who emigrated to the United States in 1939.

Today, the birthday problem is one of the most explored probability problems in the classroom.

Example 1

Sally and Craig are going to catch a train.

The probability that Sally will be early is 0.8.
The probability that Craig will be early is 0.3.

The two events are independent.

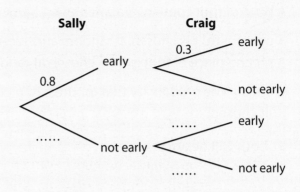

a Complete the probability tree diagram.

'Early' and 'not early' are mutually exclusive events, so:

P(Sally not early) = 1 − 0.8 = **0.2**
P(Craig not early) = 1 − 0.3 = **0.7**

The two events are independent, so the probabilities for Craig are the same on both parts of the tree diagram.

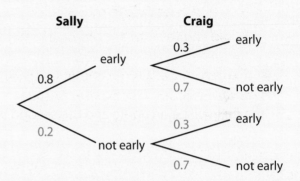

b Work out the probability that Sally and Craig will both be early.

Write the combined outcomes on the tree diagram.

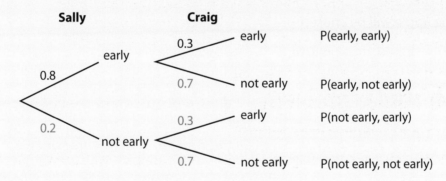

P(Sally early **and** Craig early) = P(early, early) = 0.8 × 0.3 = 0.24

c Work out the probability that just one person will arrive early.

P(just one person early)
= P(Sally early and Craig not early **or** Sally not early and Craig early)
= P(early, not early) + P(not early, early)
= (0.8 × 0.7) + (0.2 × 0.3) = 0.56 + 0.06 = 0.62

P(just one person early) = **0.62**

Example 2

A bowl of fruit contains 3 apples and 4 bananas.

A piece of fruit is chosen at random and eaten.
A second piece of fruit is then chosen at random.

Work out the probability that for the two pieces of
fruit chosen:

a **both will be apples**

1st choice: $P(A) = \frac{3}{7}$ Find the probability that the first piece of fruit will be an apple.
Of the 7 pieces of fruit, 3 are apples.

2nd choice: $P(A) = \frac{2}{6}$ First choice was an apple.
There are now only 6 pieces of fruit, 2 of which are apples.

$P(A \textbf{ and } A) = \frac{3}{7} \times \frac{2}{6} = \frac{1}{7}$ Multiply the probabilities.

b **the first will be an apple and the second will be a banana**

1st choice: $P(A) = \frac{3}{7}$ As before, find the probability that the first piece of fruit will be an apple.

2nd choice: $P(B) = \frac{4}{6}$ First choice was an apple.
There are now only 6 pieces of fruit, 4 of which are bananas.

$P(A \textbf{ and } B) = \frac{3}{7} \times \frac{4}{6} = \frac{2}{7}$ Multiply the probabilities.

c **at least one apple will be chosen**

$P(\text{at least one apple}) = 1 - P(B, B)$ The outcomes are mutually exclusive so
$P(\text{at least one apple}) + P(\text{no apples}) = 1$

1st choice: $P(B) = \frac{4}{7}$ Find the probability that the first piece of fruit will be a banana.
Of the 7 pieces of fruit, 4 are bananas.

2nd choice: $P(B) = \frac{3}{6}$ First choice was banana so there are now only 6 pieces of fruit, 3 of which are bananas.

$P(B, B) = \frac{4}{7} \times \frac{3}{6} = \frac{2}{7}$ Multiply the probabilities.

$P(\text{at least one apple}) = 1 - \frac{2}{7} = \frac{5}{7}$

①   The probability that Gary cycles to work is 0.4. If Gary doesn't cycle, he runs.
The probability that Ben walks to work is 0.8. If Ben doesn't walk, he takes the bus.
The probability that Freya drives to work is 0.5 and the probability that she runs is 0.1;
otherwise she cycles.

Work out the probability that today Gary, Ben and Freya travelled to work in different ways.

2 Shareen is packing to go away for a weekend.
She has 3 red shirts, 1 blue shirt, a grey shirt, 2 green shirts and 1 black shirt.
Shareen needs to pack two shirts. She picks two at random.
Calculate the probability that the two shirts she picks are the same colour.

3 A fair dice is labelled 3, 3, 4, 6, 6, 6.

Work out the probabilities of:

a throwing the dice three times and getting three sixes

b throwing the dice twice and getting an odd total

c throwing the dice three times and getting 3, 4 and 6 in that order

4 A bag of sweets contains 5 red, 3 green, 4 yellow and 6 brown sweets.
Three children take turns to pick a sweet at random from the bag and eat it.

Calculate the probability that:

a all three children pick a sweet of the same colour

b at least two of the children pick a brown sweet

Exercise 2B

Example

Suppose there are five pupils in a class.
What is the probability that at least two of them share the same birthday?

One way to calculate this is as 1 − probability that they all have different birthdays.

If the birthdays are all on different days of the year:

◦ there are 365 out of 365 possibilities for the 1st person's birthday;

◦ there are 364 out of 365 possible days for the second person's birthday;

◦ there are 363 out of 365 possible days for the third person's birthday, and so on.

P(they all have different birthdays) $= \frac{365}{365} \times \frac{364}{365} \times \frac{363}{365} \times \frac{362}{365} \times \frac{361}{365} = 0.973$

P(at least two share the same birthday) $= 1 - 0.973 = 0.027 = 3\%$

Work with a partner. You need a copy of **S7.4 Resource sheet 2.1**.

1. Calculate the probability that at least two pupils share the same birthday for the class sizes your teacher has given you.

2. Plot the probabilities on the grid on **Resource sheet 2.1**.

3. Collect some probabilities for different class sizes from other groups and add these to your graph.

4. Join the points you have plotted with a smooth curve. Use your graph to answer the question:

> How many people do you need in a group to ensure at least a 50 per cent probability that at least 2 people in the group share a birthday?

Points to remember

⊙ For independent or non-independent combined events, you can use tree diagrams to represent outcomes and help work out probabilities.

⊙ You can also use the 'and' and 'or' rules to work out probabilities without a tree diagram.

3 Using probability 1

This lesson will help you to explore some games of chance using probability.

Did you know that...?

In about 1650, the **Chevalier de Mere**, a Frenchman, lost a lot of money because he calculated his chances of winning a game of dice incorrectly. The chevalier sought help from the mathematician **Blaise Pascal** (1623−1662), who was able to spot his error. In solving the problem, Pascal discovered a fundamental principle of probability.

Exercise 3

1. In a party game, there is one box that contains 2 yellow balls and 2 green balls.
   Another box contains 3 green balls and 1 yellow ball.
   Without looking, you pick a ball at random from each box.
   You win a prize if the two balls are the same colour.
   Is this game fair? Explain your answer.

2. In these party games, the rules are the same as in question 1 but there are different numbers of balls in the boxes.

Work out whether each game is fair or not. Explain your answer each time.

   a Game 1: Box A: 2 yellow and 2 green, Box B: 2 yellow and 2 green

   b Game 2: Box A: 1 yellow and 2 green, Box B: 4 yellow and 2 green

   c Game 3: Box A: 2 yellow and 2 green, Box B: 4 yellow and 2 green

   d Game 4: Box A: 2 yellow and 1 green, Box B: 3 yellow and 2 green

3. Ben and Josh are playing Bingo.
   They have each picked six numbers from this list and written them on their Bingo cards.

   1, 2, 3, 4, 5, 6, 8, 9, 10, 12, 15, 16, 18, 20, 24, 25, 30, 36

   Ben has picked the numbers 1, 2, 3, 4, 5, 6.
   Josh has picked the numbers 8, 10, 12, 18, 24, 30.

   They throw two dice and multiply the scores.
   If one of their numbers comes up they cross it off their Bingo card.

   a Who do you think will win? Why?

   b Which are the best numbers to choose to win this game of Bingo?

   c Which are the worst numbers to choose?

4. This time Ben and Josh are playing a different game of Bingo.
   They have each picked three numbers from this list:

   0, 1, 2, 3, 4, 5

   Ben has picked the numbers 0, 1, 2.
   Josh has picked the numbers 3, 4, 5.

   They throw the two dice and subtract the smaller score from the larger.
   If one of their numbers comes up they cross it off their Bingo card.

   a Who do you think will win? Why?

   b Which is the best number to choose to win this game of Bingo?

   c Which is the worst number to choose?

   d How can you change the rules of this game to make it fair?

5. Make up two party games of your own like the ones in question 2, one fair and one not fair.

Did you know that...?

The probability of any set of six numbers being chosen at random in a fair draw are identical. However, many people assume that:

⊙ numbers that appeared in the last draw are more likely to appear in the next;

⊙ numbers that have not appeared for some time are more likely to appear;

⊙ there are trends in the colours of the balls drawn;

⊙ a combination that has never won previously is more likely to win next time.

6 In a game, you have to match six numbers that are drawn at random without replacement from the numbers 1 to 50.

Explain why each of the four assumptions above is false.

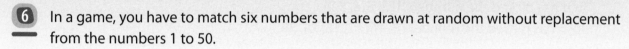

Points to remember

⊙ You can sometimes use probability to analyse games to work out the chances of winning them and to decide whether or not they are fair.

4 Using probability 2

This lesson will help you to use experimental probability to explore some dice games.

Exercise 4

Did you know that...?

Pig is a jeopardy dice game first described in 1945 by the American stage magician **John Scarne** (1903−1985).

A jeopardy dice game is one where the main decision to make is whether or not to jeopardise your previous score by rolling again for a potentially greater score.

John left school at 14. He became an expert on card and dice games and wrote a number of popular books on them.

You need three dice.

(1) **Pig** is a game for any number of players but it works best with 2–4 people.

Here are the rules for some games of Pig.

Simple pig

◎ Player 1 keeps rolling the dice and adding the scores, e.g. 2, 3, 5 scores 10:

- the player can decide when to stick;
- if the player rolls **1**, their score for that turn is zero and their turn ends.

◎ It is then the next player's turn.

◎ The winner is the first player to reach a score of 100.

Two-dice pig

◎ In the two-dice game:

- rolling a 1 ends your turn with no score for that turn;
- rolling a double 1 reduces your overall score for the game to 0;
- rolling any other score adds the total of the dice to your overall score.

◎ Other rules remain the same.

Big pig

◎ In this variation of Two-dice pig:

- rolling a double 1 adds 25 to your score for that turn;
- rolling any other double adds twice the amount shown to your score.

Hog

◎ At the start of your turn you decide how many dice you want to roll, 1, 2 or 3 dice, and then roll that number of dice all at once.

- rolling one or more 1s ends your turn with no score for that turn;
- rolling any other score adds the total of the dice to your overall score.

Other variations

◯ Instead of winning by reaching a score of 100, play for a fixed number of rounds. The winner is then the player with the greatest total score.

◯ Play simultaneously. All players share the same dice rolls but choose whether to stick or continue.

◯ Play with two dice. A score of 7 ends your turn with no score for that turn.

Here are some questions about the game of Pig.

a Is there an optimal number of rolls after which you should end your turn?

b Is there an optimal number of points at which you should end your turn?

c What is the expected score if you throw the dice twice, three times, …?

d What are good winning strategies?

e What factors affect who wins?

f How does your knowledge of probability help you to choose winning strategies?

Points to remember

⊙ You can use probability to help you to make decisions and choose good strategies in games of chance and other situations.

5 Quincunx

This lesson will help you to apply your understanding of probability to an unfamiliar situation.

Did you know that...?

In the western world, the arrangement of numbers where each number is the sum of the two numbers above it is called **Pascal's triangle**.

It is named after the French mathematician and philosopher **Blaise Pascal** (1623–1662).

Other mathematicians in India, Persia, China and Italy studied the triangle's properties centuries before Pascal. In China, the triangle is called the **Yang Hui triangle** after the Chinese mathematician **Yang Hui** (about 1238–1298), who wrote about it in 1261.

Did you know that...?

In 1873–74, **Sir Francis Galton** (Charles Darwin's cousin) designed a triangular arrangement of pegs that he named the **quincunx**.

A ball is dropped onto the top peg. When it hits a peg, it bounces either left or right. The ball bounces its way down to the bottom where it is collected.

The apparatus is also known as the Galton board or the binostat.

A quincunx can be used to demonstrate some principles of probability and a normal distribution.

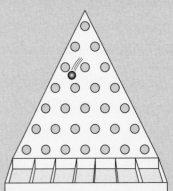

Work with a partner.
You need a coin and a copy of **S7.4 Resource sheet 5.2** between you.

1 **Quincunx simulation**

- Choose a quincunx on the resource sheet.
- Plot the paths of 20 balls as they fall through the pins.
- One of you should flip a coin to decide whether to go left or right at each pin. The other should record the path of the ball.
  Draw a dot in the bin when the ball arrives at the bottom of the quincunx.
- Count the dots in each bin and record the number.
- Repeat for each of the other two quincunxes on the Resource sheet.
- Give your results to your teacher to combine with the results of other pairs.

2 **a** Work out the number of routes there are to each of the bins A–E on this 4-row quincunx.

b What is the probability of a ball landing in bin A?

c What is the probability of a ball landing in bin B?

d What is the probability of a ball landing in bin C?

e How can you check that the probabilities are correct?

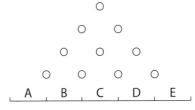

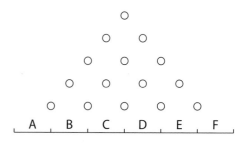

3 a Work out the number of routes there are to each of the bins A–F on this 5-row quincunx.

b Can you work out a quick way of counting all the routes using the results of the 4-row quincunx?

c What is the probability of a ball landing in each of the bins?

4 The number of routes to each bin should remind you of Pascal's triangle.

a Use Pascal's triangle to work out the number of routes for each bin in an 8-row quincunx.

b Work out the probability of a ball landing in each of the bins for this quincunx.

Extension problem

5 In a fair quincunx the ball has a probability of $\frac{1}{2}$ of going left and $\frac{1}{2}$ of going right at each peg.

Kim has a 4-row quincunx in which the ball has a probability of $\frac{1}{4}$ of going right at each peg.

a Sketch what you think the distribution of 50 balls would look like in Kim's quincunx.

b Design a simulation in which you flip two coins to decide which way the ball goes. Carry out an experiment of 50 trials to test your prediction for Kim's quincunx.

c Calculate the theoretical probability of a ball landing in each of the bins of Kim's quincunx.

d Use the theoretical probabilities to predict how many times a ball will land in each pocket for 50 trials.

e Compare your experimental and theoretical results. How close together were they?

Points to remember

⊙ You can solve problems involving probability using the addition and multiplication rules.

⊙ **Pascal's triangle**, in which each number is the sum of the two numbers above it, helps to work out probabilities in the quincunx.

How well are you doing?

Probability 2 (no calculator)

1 *2002 level 8*

I have a bag that contains blue, red, green and yellow counters. I am going to take out one counter at random. The table shows the probability of each colour being taken out.

	Blue	Red	Green	Yellow
Probability	0.05	0.3	0.45	0.2

a Explain why the number of yellow counters in the bag cannot be 10.

b What is the smallest possible number of each colour of counter in the bag?

2 *2002 level 8*

A robot can move N, S, E or W along the lines of a grid. It starts at the point marked ● and moves one step at a time. For each step, it is equally likely that the robot will move N, S, E or W.

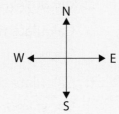

a The robot is going to move 3 steps from the point marked ●.

What is the probability that it will move along the path shown? Show your working.

b The robot is going to move 3 steps from the point marked ●.

What is the probability that it will reach the point marked × by any route?

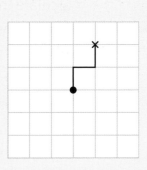

③ In a study of alligators in an area of central Florida, 47 of them were captured using cages baited with fish heads. The alligators were marked and released.
A week later, 82 alligators were captured, 39 of which had been marked.

a Estimate the size of the alligator population in the area.

b Describe one factor that might interfere with the accuracy of the alligator population estimate.

④ *1999 Exceptional performance*

In archery, you can score from 1 to 10 points with a single arrow hitting the target. If you miss the target you score 0 points.

Points scored	Probability
10	0.23
9	0.17
8	0.14
7	0.12
6	0.09
5	0.08
4	0.07
3	0.05
2	0.02
1	0.02
0	0.01

Ellen is taking part in a competition. She has to shoot 5 arrows at the target. The table shows the probability of Ellen scoring each number of points with a single arrow.

a Calculate the probability of Ellen scoring a total of 50 points with her 5 arrows. Show your working.

b Calculate the probability of Ellen scoring a total of 49 points. Show your working.

c Calculate the probability of Ellen hitting the target with all 5 arrows, but scoring no more than 4 points with any arrow. Show your working.

d Ellen needs to score 18 points or more with her final two arrows to win the competition.
Calculate the probability that Ellen scores 18 points or more with two arrows. Show your working.

In the game of SCRABBLE there are 100 tiles with letters written on them.
12 tiles have the letter E, 6 have N, and 4 have D.

a 3 of the letters are removed at random from a bag, without replacement.
Find the probability that the letters will spell the word END in the order they are taken out of the bag. Show your working.

b What is the probability that the letters E, N, D, in any order, will be chosen?
Show your working.

Steve and Ann make up their own game.
The game starts with all 100 tiles in a bag. 42 of the tiles are vowels.
The rules of their game are:

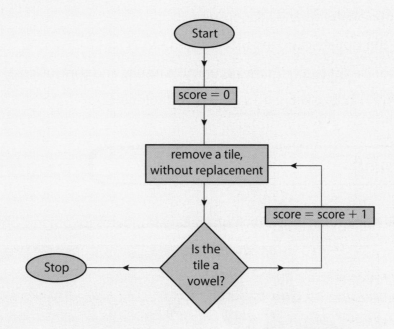

c Ann plays first.
What is the probability that Ann has scored exactly 2 points when she has to stop?
You may wish to draw a tree diagram.
Show your working.

d All the tiles are put back in the bag, and Steve plays.
What is the probability that Steve has scored 2 points or fewer when he has to stop?
Show your working.

Functional skills 7

Free-range organic chickens

This group activity will help you to:

- solve problems in unfamiliar contexts;
- choose and combine representations from a range of perspectives;
- select and apply a range of methods, operations and tools, including ICT;
- examine patterns and relationships;
- use appropriate checking procedures;
- recognise limitations in the accuracy of results and conclusions;
- interpret and communicate results and solutions.

Background

The Soil Association insists on high welfare standards for organic poultry.

- The chickens are looked after in small flocks of less than 500 birds.
- They are truly free range. They can roam freely outdoors with access to fresh grass and fresh air, with at least $4\,m^2$ of roaming space for each bird.
- They have plenty of space in their shelters.
- They are fed on a diet rich in organic cereals.

A farmer in Wales wants to form pens for his chickens so that they will have access to the greatest area of grass on which to roam.

Work in a small group. You need paper, rulers and scientific calculators.

1   The farmer has a barn where the chickens will have shelter.
   One long straight wall of the barn can act as one side of the pen.

   a   The farmer has just 100 m of fence available.

      What is the largest area that he can enclose using the wall of the barn as one side?
      What is the maximum number of organic free-range chickens he can keep?

   b   The farmer can make two straight pieces of fence 30 m and 40 m long.

      What is the largest area that he can enclose using the wall and two lengths of fence?
      What is the maximum number of organic free-range chickens he can keep?

Extension problem

2   The farmer has a rectangular field.
   He can make one straight fence 100 m long to fence off a corner of the field.

   What is the greatest area he can enclose with this single fence?

   What is the maximum number of organic free-range chickens he can keep?

Be prepared to justify your decisions, assumptions and conclusions to other groups.

Exploring graphs

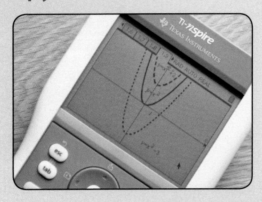

- know some properties of the graphs of more complex functions, including polynomial, reciprocal, exponential and trigonometric functions;
- know some properties of transformations of functions;
- construct the graphs of simple loci;
- use algebra to solve problems.

1 Exploring quadratic and cubic functions

This lesson will help you to know and use some of the properties of quadratic and cubic graphs.

Exercise 1

The graph of a quadratic equation $y = ax^2 + bx + c$ is a U-shaped graph.

When a is positive, for example $y = 2x^2 + 3x - 2$, it looks like this.

When a is negative, for example $y = -2x^2 + 3x + 2$, it looks like this.

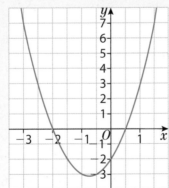

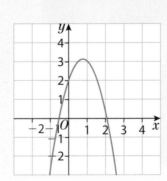

y is a **minimum** when $x = -0.75$.

y is a **maximum** when $x = 0.75$.

The graph of a cubic equation $y = ax^3 + bx^2 + cx + d$ is an S-shaped graph.

When a is positive, for example
$y = 2x^3 + 3x^2 - 2x + 1$, it looks like this.

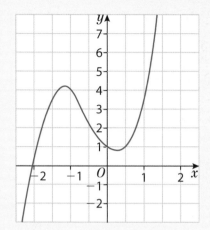

When a is negative, for example
$y = -2x^3 - 3x^2 + 2x - 1$, it looks like this.

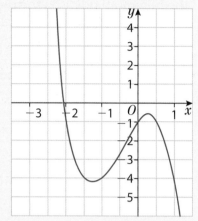

The graph has two **turning points** at approximately $x = -1.3$ and 0.3.

The graph has two **turning points** at approximately $x = -1.3$ and 0.3.

Work with a partner.
You need a graphics calculator, or a computer with a graph plotter and a scientific calculator.

(1) Exploring quadratic graphs

a Draw the graph of $y = x^2 - 4x + 4$.

b Where does the graph cross or touch the x-axis?

c Factorise the expression $x^2 - 4x + 4$.

d What do you notice?

e Draw the graph of $y = x^2 - 4x + 1$.

f Write the expression $x^2 - 4x + 1$ in the form $(x - 2)^2 + k$.
What is the value of k?

g What do you notice?

(2) **Maximum and minimum**

a Draw the graph of $y = x^2 + 6x + 9$.

b What is minimum point on the graph?

c Without drawing the graph, work out the values of x and y at
the minimum point on the graph of $y = x^2 + 6x + 5$.
Check by drawing the graph.

d Without drawing the graph, work out the values of x and y at
the minimum point on the graph of $y = x^2 - 8x + 6$.
Check by drawing the graph.

e Without drawing the graph, work out the values of x and y at the maximum point on the graph of $y = -x^2 - 10x - 22$.
Check by drawing the graph.

f Without drawing the graph, work out the values of x and y at the minimum point on the graph of $y = x^2 - x$.
Check by drawing the graph.

③ The gradient of a curve at any point is the gradient of the tangent at that point.

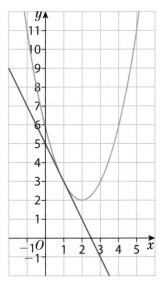

a Draw the graph of $y = x^2 - 4x + 6$.

b The diagram shows the tangent to the curve at (1, 3). What is the gradient of the tangent at (1, 3)?

c What is the gradient of the tangent at (2, 2)?

d Describe what happens to the gradient of the tangent to the curve as x increases from -1 to 5.

e What can you say about the gradient of the tangent at the minimum point of the curve?

f Describe what happens to the gradient of the tangent to the curve $y = -x^2 + 4x + 6$ as x increases from -1 to 5.

④ **Exploring cubic graphs**

a Draw the graph of $y = x^3$.

b Describe what happens to the gradient of the tangent to the curve as x increases from -2 to 2.

c Draw the graph of $y = x^3 - x$.

d Describe what happens to the gradient of the tangent to the curve as x increases from -2 to 2.

e Draw the graphs of $y = x^3 - x, y = x^3 - 2x, y = x^3 - 3x, y = x^3 - 4x, \ldots$.

f Describe the graphs you have drawn in part **e**.

g Draw the graphs of $y = x^3 + x, y = x^3 + 2x, y = x^3 + 3x, y = x^3 + 4x, \ldots$.

h Explain how the graphs in part **g** are different from those in part **e**.

i Investigate the graphs of $y = x^3 - x^2, y = x^3 - 2x^2, y = x^3 - 3x^2, y = x^3 - 4x^2$. Write down what you notice.

Points to remember

- The **quadratic equation** $y = ax^2 + bx + c$ has a U-shaped graph, which:
  - when a is positive, has a minimum value at its turning point;
  - when a is negative, has a maximum value at its turning point.
- The **cubic equation** $y = ax^3 + bx^2 + cx + d$ has an S-shaped graph, which:
  - when a is positive, starts in the 3rd quadrant and ends in the 1st quadrant;
  - when a is negative, starts in the 2nd quadrant and ends in the 4th quadrant;
  - has two turning points, with one maximum and one minimum value, or no turning points.

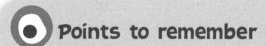

2 Properties of polynomial functions

This lesson will help you to learn some general properties of the graphs of polynomials.

Did you know that...?

In a polynomial function, the powers of x are positive integers.

$y = 2x - 3$, $y = x^4 + 3$, $y = x^7 - 2x^4 + 5x$ are all examples.

Thomas Harriot (1560–1621) was an English mathematician who contributed to a better understanding of polynomial functions. He has been described as the greatest mathematician that Oxford has produced, though not a lot is known about him. At one time he worked for Sir Walter Raleigh as accountant, instructor in navigation and designer of ships.

Exercise 2

This is the graph of $y = x^5 - 5x^3 + 4x - 3$.

The graph cuts the x-axis in three places.

The graph has four turning points.

The graph begins in the 3rd quadrant and ends in the 1st quadrant.

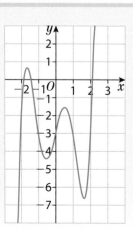

Work with a partner.
You need a graphics calculator, or a computer with a graph plotter and a scientific calculator.

1 **Linear graphs** $y = ax + b$

   a Draw the graphs of $y = x - 2$, $y = x - 1$, $y = x$, $y = x + 1$, $y = x + 2$, ...

   b Draw the graphs of $y = x$, $y = 2x$, $y = 3x$, $y = 4x$, ...

   c Describe the shape of the graphs.

   d Does a linear graph always cross the x-axis? If so, how many times does it cross?

   e In which quadrants do the graphs start and finish?

   f Describe what happens when the coefficient of x is negative, e.g. $y = -3x + 4$.

2 **Quadratic graphs** $y = ax^2 + bx + c$

   a Draw the graphs of:
     i $y = x^2 - 4x + 6$
     ii $y = x^2 - 4x + 4$
     iii $y = x^2 - 4x$

   b Describe the shape of the graphs.

   c Do all the graphs cross the x-axis?
     Explain your answer.

   d How many turning points do the graphs have?

   e In which quadrants do the graphs start and finish?

   f Describe what happens when a, the coefficient of x^2, is negative, e.g. $y = -x^2 - 4x + 6$.

3 **Cubic graphs** $y = ax^3 + bx^2 + cx + d$

   a Draw the graphs of $y = x^3$ and $y = x^3 - x^2 - 5x + 2$.

   b Draw some more cubic graphs by changing the values of a, b, c and d.

   c Do cubic graphs always cross the x-axis?
     If so, what is the maximum number of times a cubic can cross the x-axis?

   d Describe the turning points on a cubic graph.

   e In which quadrants do the graphs start and finish when a is positive?

   f In which quadrants do the graphs start and finish when a is negative?

4 **Polynomials of order 4**

    a Draw graphs of:

       i $y = x^4$

       ii $y = x^4 - 5x^2 + 4$

       iii $y = x^4 - 5x^2 + 7$

    b Do all polynomial graphs of order 4 cross the x-axis?

    c What is the maximum number of times a polynomial graph of order 4 can cross the x-axis?

    d Describe the turning points on the graphs.

    e In which quadrants do the graphs start and finish when a is positive?

    f Describe what happens when a is negative.

    g Write a general description of a polynomial graph of order 4.

5 **Polynomials of order 5**

    a Investigate polynomial graphs of order 5 by considering the way they cross the x-axis, their turning points and where the graphs start and finish.

    You could begin by drawing the graphs of $y = x^5$ and $y = x^5 - 5x^3 + 4x - 3$.

    b Write a general description of a graph of a polynomial of order 5.

Extension problem

6 Generate graphs that look like these.

  a

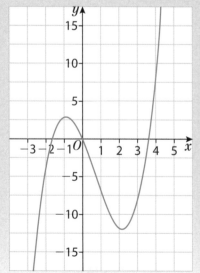

  b

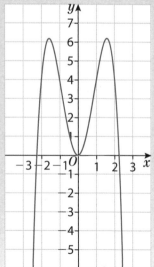

  c

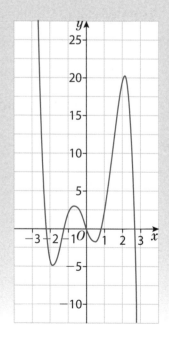

Points to remember

⊙ $y = ax + b$, $y = ax^2 + bx + c$, $y = ax^3 + bx^2 + cx + d$ and so on are examples of **polynomial functions**. Each power of x is a positive integer.

⊙ When the highest power is x^n, the polynomial is of **order n**.

⊙ When the order is even, a polynomial graph starts and ends on the same side of the x-axis. It either:
  – starts in the 2nd quadrant and ends in the 1st quadrant; or
  – starts in the 3rd quadrant and ends in the 4th quadrant.

⊙ When the order is odd, a polynomial graph crosses the x-axis at least once. It either:
  – starts in the 3rd quadrant and ends in the 1st quadrant; or
  – starts in the 2nd quadrant and ends in the 4th quadrant.

⊙ As the order of a polynomial graph increases:
  – the number of 'bends' in the graph increases;
  – the more times it can cross the x-axis.

3 Reciprocal functions

This lesson will help you to learn some of the characteristics of reciprocal graphs.

Exercise 3

In mathematics the word **reciprocal** means 'multiplicative inverse'.

The reciprocal of 3 is $\frac{1}{3}$ and the reciprocal of $\frac{1}{3}$ is 3.

The reciprocal of x is $\frac{1}{x}$ and the reciprocal of $\frac{1}{x}$ is x.

Example 1

The area of a triangle is $10\,\text{cm}^2$. Show the relationship between the base x and height y on a graph.

Area of triangle: $10 = \frac{1}{2}xy$

Make y the subject of the formula: $y = \dfrac{20}{x}$

The graph shows the relationship between x and y.

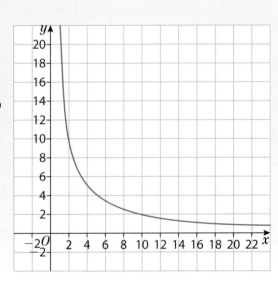

Example 2

Draw the graph of $y = \dfrac{12}{x}$.

y is inversely proportional to x.

Make a table of values.

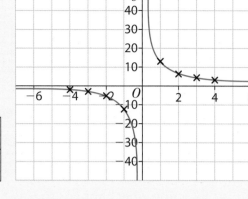

x	-4	-3	-2	-1	1	2	3	4
y	-3	-4	-6	-12	12	6	4	3

Plot the points on a graph.

Work with a partner. You need graph paper and copies of **A7.4 Resource sheet 3.1**.
You also need a graphics calculator, or a computer with a graph plotter and a scientific calculator.

① **a** The force, y, exerted by a magnet on a metal sphere is inversely proportional to x, the distance between them.
The relationship between x and y is given by the formula $y = \dfrac{10}{x}$.

Use graphing software to draw a graph to show this relationship.

b Describe what happens to the force as the distance between the magnet and the metal sphere increases.

② **a** An electric current, I, is inversely proportional to the resistance, R, of the circuit.

The relationship between I and R for a particular circuit is given by the formula:

$I = \dfrac{500}{R}$.

Draw a graph to show this relationship.

b Describe what happens to I as R increases.

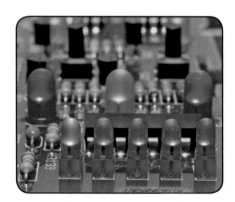

③ **Investigating graphs of $y = \dfrac{a}{x}$**

Generate graphs of these equations on the computer or graphics calculator.
Sketch each graph on a new grid, using the grids on **Resource sheet 3.1**.
Write some comments describing the curves.

a $y = \dfrac{1}{x}$ **b** $y = \dfrac{2}{x}$ **c** $y = \dfrac{3}{x}$ **d** $y = \dfrac{4}{x}$ **e** $y = \dfrac{5}{x}$ **f** $y = \dfrac{6}{x}$

(4) **a** Copy and complete the table for $y = \dfrac{8}{x}$. Calculate the values of y to 1 decimal place.

x	-8	-7	-6	-5	-4	-3	-2	-1	1	2	3	4	5	6	7	8
y																

b Draw an accurate graph of the equation using graph paper.

c Describe what happens to y as x increases from -8 to 8.

d Describe what happens to y as x increases beyond 8.

e Describe what happens to y as x decreases from 1 towards zero.

Extension problem

5 Generate graphs of these equations on the computer.
Sketch the graphs on **separate** grids on **Resource sheet 3.1**.
In the space on the resource sheet, write some comments describing the graphs.

a $y = -\dfrac{12}{x}$ **b** $y = \dfrac{12}{x} + 10$ **c** $y = \dfrac{12}{x} + x$

d $y = \dfrac{12}{x} + x^3$ **e** $y = \dfrac{12}{x} + x^2$ **f** $y = \dfrac{12}{x} - x^3$

 Points to remember

⊙ A **reciprocal function** has an equation of the form $y = \dfrac{a}{x}$. Its graph:

- has two parts in diagonally opposite quadrants;
- does not cross or touch the x-axis or the y-axis;
- has no maximum or minimum points;
- is discontinuous, since the function has no value at $x = 0$;
- approaches the x-axis, without crossing or touching it, at each end.

4 Exponential functions

This lesson will help you to know some features of the graphs of exponential functions.

Exercise 4

The word **exponential** means: 'rapidly becoming greater in size'.

$f(x) = a^x$ is an **exponential function**.

Work with a partner. You need some graph paper.
You also need a graphics calculator, or a computer with a graph plotter and a scientific calculator.

1   **a**   Copy and complete the table for $y = 2^x$. Calculate the values of y to 1 decimal place.

x	-5	-4	-3	-2	-1	0	1	2	3	4	5
y											

    b   Plot the points and draw the graph of $y = 2^x$.

    c   Use graphing software to draw the graph of $y = 2^x$.

    d   Write what you notice about the value of y as x increases positively.

    e   Write what you notice about the value of y as x increases negatively.

    f   Can the value of y ever be negative?

    g   Can the value of y ever be zero?

2   **a**   Use graphing software to draw the graphs of $y = 3^x$, $y = 4^x$, $y = 5^x$ and $y = 6^x$.

    b   On the same axes on graph paper, sketch and label the graphs of
$y = 3^x$, $y = 4^x$, $y = 5^x$ and $y = 6^x$.

    c   What point is common to all the graphs?

    d   Compare the graphs.

3   **a**   Think about the graph of $y = 2^x$ that you drew
in question 1. On the same axes on graph paper,
sketch and label the graphs of $y = 2^x$ and $y = 2^{-x}$.

    b   What is the relationship between $y = 2^x$ and $y = 2^{-x}$?

    c   Comment on the y-values of $y = 2^{-x}$.

    d   On new axes on graph paper, sketch and label
the graphs of $y = -2^x$ and $y = -2^{-x}$.

    e   Describe the graphs you have drawn.

4   **a**   Think about the graph of $y = 2^x$ that you drew in question 1.
On graph paper, sketch and label the graph of $y = 2^x + 3$.
Describe what happens to $y = 2^x$ when you add the constant 3.

    b   On the same axes as for part **a**, sketch and label the graph of $y = 2^x - 1$.

5 **a** Think about the graph of $y = 2^x$ that you drew in question 1.
On graph paper, sketch and label the graph of $y = 3 \times (2^x)$.
Describe what happens to $y = 2^x$ when you multiply by 3.

  b On the same axes as for part **a**, sketch and label the graph of $y = -3 \times (2^x)$.

Extension problem

6 Write the equation of each graph.

a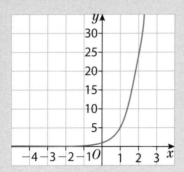

b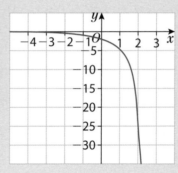

c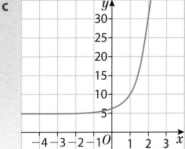

d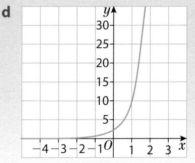

⊙ **Points to remember**

⊙ When a number is raised to a power, the power is called the **exponent**.

⊙ As the power is increased, so the number increases rapidly.

⊙ The equation $y = a^x$, where a is a constant, represents an **exponential function**. Its graph:
 – is a continuous curve and is always positive (i.e. above the x-axis);
 – crosses the y-axis at (0, 1);
 – has no maximum or minimum points;
 – increases very rapidly at one end and approaches the x-axis, without crossing or touching it, at the other end.

5 Generating trigonometric functions

This lesson will remind you to how to draw and use graphs of trigonometric functions.

 Did you know that...?

Trigonometric functions arose out of links between mathematics and astronomy.

The Greek astronomer **Hipparchus** (190–120 BC) is often thought of as the founder of trigonometry.

The French mathematician **Hérigone** (1580–1643) was the first person to use the term sine derived from the Latin word *sinus* meaning 'a fold'.

Hipparchus

Exercise 5

Here are the graphs of $y = \sin x$ and $y = \cos x$ which you met in unit G7.5.

$y = \sin x$

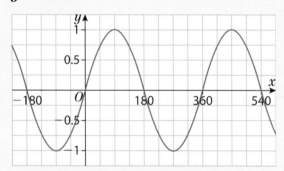

$y = \cos x$

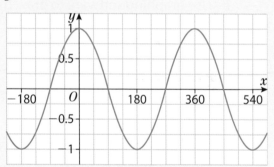

Trigonometric functions are periodic.

Different trigonometric functions are positive in different quadrants.

sin +	sin +
cos −	cos +
tan −	tan +
2nd	**1st**
3rd	**4th**
sin −	sin −
cos −	cos +
tan +	tan −

Work with a partner. You need some centimetre squared paper.
You also need a graphics calculator, or a computer with a graph plotter and a scientific calculator.

1.
   a Use graphing software to generate the sine and cosine curves on the same axes.

   b Describe the relationship between the two graphs.

2 a What is the maximum value that $\sin a$ can take?

   b What is the minimum value that $\sin a$ can take?

   c For what angles is $\sin a$ equal to $\cos a$?

   d What do you notice about $\sin 70°$ and $\cos 20°$?

   e Explain how you calculate a in the equation
      $\sin a = \cos 50°$.

   f Explain how you calculate b in the equation
      $\sin 25° = \cos b$.

   g Use your answers to parts **e** and **f** to complete the general statement:
      $\sin c = \cos \ldots$
      Use your calculator to check the statement for angles between $0°$ and $360°$.

3 You can find the tangent of an angle when you know the sine and the cosine,
   using the relationship $\tan a = \dfrac{\sin a}{\cos a}$.

   a Explain why $\tan 90°$ and $\tan 270°$ cannot be calculated.

   b Use graphing software to draw the graph of $\tan x$.

   c Describe the graph of $\tan x$.

   d Use the graph to find the next positive angle that has the same value as $\tan 60°$.

   e Explain how to work out the next angle that has the same value as $\tan a$.

4 a Use your calculator to copy and complete this
      table for angles $0°$ to $360°$ in steps of $30°$. Write
      the sine of the angles to two decimal places.

   b Use centimetre squared paper.
      On the same axes, sketch and label the graphs
      of $y = \sin x$ and $y = \sin (x + 30°)$ for values of x
      from $0°$ to $360°$.

Angle x	$\sin x$	$\sin (x + 30°)$
$0°$	1	0.5
$30°$	0.5	...
$60°$	...	...

   c Describe the relationship between the two graphs.

   d Use your graphs to estimate the solutions in the interval $0 \leqslant x \leqslant 360°$ to the equation
      $\sin x = \sin (x + 30°)$.

   e Use your calculator to check your solutions.

(5) Do this question without using a calculator.
A unit circle has its centre at O.

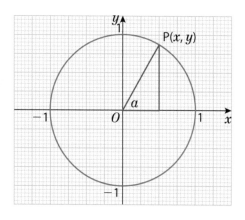

a P is a point on the circle with coordinates (x, y). Use Pythagoras' theorem to write a relationship between x and y.

b Use your answer to part **a** to complete the statement:

$\cos^2 a + \sin^2 a = \ldots$

c If $\cos a = 0.8$, what is $\sin a$?

⊙ Points to remember

- ⊙ When a point travelling around a unit circle anticlockwise makes an angle a with the x-axis, its vertical distance from the x-axis is $\sin a$ and its horizontal distance from the y-axis is $\cos a$.
- ⊙ Plotting the vertical distance against the angle gives a **sine curve**.
- ⊙ Plotting the horizontal distance against the angle gives a **cosine curve**.
- ⊙ Trigonometric functions are periodic.
- ⊙ Different trigonometric functions are positive in different quadrants.

	2nd	1st	
sin	+	sin	+
cos	−	cos	+
tan	−	tan	+

	3rd	4th	
sin	−	sin	−
cos	−	cos	+
tan	+	tan	−

---

6 Exploring trigonometric functions

This lesson will help you to understand more about the graphs of trigonometric functions.

Exercise 6

This is the graph of $y = \sin x$.

It is a **periodic graph**.

Its **period** is 360°.

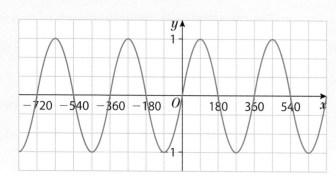

This is the graph of $y = \cos x$.

It is a periodic graph.

Its period is 360°.

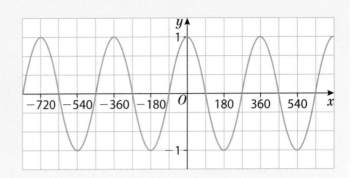

Work with a partner.
You also need a graphics calculator, or a computer with a graph plotter and a scientific calculator.

1 **a** Draw the graph of $y = \sin x$.

   b On the same axes, draw the graph of $y = \sin x + 1$. Describe the transformation.

   c On the same axes, draw the graph of $y = \sin x - 1$. Describe the transformation.

   d On the same axes, draw the graphs of $y = \sin x + 2$, $y = \sin x + 3$ and $y = \sin x - 4$.

   e For function $f(x) = \sin x$, describe the transformation $f(x) = \sin x + a$, where a is a constant.

2 **a** Draw the graph of $y = \cos x$.

   b On the same axes, draw the graph of $y = \cos (x + 30°)$. Describe the transformation.

   c On the same axes, draw the graph of $y = \cos (x - 30°)$. Describe the transformation.

   d On the same axes, draw the graphs of $y = \cos (x + 60°)$, $y = \cos (x + 90°)$, $y = \cos (x + 180°)$ and $y = \cos (x - 60°)$.

   e For $f(x) = \cos x$, describe the transformation $f(x) = \cos (x + a)$, where a is a constant.

3 **a** Draw the graph of $y = \sin x$.

   b Write the period and amplitude of $y = \sin x$.

   c On the same axes, draw the graph of $y = 2 \sin x$. Describe the transformation.

   d Write the period and amplitude of $y = 2 \sin x$.

   e On the same axes, draw the graphs of $y = 0.5 \sin x$, $y = 3 \sin x$ and $y = 4 \sin x$.

   f For $f(x) = \sin x$, describe the transformation $f(x) = a \sin x$, where a is a positive constant.

   g Write the period and amplitude of the function $f(x) = a \sin x$.

   h Describe what happens when a is negative.

4 **a** Draw the graph of $y = \cos x$.

   b Write the period and amplitude of $y = \cos x$.

   c On the same axes, draw the graph of $y = \cos 2x$. Describe the transformation.

   d Write the period and amplitude of $y = \cos 2x$.

   e On the same axes, draw the graphs of $y = \cos 0.5x$, $y = \cos 3x$ and $y = \cos 4x$.

   f For $f(x) = \cos x$, describe the transformation $f(x) = \cos ax$, where a is a positive constant.

   g Write the period and amplitude of the function $f(x) = \cos ax$.

   h What happens when a is negative?

Extension problem

5 Write the equation, period and amplitude of each graph.

   a

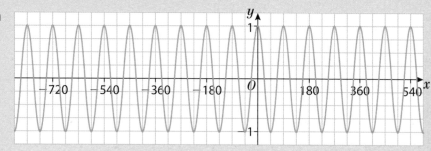

   b

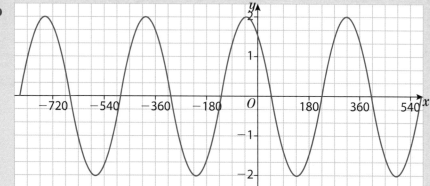

   c

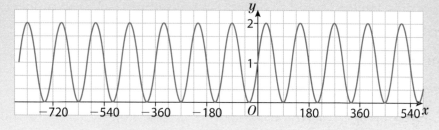

   d

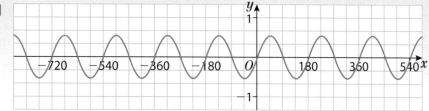

Points to remember

- Trigonometric graphs are periodic.
- $y = \sin x$ and $y = \cos x$ each have a **period** of 360° and an **amplitude** of 1.
- Trigonometric graphs can be transformed by introducing constants.

7 Transformations of functions

This lesson will help you to use function notation and describe simple transformations of graphs.

Exercise 7A

Function notation

The letter f can represent the **rule for a function**. For example,

f might stand for the rule 'treble the input and then add 2'. $x \rightarrow \boxed{f} \rightarrow 3x + 2$
If x is the input, the output will be $3x + 2$.

This rule or function can be written as $f(x) = 3x + 2$.

f(5) means work out the output when the input is 5. $5 \rightarrow \boxed{f} \rightarrow 3 \times 5 + 2 = 17$

Example 1

$f(x) = 2x - 5$ and $g(x) = x^2 + 4$.

a   Find the value of f(9).   Substitute 9 for x in f(x), which gives $2 \times 9 - 5 = \mathbf{13}$.

b   Find the value of g(−4).   Substitute −4 for x in g(x), which gives $(-4)^2 + 4 = 16 + 4 = \mathbf{20}$.

Example 2

$g(x) = x^2 + 4$. Find an expression for $3g(x) - 5$.   Replace g(x) with $x^2 + 4$, then simplify.

$$3(x^2 + 4) - 5 = 3x^2 + 12 - 5 = \mathbf{3x^2 + 7}$$

1   $f(x) = 3x + 4$ and $g(x) = 2x^2 - 1$. Find the value of:

   a   f(3)   b   f(10)   c   f(−5)   d   f(0)   e   f(0.5)

   f   g(3)   g   g(10)   h   g(−5)   i   g(0)   j   g(0.5)

2   $p(x) = 2x - 3$ and $q(x) = x^2$. Find an expression for:

   a   p(x) + 4   b   p(x + 4)   c   p(4x)   d   p(−x)   e   −p(x)

   f   q(x + 1)   g   q(x − 3)   h   q(−5x)   i   7q(x) − 1   j   q(3x − 1)

A **translation** moves a shape to the right or left and/or up or down.
The shape does not change in size or orientation.

A **reflection** produces a mirror image of a shape in a mirror line.
The perpendicular distance of every point on the image from the mirror line is equal to the perpendicular distance of the corresponding point of the object from the mirror line.

A **stretch** increases or decreases lengths in one direction by the same scale factor.
Lengths in the perpendicular direction stay the same.

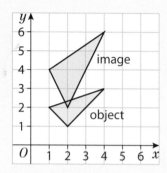   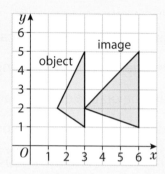

In the stretch shown above, at each vertex of the image, the x-coordinate is unchanged and the y-coordinate has been multiplied by **2**.

The **scale factor** is 2 and the direction of the stretch is **parallel to the y-axis**.

In the stretch shown above, at each vertex of the image, the y-coordinate is unchanged and the x-coordinate has been multiplied by **2**.

The **scale factor** is 2 and the direction of the stretch is **parallel to the x-axis**.

Work with a partner.
You also need a graphics calculator, or a computer with a graph plotter and a scientific calculator.
If necessary, simplify the right-hand side of the equation before you draw the graph.

① **a** Draw the graphs of $y = 3x$, $y = 3x - 2$, $y = 3x - 1$, $y = 3x + 1$ and $y = 3x + 2$.

b Describe the effect of adding a constant a to any linear function.

c Draw the graphs of $y = x^2$, $y = x^2 - 4$, $y = x^2 - 1$, $y = x^2 + 2$ and $y = x^2 + 4$.

d Describe the effect of adding a constant a to any quadratic function.

e Predict the effect of adding a constant a to any polynomial function.

f Check by drawing graphs of $y = x^3$, $y = x^3 + 5$ and $y = x^3 - 7$.

g If f(x) is any polynomial function, what can you say about the graph of $y = $ f$(x) + a$?

2

   a Draw the graphs of $y = 3x$, $y = 3(x - 2)$, $y = 3(x - 1)$ and $y = 3(x + 1)$.

   b Describe the effect of adding a constant a to x in any linear function.

   c Draw the graphs of $y = x^2$, $y = (x - 4)^2$, $y = (x - 1)^2$ and $y = (x + 2)^2$.

   d Describe the effect of adding a constant a to x in any quadratic function.

   e Predict the effect of adding a constant a to x in any polynomial function.

   f Check by drawing graphs of $y = x^3$ and $y = (x + 1)^3$.

   g If f(x) is any polynomial function, what can you say about the graph of $y = $ f($x + a$)?

3

   a Draw the graphs of $y = 3x$ and $y = -3x$, then $y = 3x + 4$ and $y = -3x + 4$.

   b Describe the effect of making x negative in any linear function.

   c Draw the graphs of $y = x^2$ and $y = (-x)^2$, then $y = (x - 4)^2$ and $y = (-x - 4)^2$.

   d Describe the effect of making x negative in any quadratic function.

   e Predict the effect of making x negative in any polynomial function.

   f Check by drawing graphs of $y = x^3$ and $y = (-x)^3$.

   g If f(x) is any polynomial function, what can you say about the graph of $y = $ f($-x$)?

4

   a Draw the graphs of $y = 3x$ and $y = -3x$, $y = 3x + 4$ and $y = -(3x + 4)$.

   b Describe the effect of multiplying a linear function by -1.

   c Draw the graphs of $y = x^2$, $y = -(x)^2$, $y = (x - 4)^2$ and $y = -(x - 4)^2$.

   d Describe the effect of multiplying a quadratic function by -1.

   e Make a conjecture about the effect of multiplying any function by -1.

   f Check your conjecture by drawing graphs of $y = x^3$, $y = -(x)^3$ etc.

   g If f(x) is any function, what can you say about the graph of $y = -$f(x)?

5

   a Draw the graphs of $y = x + 1$, $y = 3(x + 1)$, $y = 6(x + 1)$ and $y = 7(x + 1)$.

   b Describe the effect of multiplying a linear function by a constant a.

   c Draw the graphs of $y = x^2$, $y = 2x^2$, $y = 3x^2$ and $y = 4x^2$.

   d Describe the effect of multiplying a quadratic function by a constant a.

   e Predict the effect of multiplying any polynomial function by a constant a.

   f Check your conjecture by drawing graphs of $y = x^3$, $y = 2x^3$, $y = 3x^3$ and $y = 4x^3$.

   g If f(x) is any polynomial function, what can you say about the graph of $y = a$f(x)?

6 a Draw the graphs of $y = x + 1$, $y = 3x + 1$, $y = 6x + 1$ and $y = 7x + 1$.

b Describe the effect of multiplying x by a constant a in any linear function.

c Draw the graphs of $y = x^2$, $y = (2x)^2$, $y = (3x)^2$ and $y = (4x)^2$.

d Describe the effect of multiplying x by a constant a in any quadratic function.

e Predict the effect of multiplying x by a constant a in any polynomial function.

f Check your conjecture by drawing graphs of $y = x^3$ and $y = (2x)^3$.

g If f(x) is any polynomial function, what can you say about the graph of $y = $ f(ax)?

Extension problem

7 The graph on the left below is the graph of $y = x^3 - x^2 - 5x$.
For each of **a** and **b**, describe the transformation and work out the equation of the graph.

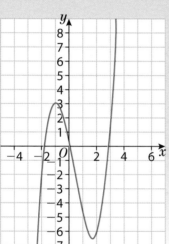   **a** 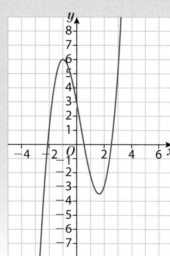   **b**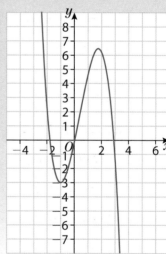

⊙ Points to remember

- ⊙ A function $y = $ f(x) can be transformed in several ways.
- ⊙ $y = $ f$(x) + a$ is a translation of a units in the y-direction.
- ⊙ $y = $ f$(x + a)$ is a translation of $-a$ units in the x-direction.
- ⊙ $y = -$f(x) is a reflection in the x-axis.
- ⊙ $y = $ f$(-x)$ is a reflection in the y-axis.
- ⊙ $y = a$f(x) is a stretch of scale factor a in the y-direction.
- ⊙ $y = $ f(ax) is a stretch of scale factor $\dfrac{1}{a}$ in the x-direction.

8 Loci

This lesson will help you to explore graphs of loci.

Exercise 8

A **locus** is a set of points obeying a rule.

Example 1

What is the equation of the set of points equidistant from A and B?

The set of points equidistant from A and B is the perpendicular bisector of AB, shown by the blue line.

Gradient of AB $= -\frac{1}{3}$
Gradient of blue line $= 3$
Midpoint of AB $= (2.5, 4.5)$
Equation of the blue line is: $y = 3x - 3$

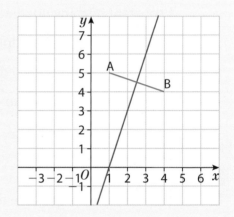

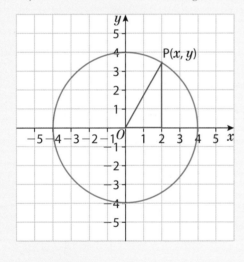

Example 2

What is the equation of the set of points 4 units from the origin?

The set of points is a circle, centre (0, 0).

Using Pythagoras' theorem:
$x^2 + y^2 = OP^2 = 16$

This is the equation of the circle.

Example 3

What is the equation of the set of points 3 cm from (2, 3)?

The set of points is a circle, centre (2, 3).

Using Pythagoras' theorem in the blue triangle:
$(x - 2)^2 + (y - 3)^2 = \text{radius}^2 = 9$

This is the equation of the circle.

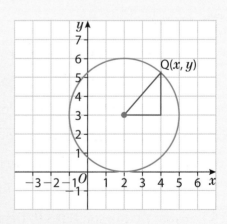

Work with a partner. You need some centimetre squared paper.
You also need a graphics calculator, or a computer with a graph plotter and a scientific calculator.

1 **Straight lines**

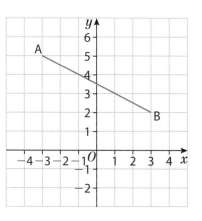

   a What are the coordinates of the midpoint of AB?

   b What is the gradient of AB?

   c What is the gradient of any line perpendicular to AB?

   d What is the equation of the perpendicular bisector of AB?

   e What is the equation of the perpendicular bisector of
      the line CD where C is $(-3, -3)$ and D is $(1, 5)$?

   f Check by drawing the graph.

2 A point P moves so that it is equidistant from the given points.
Write the equation of the locus of point P.
Check by drawing the graph.

   a $(5, 0)$ and $(0, 5)$ **b** $(-4, 0)$ and $(0, 4)$ **c** $(1, -1)$ and $(3, 3)$

   d $(-1, 2)$ and $(-2, 1)$ **e** $(2, 3)$ and $(3, 2)$ **f** $(-2, 5)$ and $(-4, -1)$

3 P is the point (x, y).
Write the equation of the locus of point P for these rules.

   a P moves so that it is the same distance from the x-axis and the y-axis.

   b P moves so that its distance from the y-axis is three times the distance from the x-axis.

   c P moves so that its distance from the y-axis is 4 more than its distance from the x-axis.

   d P moves so that it is an equal distance from the lines $x = 2$ and $y = 1$.

   Check by drawing the graphs.

4 **Circles**

   Write the equations of these circles.
   Check your answers by drawing the graphs.

   a centre $(0, 0)$, radius 6 units   **b** centre $(0, 0)$, radius 13 units

   c centre $(0, 0)$, radius 3.5 units   **d** centre $(0, 0)$, radius 7.2 units

   e centre $(3, 5)$, radius 7 units   **f** centre $(2, -1)$, radius 4 units

5 Estimate the solutions to these pairs of simultaneous equations by drawing the graphs.

   a $x^2 + y^2 = 9$ and $y = 2x + 1$ **b** $x^2 + y^2 = 64$ and $3x + y = 9$

   c $(x - 3)^2 + (y - 2)^2 = 25$ and $y - x = 1$ **d** $(x + 7)^2 + (y + 6)^2 = 81$ and $y = 2x - 5$

6 Find algebraically the coordinates of the points of intersection of each circle and straight line. Give your answers correct to 3 significant figures. Check your answers by drawing graphs.

a $x^2 + y^2 = 49$ and $y = x + 3$ **b** $x^2 + y^2 = 36$ and $x + y = 4$

Extension problem

7 Q is the point (x, y).

   a Write an expression for the distance of Q from the line $y = 2$.

   b Write an expression for the distance of Q from the point $(0, 4)$.

   c Q moves so that it is equidistant from the line $y = 2$ and the point $(0, 4)$.

      Find the equation of the locus of Q. Give your answer in its simplest form.

   d Check by drawing the graph.

◉ Points to remember

⊙ The set of points equidistant from two given points A and B is the perpendicular bisector of AB.

⊙ The set of points a fixed distance from point A is a circle, centre A.

⊙ The equation of a circle, centre $(0, 0)$, radius r, is $x^2 + y^2 = r^2$.

⊙ The equation of a circle, centre (a, b), radius r, is $(x - a)^2 + (y - b)^2 = r^2$.

9 Solving problems

This lesson will help you to solve problems using mathematics.

Exercise 9

You can use **algebra** to solve many different problems.

Work systematically and logically following the **problem solving cycle**.

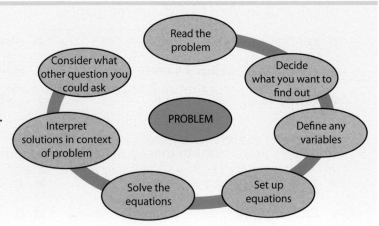

1. **a** Hamish is making an open-topped box with a square base.

   He wants to make it so that it has the greatest volume possible using a piece of card that measures 10 cm by 10 cm.

   He cuts out square corners measuring x cm by x cm.

   For what value of x is the volume of the box at its maximum? Give your answer to 1 decimal place.

   b Hamish then makes boxes with square card measuring 12 cm by 12 cm. For what value of x does the box have a maximum volume?

   c Investigate for different-sized cardboard squares. Find a formula for the value of x when the cardboard is a square of side a cm.

2. Mandy and Dan have a square lawn. They agreed that they should each cut exactly half of the area of grass.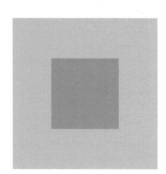

   Mandy cut a border 4 metres wide all around the inside edge of the lawn. What is the area of the lawn? Give your answer to the nearest square metre.

Extension problem

3. The drawing (which is not to scale) shows a garden in the shape of a trapezium. The garden has two parallel sides 5 m long and 3 m long.

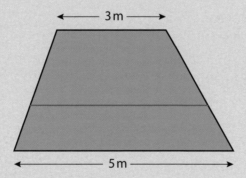

A fence which is parallel to the two parallel sides divides the garden into two parts equal in area.

The area of the whole garden is 24 m².

How far is the fence from the 5 m side? Give your answer to the nearest tenth of a metre.

Points to remember

- Read through the problem and decide what mathematics to use.
- Define any variables you are going to use.
- Set up any expressions or equations using the information given.
- Solve the mathematical problem.
- Interpret the solution in the context of the original problem.
- Ask your own questions.

How well are you doing?

Can you:

- remember and visualise some properties of the graphs of polynomial, reciprocal, exponential and trigonometric functions?
- give some general properties of transformations of functions?
- draw graphs from a set of points obeying a rule?
- solve problems using mathematics?

1 *2008 level 8*

The graph shows a circle with centre (0, 0).

The circle has the equation: $x^2 + y^2 = 25$.

a There are two points on the circumference of the circle with an x-coordinate of 3.
Write the coordinates of these two points.

b What is the radius of the circle?

c Point P is on the circumference of the circle. Its x-coordinate is equal to its y-coordinate. What are the coordinates of point P, correct to 1 decimal place?

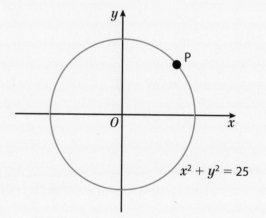

2 *GCSE 1387 June 2003*

The graph of $y = a - b\cos(kt)$ for values of t between 0° and 120°, is drawn on the grid.

Use the graph to find an estimate for the value of:

   i a

  ii b

 iii k

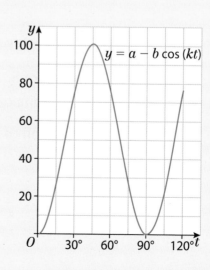

Match each graph to the correct equation.

A

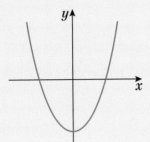

B

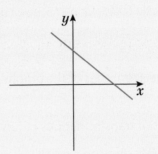

C

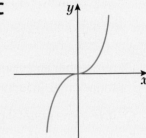

D

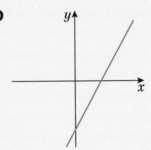

E

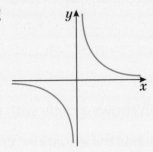

a $y = 2x - 6$ b $y = 6x^3$ c $y = 6 - x$

d $y = x^2 - 6$ e $y = \dfrac{1}{6x}$

④ *2001 level 8*

The diagram shows a sketch of the curve $y = 16 - x^2$.

a What are the coordinates of points A, B and C?

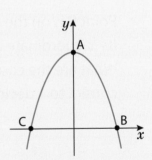

The curve $y = 16 - x^2$ is reflected in the line $y = 12$.

b B_1 is the reflection of B.
What are the coordinates of B_1?

c What is the equation of the new curve?

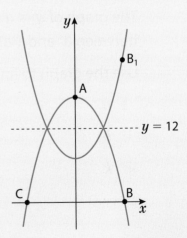

(5) *GCSE 1387 November 2005*

The sketch graph shows a curve with equation $y = pq^x$.

The curve passes through the points (1, 5) and (4, 320).

Calculate the value of p and the value of q.

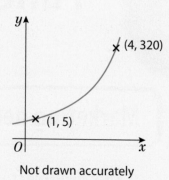

Not drawn accurately

(6) *2001 Exceptional performance*

This curve is named after a mathematician called Maria Agnesi, who studied it in 1748.

The curve touches a circle of radius a, centre (0, a).

The equation of the curve is $y = \dfrac{8a^3}{x^2 + 4a^2}$.

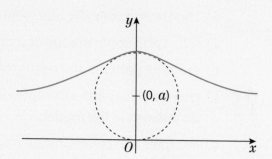

a For the curve when $a = 5$, what is the maximum value of y?

b When $a = 2$ and $y = 1.5$, what are the values of x? Show your working.

c When $y = \dfrac{2a}{5}$ what, in terms of a, are the values of x? Show your working.

Marketing new designer jeans

This group activity will help you to:

- ☉ solve problems in unfamiliar contexts;
- ☉ choose and combine representations from a range of perspectives;
- ☉ select and apply a range of methods, operations and tools, including ICT;
- ☉ examine patterns and relationships;
- ☉ change values and assumptions or adjust relationships to see the effects on answers in the model;
- ☉ interpret and communicate results and solutions.

Background

A company that wants to market a new pair of designer jeans has to think about a number of things so that they make a profit. Here are some of the factors that have to be considered.

- ☉ **Costs**
  What do materials cost? What are the labour costs?

- ☉ **The market**
  Who is likely to buy the new jeans? Where do they live?

- ☉ **Sales**
  What should the selling price of the new jeans be? How many pairs of new jeans are likely to be sold? How much profit can the company make?

Blue Moon, an up-market clothes manufacturer, has designed a new pair of jeans.

Blue Moon has estimated its **production costs** (£C) are the sum of a fixed cost of £4000 for research and machinery, and a variable cost which is directly proportional to the number of pairs of jeans (n) that are made. The company's formula is $C = 4000 + 25n$.

The Board is now discussing the **selling price** of the jeans. This price will influence the number of pairs of jeans that are sold and hence the number that should be produced.

The Head of Marketing estimates that if the selling price is fixed at £50, then 5500 pairs of jeans will be sold in the first month, whereas if the price is £100, only 1000 pairs will be sold.

She believes that the approximate relationship between the selling price (£s) and the number of pairs of jeans sold (n) is shown in the diagram opposite.

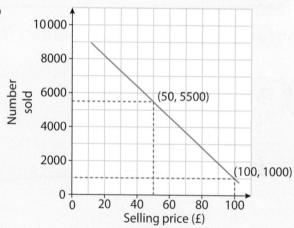

Work in a small group. You need either graphics calculators and a computer with spreadsheet software, or graph paper and calculators.

1. The **sales revenue** (£R) is the product of the selling price (£s) and the number of pairs of jeans sold (n). What should the selling price be to maximise the sales revenue?

Extension problem

2. The **profits from sales** are found by subtracting production costs from the sales revenue. What should the selling price be to maximise the profits?

Be prepared to justify your decisions, assumptions and conclusions to other groups.

Using and applying maths

This unit will help you to:

- ◉ gain a sense of the rich historical and cultural roots of mathematics;
- ◉ solve routine and non-routine problems in familiar and unfamiliar contexts;
- ◉ select and apply a range of mathematical techniques to find solutions;
- ◉ use algebra to prove that a statement is true;
- ◉ communicate convincing arguments and solutions;
- ◉ be aware of some current applications of mathematics.

1 The history of convex polyhedra

This **double lesson** will help you to appreciate some of the historical and cultural roots of mathematics.

Did you know that...?

The five Platonic solids are named after the Greek philosopher **Plato** (427 BC–347 BC), who knew of them and related four of them to the elements of earth, fire, air and water.

The renowned Greek mathematician **Archimedes** (287 BC–212 BC) wrote about the five solids, and eight further solids whose faces are also regular polygons but of more than one type. The record of his work on these 13 Archimedean solids is lost. However, it is referred to in the fifth book of the Greek mathematician **Pappus of Alexandria**, who lived in the beginning of the fourth century AD.

Exercise 1

The five **Platonic solids** are regular concave polyhedra. Each of the solids has faces of exactly the same size and shape and the same number of faces meet at each vertex. The five Platonic solids are:

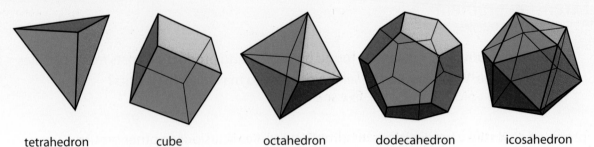

| tetrahedron | cube | octahedron | dodecahedron | icosahedron |

1 **a** What is a deltahedron? How does a deltahedron differ from a Platonic solid?

   b Give at least one example of a deltahedron that is not a Platonic solid.

2 A Platonic tiling is a tessellation of the plane by identical regular polygons.

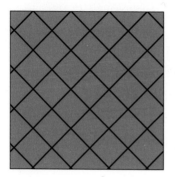 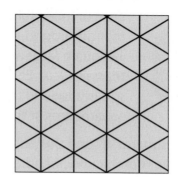 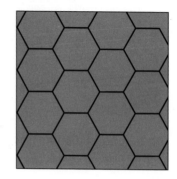

Prove that there are only three possible Platonic tilings.

3 **a** Copy and complete this table for the Platonic solids.

Name of solid	Vertices	Edges	Faces	Sides of face	Faces at vertex
Tetrahedron	4	6	4	3	3
Cube	8	12	6	4	3
Octahedron	6	12	8	3	4
Dodecahedron	20	30	12	5	3
Icosahedron	12	30	20	3	5

   b Write down the formula that connects the number of faces, edges and vertices.

   c The formula is named after the mathematician who discovered it.
   Who was the mathematician?

4 **a** How many pentagons and hexagons are there on a football?

   b What is the mathematical name of the shape of a football?

5 Draw the net of a truncated octahedron.

truncated octahedron

6 You can colour the Platonic solids so no two faces that meet along an edge have the same colour.
What is the minimum number of colours that you need to colour each of the five solids?

7 Prove that there are only five possible Platonic solids.

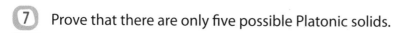

Extension problems

Did you know that...?

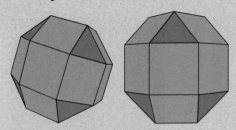

Each of these solids has 3 squares and a triangle around each vertex. Each has 18 square faces and 8 equilateral triangle faces. Each has a band of 8 squares around the 'equator' and two square faces at the top and bottom.

The first solid also has a band of squares around the 'poles'. It is one of the 13 Archimedean solids and is called a rhombicuboctahedron. The second was only made known by the British mathematician, **J.C.P. Miller** (1906–1981), in the 1930s.

8 Triangles are formed by joining three different corners of a cube.
How many different shapes can the triangles have?
Draw and label sketches of the possible shapes.

9 **a** Blue paint is splodged on one corner of a cube.

    i How many edges have blue paint at one end?

    ii How many faces have blue paint at one corner?

b Blue paint is now splodged on a second corner.
One edge now has blue paint at both ends.

    i How many edges now have blue paint at one end?

    ii How many faces now have blue paint at one corner?

    iii How many faces have blue paint at two corners?

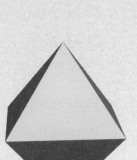

c Blue paint is now splodged on a third corner.
One face now has blue paint at three of its corners.

    i How many edges now have blue paint at one end?

    ii How many faces now have blue paint at one corner?

    iii How many faces now have blue paint at two corners?

d Repeat questions **a**, **b** and **c** for an octahedron.

10 A Platonic solid of side 3 cm can be fitted inside a sphere, cylinder or cone so that each vertex touches a face or vertex of the container.

Find the smallest possible volume of the container when the Platonic solid is:

a a cube of side 3 cm;   **b** a tetrahedron of side 3 cm.

Points to remember

- People from many different cultures have contributed to what we now know about convex polyhedra, including mathematicians from Ancient Greece, Europe and America.
- There are five different Platonic solids, which are regular concave polyhedra with congruent vertices.
- There are eight different deltahedra and 13 different Archimedean solids.
- The Internet is a good source of information about mathematics and its history.

3 Algebraic proof

This lesson will help you to use algebra to prove results.

Did you know that...?

Fibonacci of Pisa

You can generate interesting sequences by starting with any two numbers, then making every subsequent term the sum of the two previous terms.

The most famous example is the sequence named after the Italian **Leonardo Fibonacci**, who died about 1250.

1, 1, 2, 3, 5, 8, 13, …

Another example is the Lucas sequence:

2, 1, 3, 4, 7, 11, 18, …

This is named after the French mathematician **Edouard Lucas** (1842–1891), who was the first to give a formula for finding the nth term of the Fibonacci sequence.

Exercise 3

Here are some ways to represent numbers when you use algebra to prove results.
When a and b are integers, you can represent:

- three consecutive integers as a, $a + 1$, $a + 2$ or as $a - 1$, a, $a + 1$;
- an even number as $2a$ and two consecutive even numbers as $2a$ and $2a + 2$;
- an odd number as $2a + 1$ and two consecutive odd numbers as $2a - 1$ and $2a + 1$;
- a multiple of, say, 7 as $7a$;
- a two-digit number as $10a + b$.

To prove that a number is divisible by 7, or a multiple of 7, prove that 7 is a factor.

To prove that a number is even, prove that 2 is a factor.

Example

Prove that the sum of any three consecutive integers is a multiple of 3.

Let the numbers be a, $a + 1$, $a + 2$.

The sum of the three numbers is $a + (a + 1) + (a + 2) = 3a + 3 = 3(a + 1)$.

Since 3 is a factor of the sum of the three numbers, the sum is a multiple of 3.

1. Prove that the sum of any two odd numbers is an even number.

2. Prove that the sum of any four consecutive odd numbers is a multiple of 8.

3. Prove that the product of two consecutive odd numbers is always 1 less than a multiple of 4.

4. Think of a number, multiply it by 3, add 5, double the result, subtract 4, divide the result by 6. Now subtract the original number. Prove that the final answer is always 1.

5. Write down any three consecutive integers.
   Find the sum of the last two numbers.
   Find the sum of the first two numbers.
   Prove that the difference between the two sums is always equal to 2.

6. Choose a two-digit integer.
   Reverse the digits to form another two-digit integer.
   Subtract the smaller two-digit integer from the larger.
   Prove that the answer is always a multiple of 9.

7. Write down any two-digit number.
   Multiply the units digit by 4.
   Add the answer to the tens digit.
   Prove that if the final answer is a multiple of 13 then so is the original number.

8. Write down any two positive integers.
   Make these the first two terms of a Fibonacci-type sequence.

   a Prove that the sum of the first and fifth terms is always a multiple of 3.

   b Prove that the sum of the first and ninth terms is always seven times the fifth term.

9. Prove that the difference between the squares of any two consecutive even numbers is twice the sum of the two even numbers.

10 Write down any three consecutive integers.

   a Prove that the product of the first and last numbers is always 1 less than the square of the middle number.

   b Prove that the difference between the product of the last two numbers and the product of the first two numbers is always equal to two-thirds of the sum of all three integers.

Extension problem

11 Which is larger, the average of the squares of two numbers, or the square of their average?

> ## ⊙ Points to remember
>
> ⊙ You can verify that an expression or formula is true or not true for a particular value by substituting that value into the expression or formula.
>
> ⊙ Verifying that a statement is true for a particular value does not prove that it is always true.
>
> ⊙ You can prove that a statement is true by using algebraic reasoning.

4 Careers in mathematics

This lesson will help you to understand how maths is used at home and work.

Exercise 4

Maths is used in many different ways in our lives at home, school and work.

Surveyor

Tennis player

Potter

Did you know that...?

The largest employer of mathematicians in the world is Pixar Animations, who made *Toy Story* and *Finding Nemo*.

1 a Do some Internet research to find out more about how maths is used in three different occupations. Make notes while you do this.

Here are some useful websites.

www.mathscareers.org.uk/11_-_14/maths_in_everyday_life.cfm
www.mathscareers.org.uk/14_-_16/maths_in_everyday_life.cfm
plus.maths.org/interview.html
www.rss.org.uk/main.asp?page=1999

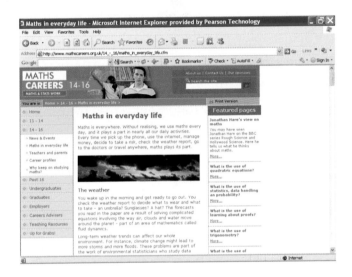

b Prepare three PowerPoint slides, one on each of the occupations.
Make sure that you include some details on how maths is used.
Be prepared to show your slides to the rest of the class at the end of the lesson.

Points to remember

⊙ The use of maths is widespread in everyday life, from sports, games and leisure pursuits, to driving and shopping, and practical tasks around the home or garden.

⊙ Many different occupations use maths in some way, sometimes in ways that are not immediately obvious.

How well are you doing?

Can you:

- ◉ solve routine and non-routine problems?
- ◉ select and apply a range of mathematical techniques to find solutions?
- ◉ use algebra to prove that a statement is true?
- ◉ communicate convincing arguments and solutions?

Using and applying maths (no calculator)

1   *1999 Exceptional performance*

a   Show that the area of triangle PQR is 2 units.
You should not find the square root of 6 or 2.
Show each step in your working.

b   Show that length QR is 4 units.
You should not find the square root of 6 or 2.
Show each step in your working.

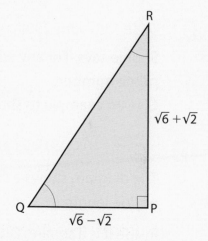

2   *GCSE 1387 June 2007*

Martin is organising a summer fair.
He needs bread buns and burgers
for the barbecue.

Bread buns are sold in packs.
Each pack contains 40 bread buns.

Burgers are sold in packs.
Each pack contains 24 burgers.

Martin buys exactly the same number
of bread buns as burgers.

What is the least number of each pack that Martin buys?

3 *GCSE 1387 November 2005*

Prove algebraically that the sum of the squares of any two odd numbers leaves a remainder of 2 when divided by 4.

4 *2000 Exceptional performance*

The lowest of four consecutive integers is n.

a Write the sum of the four consecutive integers as simply as possible in terms of n.

b Write the product of the lowest and the highest of the four consecutive integers in terms of n.

c Use your answers to parts **a** and **b** to show there are only two sets of four consecutive integers whose sum is equal to the product of the lowest and the highest integers.

d Write down the two sets of four consecutive integers.

5 *GCSE 1387 June 2006*

Sophie says, 'For any whole number, n, the value of $6n - 1$ is always a prime number'.

Give an example to show that Sophie is wrong.

6 *2001 Exceptional performance*

The diagram shows a square, ABCD, of side length $(p + q)$.

Inside it is a square, EFGH, of side length r.

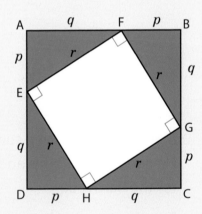

a Write a simplified expression for:

   i area of square EFGH (in terms of r);

   ii area of triangle DEH (in terms of p and q);

   iii area of square ABCD (in terms of p and q).

b Square ABCD is made up from four triangles and square EFGH.

The four triangles are all congruent to triangle DEH.

Use this information to write an expression in terms of p, q and r for the area of square ABCD.

c Use the two different expressions for the area of square ABCD to express r^2 in terms of p^2 and q^2.

a A solid cuboid, a cm $\times$ b cm $\times$ c cm, is made out of 1 cm cubes.

a, b and c are all greater than or equal to 2.

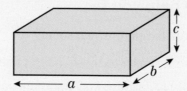

The outside of the cuboid is covered completely in green paint.

The eight corner cubes have 3 faces painted green.

Write an expression for:

  i the number of 1 cm cubes that have exactly 2 faces painted green;

  ii the number of 1 cm cubes that have exactly 1 face painted green;

  iii the number of 1 cm cubes that have 0 faces painted green.

b If $a = b = c$, the cuboid is a cube of side a. The cube is also covered in green paint.

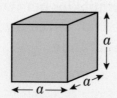

The table shows how many 1 cm cubes have 0, 1, 2 or 3 faces covered.

No. of faces covered	No. of 1 cm cubes
3	8
2	$12(a - 2)$
1	$6(a - 2)^2$
0	$(a - 2)^3$

The total number of 1 cm cubes in the cube is a^3.

You can tell from the table that:

$$8 + 12(a - 2) + 6(a - 2)^2 + (a - 2)^3 = a^3$$

Use an algebraic method to show that this is true.

Show each step in your working.

Revision unit 1

This unit will help you to:

- ⊙ revise your work during the year so far;
- ⊙ answer questions similar to those in tests and examinations;
- ⊙ help you to decide whether you are achieving National Curriculum level 8.

1 Percentages and ratios

This lesson will remind you how to calculate fractions, percentages and ratios.

Did you know that...?

The **symbol for per cent (%)** is thought to have evolved from an earlier symbol representing the Italian *per cento*.

This first appeared in an anonymous Italian manuscript of about 1425.

Exercise 1

You can solve percentage problems by using the unitary method to find 1% as an interim step, or by using decimal multipliers.

Example 1

The price of a new tumble dryer is £350.15. This includes Value Added Tax (VAT) at 17.5%. Work out the cost of the tumble dryer before VAT was added.

Method 1: Unitary method	£350.15 represents 117.5%.
Find the value of 1%.	£350.15 ÷ 117.5 = £2.98 represents 1%.
Find the value of 100%.	100% = £2.98 × 100 = £298
Method 2: Using a multiplier	£350.15 is the price after an increase by a factor of 1.175.
Divide £350.15 by 1.175.	£350.15 ÷ 1.175 = £298

When a quantity is divided into two parts in the ratio $a:b$, the two parts are the fractions $\dfrac{a}{a+b}$ and $\dfrac{b}{a+b}$ of the quantity.

Given a ratio and the size of one part, you can find the other part.

Example 2

Jim and Carol share an inheritance in the ratio $5:7$. Jim gets £16 000.
How much does Carol get?

Jim gets $\frac{5}{12}$ of the inheritance, which is £16 000.

For $\frac{1}{12}$, calculate £16 000 ÷ 5 = £3200.

For Carol's share of $\frac{7}{12}$, calculate £3200 × 7 = £22 400.

---

1 *2006 level 8*

Since 1952 the total number of people living in Wales
has increased by about one eighth.
The total number of people living in Wales now is about 3 million.
About how many people lived in Wales in 1952?

2 *2005 level 8*

a Each side of a square is increased by 10%.
By what percentage is the area increased?

b The length of a rectangle is increased by 20%. The width is decreased by 20%.
By what percentage is the area changed?

3 *2007 level 8*

Here is part of a newspaper report about wildlife in a country in Africa.

The number of gorillas has fallen by 70% in the last ten years. Only about 5000 gorillas are left.

About how many gorillas were there in this country ten years earlier?

4 *2002 level 8*

I fill a glass with orange juice and lemonade in the ratio 1 : 4.
I drink $\frac{1}{4}$ of the contents of the glass, then I fill the glass using orange juice.

Now what is the ratio of orange juice to lemonade in the glass?
Show your working, and write the ratio in its simplest form.

5 *2006 level 8*

Films at the cinema and films on television are shown at different speeds.

Cinema	Television
24 pictures per second	25 pictures per second

At the cinema a film lasts 175 minutes.
How many minutes does the same film last on television?

6 *2008 level 8*

In 1988 there was a survey of giant pandas seen in the wild in China.
In 2004 the survey was repeated. There was a 40% increase.
The table shows some of the results.

Year	Approximate number of giant pandas seen
1988	x
2004	1600

About x giant pandas were seen in 1988.

Work out the value of x and give your answer to the nearest 100.

7 *GCSE 1387 June 2004*

a A company bought a van that had a value of £12 000.
Each year the value of the van depreciates by 25%.
Work out the value of the van at the end of three years.

b The company bought a new truck.
Each year the value of the truck depreciates by 20%.
The value of the new truck can be multiplied by a single number to find
its value at the end of four years. Find this single number as a decimal.

8 *2008 Level 8*

Jane and Delia work together. Delia's pay is exactly twice as much as Jane's.
They are each going to get a pay increase.

a If they each get a pay increase of £2000, which is the true statement below?

    A Delia's pay will be more than twice as much as Jane's.

    B Delia's pay will be exactly twice as much as Jane's.

    C Delia's pay will be less than twice as much as Jane's.

    D There is not enough information to tell.

b If instead they each get a 5% pay increase, which is the true statement below?

    A Delia's pay will be more than twice as much as Jane's.

    B Delia's pay will be exactly twice as much as Jane's.

    C Delia's pay will be less than twice as much as Jane's.

    D There is not enough information to tell.

9 *1996 level 8*

A clothes shop had a closing down sale.
The sale started on Tuesday and finished on Saturday.

For each day of the sale, prices were reduced
by 15% of the prices on the day before.

a A shirt had a price of £19.95 on Monday.
Kevin bought it on Wednesday.
How much did he pay?
Show your working.

b Ghita bought a dress on Tuesday for £41.48.
What was its price on Monday?
Show your working.

c A jacket had a price of £49.95 on Monday.
What was its price on Friday?
Show your working.

d Another shop is reducing its prices each day by
12% of the prices on the day before. How many
days would it take for its original prices to be
reduced by more than 50%?
Show your working.

Extension problem

10 *1995 Exceptional performance*

Metric paper sizes such as A3, A4 and A5 are all rectangles and all have sides in the ratio $1:\sqrt{2}$. A sheet of A0 paper can be folded to make two sheets of A1. A sheet of A1 paper can be folded to make two sheets of A2, and so on.

a A pack of A4 paper is labelled 210 mm × 297 mm.
Is this an exact metric size, as defined by the ratio $1:\sqrt{2}$? Explain your answer.

b A pack of A0 paper is labelled 841 mm × 1189 mm.

Calculate the percentage error in the area of a sheet of A0 paper if it is similar to a sheet of A4 paper, 210 mm × 297 mm, instead of being its actual size, 841 mm × 1189 mm.

c The diagrams show how a sheet of metric paper can be folded to make a kite, ABCD.

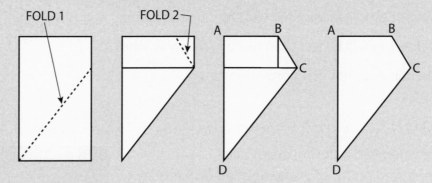

Check the instructions by folding a piece of A4 paper to make a kite if this will help you.

The shorter sides of a sheet of metric paper are each x units long.
The longer sides of a sheet of metric paper are each $\sqrt{2}x$ units long.

The sheet is folded to make a kite ABCD as above.
Find the length of side AB. Give your answer in terms of x and $\sqrt{2}x$ and simplify it.

d Find BC^2, the square of the length of the side BC.
Give your answer in terms of x and $\sqrt{2}x$ and simplify it.

e Show that $AB^2 = BC^2$ and, from this, that $AB = BC$.

◉ Points to remember

- When a quantity is divided into two parts in the ratio $a:b$, the parts are $\dfrac{a}{a+b}$ and $\dfrac{b}{a+b}$ of the whole quantity.
- Calculate percentage increases and decreases, or reverse percentages, using the unitary method or decimal multipliers.
- Use the unitary method to solve problems involving direct or inverse proportion.

2 Expressions and equations

This lesson will remind you how to expand brackets, factorise expressions and solve simultaneous linear equations.

 Did you know that...?

A graphics calculator can plot graphs and help you to estimate or check solutions to equations.

The world's first graphics calculator was made by Casio in 1985. Hewlett Packard produced one soon afterwards.

Texas Instruments has been making graphics calculators since 1990. The photograph shows the TI-84.

Exercise 2

Expanding brackets and **factorising** are the opposite of each other.

Example 1

Expand $3(4a + 7)$.

$3(4a + 7) = 12a + 21$ Multiply everything inside the bracket by the number outside.

Example 2

Factorise $ax^2 + 5ax$.

$ax^2 + 5ax = ax(x + 5)$ Remove the common factor ax, taking it outside a bracket.

Example 3

Expand $(2x + 5)(3x - 4)$.

Multiply each term in the first bracket by each term in the second bracket.

You can use a multiplication grid or the FOIL method.
F means multiply the first terms, O means multiply the outside terms,
I means multiply the inside terms and L means multiply the last terms.

$(2x + 5)(3x - 4) = 6x^2 - 8x + 15x - 20 = 6x^2 + 7x - 20$
                      F   O   I   L

Example 4

Factorise $x^2 - x - 6$.

$x^2 - x - 6 = (x - 3)(x + 2)$ A pair of factors of -6 with a sum of -1 is -3 and 2.

You can solve **simultaneous equations** using an **elimination method** or by finding a **graphical solution**.

Example 5

Find the solution of the simultaneous equations: $2x + 3y = 9$
$3x - 4y = 5$

Method of elimination

$$2x + 3y = 9 \quad \dots\dots\dots(1)$$
$$3x - 4y = 5 \quad \dots\dots\dots(2)$$

multiply (1) by 3 $6x + 9y = 27 \quad \dots\dots(3)$
multiply (2) by 2 $6x - 8y = 10 \quad \dots\dots(4)$

subtract (4) from (3) $17y = 17$
divide by 17 $y = 1$

substitute $y = 1$ in (1) $2x = 6$
divide by 2 $x = 3$

Check by substituting $y = 1$, $x = 3$ in (2): $9 - 4 = 5$

Graphical solution

The red line is $2x + 3y = 9$.
The blue line is $3x - 4y = 5$.
The lines cross at the point (3, 1).

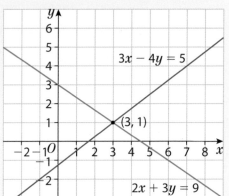

You need graph paper.

① *2007 level 7*

   a Jenny wants to multiply out the brackets in the expression $3(2a + 1)$. She writes:

$$3(2a + 1) = 6a + 1$$

   Show why Jenny is wrong.

   b Sandeep wants to multiply out the brackets in the expression $(k + 4)(k + 7)$. He writes:

$$(k + 4)(k + 7) = k^2 + 28$$

   Show why Sandeep is wrong.

② *2006 level 7*

   Multiply out these expressions. Write your answers as simply as possible.

   a $5(x + 2) + 3(7 + x)$ **b** $(x + 2)(x + 5)$

③ Multiply out these expressions. Write your answers as simply as possible.

   a $(2x + 3)(3x + 7)$ **b** $(4x - 5)(6x + 9)$ **c** $(5x - 2)(3x - 2)$

   d $(6x + 5)^2$ **e** $(2x - 7)(2x + 7)$

4 Factorise these expressions.

a $x^2 + 11x + 28$ **b** $x^2 + 5x - 36$ **c** $x^2 - 10x + 25$

5 *2004 level 8*

Look at these expressions.

$$5y - 8$$

first
expression

$$3y + 5$$

second
expression

a What value of y makes the two expressions equal? Show your working.

b What value of y makes the first expression twice as great as the second expression?

6 *2004 level 8*

y^2 represents a square number; y is an integer.

a Think about the expression $9 + y^2$.

Explain how you know there are values of y for which this expression does not represent a square number.

b Explain why the expression $16y^2$ must represent a square number.

7 **a** Use graph paper. Draw graphs to solve these simultaneous equations.

$$x + y = 6$$
$$3x - y = 2$$

b Use the method of elimination to solve these simultaneous equations.

$$2x + 5y = 12$$
$$3x - 5y = 3$$

8 *1996 level 8*

Lena thought of two numbers which she called a and b.
She wrote down this information about them in the form of equations:

$$a + 3b = 25$$
$$2a + b = 15$$

Work out the values of a and b.
Show your working.

(9) *GCSE 1387 June 2003*

Factorise $2x^2 - 7x + 6$.

(10) *GCSE 1387 June 2006*

Solve this quadratic equation:

$x^2 - 5x - 8$

Give your answer to 3 significant figures.

● Points to remember

- To work out the product of two expressions, multiply each term of the first expression by each term of the second expression.
- Factorising an expression is the opposite of expanding brackets. Work backwards to find the two brackets whose product is the expression.
- Two linear equations have a simultaneous solution when you can find a value for each variable that satisfies both equations.
- Two linear equations have no simultaneous solution when their graphs are parallel.

---

3 Formulae, functions and graphs

This lesson will remind you how to manipulate and evaluate algebraic formulae and to use the properties of straight-line graphs.

Exercise 3

Example 1

Evaluate the formula $V = \frac{1}{3}\pi h\left(\frac{a^3 - b^3}{a - b}\right)$ when $h = 12$, $a = 7$ and $b = 4$.

Use $\pi = 3.14$ and give your answer to 3 significant figures.

Substituting the given values for h, a and b in $V = \frac{1}{3}\pi h\left(\frac{a^3 - b^3}{a - b}\right)$ gives:

$\frac{1}{3}\pi \times 12\left(\frac{7^3 - 4^3}{7 - 4}\right) = 4\pi\left(\frac{343 - 64}{3}\right) = 4\pi \times 93 = 1170$ (to 3 s.f.)

Example 2

Make t the subject of the formula $v = u + at$.

Isolate any terms containing t $v - u = at$

Reverse the equation $at = v - u$

Divide by a $t = \dfrac{v - u}{a}$

Example 3

a What is the equation of the line?

Any straight line has equation $y = ax + b$.
The gradient of the line is 3 and the intercept on
the y-axis is (0, 2) so the equation of the line is
$y = 3x + 2$.

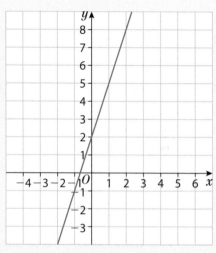

b Write the equation of a line parallel to the given line.

Any line parallel to this line has equation
$y = 3x + b$, for example the line $y = 3x + 9$.

c Write the equation of a line perpendicular to the
given line.

A line perpendicular to this line has equation
$y = -\frac{1}{3}x + b$, for example the line $y = -\frac{1}{3}x + 4$.

---

(1) *2002 level 7*

  a The subject of the equation $p = 2(e + f)$ is p.

     Rearrange the equation to make e the subject.

  b Rearrange the equation $r = \frac{1}{2}(c - d)$ to make d the subject.

     Show your working.

(2) *GCSE 2540 November 2007*

$v^2 = u^2 + 2as$

$u = 6$
$a = 2.5$
$s = 9$

  a Work out a value of v.

  b Make s the subject of the formula $v^2 = u^2 + 2as$.

3 *GCSE 1387 November 2007*

    a Simplify $(2x^4y^5)^3$.

    b Rearrange the formula $y = \dfrac{2pt}{p - t}$ to make t the subject.

4 *2007 level 8*

Look at the cube. The area of a face of the cube is $9x^2$.

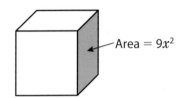

Area $= 9x^2$

    a Write an expression for the total surface area of the cube.
Write your answer as simply as possible.

    b Write an expression for the volume of the cube.
Write your answer as simply as possible.

5 *GCSE 1387 June 2006*

The distance, D, travelled by a particle is directly proportional to the square of the time, t, taken.

When $t = 40$, $D = 30$.

    a Find a formula for D in terms of t.

    b Calculate the value of D when $t = 64$.

    c Calculate the value of t when $D = 12$.

       Give your answer correct to 3 significant figures.

6 *2005 level 8*

To change temperatures measured in °C to °F you can use an exact formula or an approximate formula.

Exact formula	Approximate formula
$F = \dfrac{9C}{5} + 32$	$F = 2C + 30$

F is the temperature in °F and C is the temperature in °C.

At what temperature in °C do these formulae give an equal value for F?
You must show an algebraic method.

7 *GCSE 2540 May 2008*

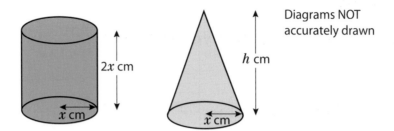

Diagrams NOT accurately drawn

A cylinder has base radius x cm and height $2x$ cm.
A cone has base radius x cm and height h cm.

The volume of the cylinder and the volume of the cone are equal.

Find h in terms of x.
Give your answer in its simplest form.

8 *2005 level 8*

The diagram shows the straight line with equation $y = 4(x - 2)$.
It is not drawn accurately.

a Work out the coordinates of the points marked A and B.

b A different straight line goes through the points (0, 0) and (3, 6).

Write the equation of this line.

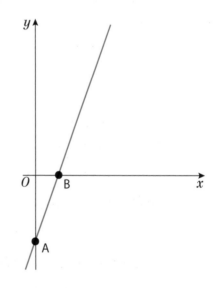

9 *GCSE 1387 June 2005*

The diagram shows three points A(-1, 5), B(2, -1) and C(0, 5).

The line **L** is parallel to AB and passes through C.

Find the equation of the line **L**.

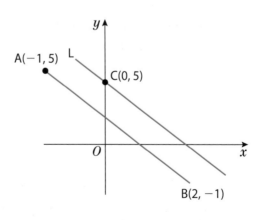

Not drawn accurately

Look at this octagon:

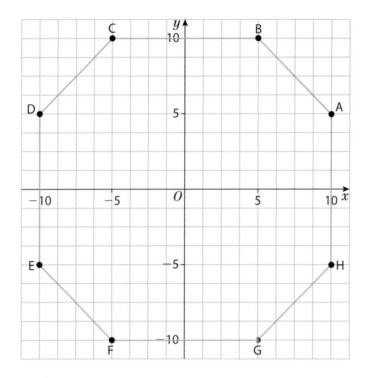

a The line through A and H has the equation $x = 10$.
What is the equation of the line through F and G?

b $x + y = 15$ is the equation of the line through which points?

c The octagon has four lines of symmetry.
One of the lines of symmetry has the equation $y = x$.
Write the equations of the three other lines of symmetry.

d The line through D and B has
the equation $3y = x + 25$.
The line through G and H has
the equation $x = y + 15$.

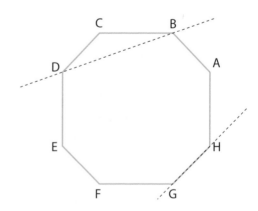

Solve the simultaneous equations

$3y = x + 25$
$x = y + 15$

Show your working.

e The line through D and B meets the line through G and H at which point?

(11) *2003 level 8*

Look at the graph.

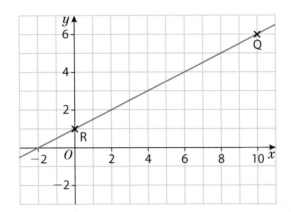

a The gradient of the line through R and Q is 0.5.
Explain how you can work this out from the graph.

b What is the equation of the straight line through R and Q?

c Write the equation of a line that is parallel to the straight line through R and Q.

(12) *GCSE 1387 November 2005*

A straight line **L** is parallel to $y = 2x - 3$ and passes through the point $(3, 4)$.

a Find the equation of line **L**.

b Which of these equations is a straight line perpendicular to the line $y = 2x - 3$?

    A $y = 2x - 3$ **B** $y = 3 - 2x$ **C** $y = \frac{1}{2}x - 3$

         D $y = 3 - \frac{1}{2}x$ **E** $y = 2x + 3$

⊙ Points to remember

- ⊙ A formula is a way of expressing a relationship using symbols.
- ⊙ When a formula starts $d = \ldots$, then d is called the subject of the formula.
- ⊙ You can rearrange a formula to make a different letter the subject, e.g.
  $s = \dfrac{d}{t}$ and $t = \dfrac{d}{s}$.
- ⊙ The graph of $y = ax + b$ has gradient a and intercept on the y-axis at $(0, b)$.
- ⊙ Parallel lines have the same gradient.
- ⊙ Any line perpendicular to $y = ax + b$ has a gradient $-\dfrac{1}{a}$.

4 Geometrical reasoning

This lesson will remind you how to use geometrical reasoning to solve problems.

Did you know that...?

Harold Scott MacDonald Coxeter (1907–2003), known as Donald, was one of the great 20th-century experts in geometry. He was born in London and studied at Cambridge but spent most of his working life in Canada. He championed the use of geometrical reasoning to solve problems.

Before he became a mathematician Coxeter wanted to become a composer but his interest in symmetry took him towards mathematics as a career. He wrote: 'I am extremely fortunate for being paid for what I would have done anyway.'

He attributed his long life to being a vegetarian, doing 50 push-ups a day until he was 89, and never being bored.

Exercise 4

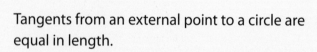

Here are some useful facts and theorems about circles.

A tangent is perpendicular to the radius at the point of contact.

    angle OTP = 90°

    angle OTQ = 90°

Tangents from an external point to a circle are equal in length.

    PA = PB

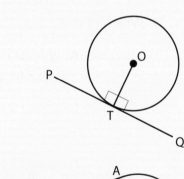

A line drawn from the centre of a circle perpendicular to a chord bisects the chord.

    When OM is perpendicular to AB, AM = BM.

A line drawn from the centre of a circle to the midpoint of a chord is perpendicular to the chord.

    When AM = MB, OM is perpendicular to AB.

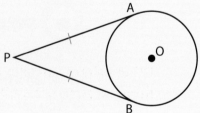
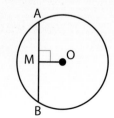

The angle at the centre of a circle is twice the angle at the circumference.

angle AOB = 2 × angle ACB

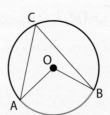

The angle in a semicircle is a right angle.

angle ACB = 90°

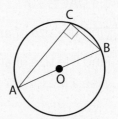

Angles in the same segment are equal.

angle APB = angle AQB

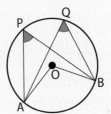

Opposite angles of a cyclic quadrilateral sum to 180°.

angle SPQ + angle SRQ = 180°

and

angle PSR + angle PQR = 180°

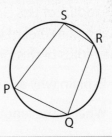

① *2000 level 8*

Two isosceles triangles have the same base, AD, so that AB = DB and AC = DC.

a Show, by calculating, that angle a is 16°.

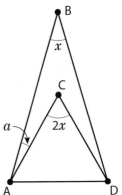

b Other pairs of isosceles triangles can be drawn from the same base, AD.

Angle ACD is twice the size of angle ABD. Call these angles $2x$ and x.

Prove that angle a is always half of angle x.

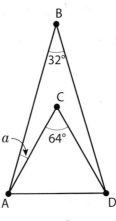

2 *GCSE 1387 November 2006*

ABCD are points on the circumference of a circle, centre O.

AC is a diameter of the circle.
Angle DAC is 20°.

a Find the size of angle ACD.

b Find the size of angle DBC.
Give a reason for your answer.

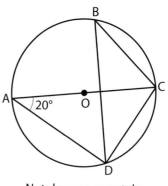

Not drawn accurately

3 *2005 level 8*

The diagram shows two circles with a point of intersection at A.

The centre of the larger circle is B.
The radius of this circle is 6 cm.
BC is a diameter of the smaller circle.
The radius of this circle is 5 cm.

a Explain why angle BAC must be a right angle.

b What is the length of AC?

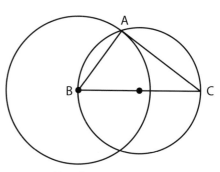

Not drawn accurately

4 *GCSE 1387 June 2006*

AED and CEB are straight lines.

AE = CE and BE = DE.

Explain why triangles ABE and CDE are congruent.

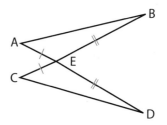

Not drawn accurately

5 *GCSE 1387 November 2006*

In the diagram, PQ = PS and PR = PT.
Angle RPT = angle SPQ.

a Prove that triangles PRQ and PTS are congruent.

b Hence, prove that PS bisects angle QST.

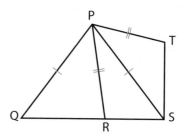

Not drawn accurately

6 *2000 level 8*

a The triangles below are similar.

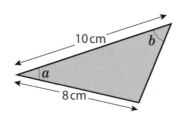 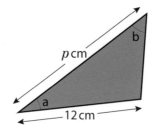

What is the value of *p*? Show your working.

b Triangles ABC and BDC are similar.

What is the length of CD?

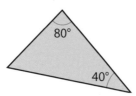

c Look at the triangles below.

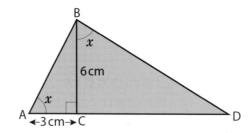

Are they similar? Show working to explain how you know.

7 *2006 level 8*

The diagram shows five points joined with four straight lines.

BC and AD are parallel.
BCE and ADE are isosceles triangles.

The total length of the four straight lines is 40 cm.

What is the length of EA?

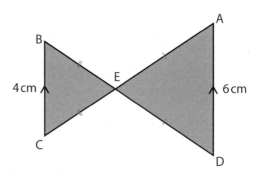

8 *1999 level 8*

Look at the diagram.

Side AB is the same length as side AC.
Side BD is the same length as side BC.

Calculate the value of x.
Show your working.

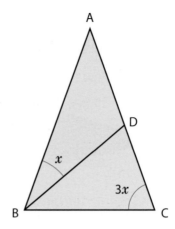

9 *2004 level 8*

A pupil has three tiles.

One is a regular octagon, one is a regular hexagon, and one is a square.
The side length of each tile is the same.

The pupil says the hexagon will fit exactly like this.

Show calculations to prove that the pupil is wrong.

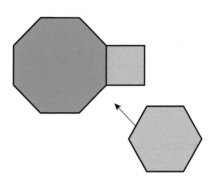

Extension problem

10 *2004 level 8*

The diagram shows a square inside a triangle.

DEF is a straight line.

The side length of square ABCE is 12 cm.
The length of DE is 15 cm.

Show that the length of EF is 20 cm.

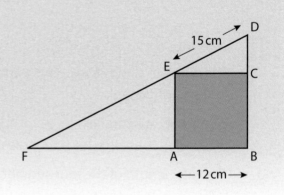

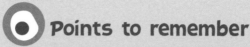

Points to remember

- Corresponding sides of **similar shapes** are in the same ratio.
- Triangles are **congruent** if they satisfy SSS, SAS, ASA or RHS.
- In a circle, the angle between a tangent and chord is a right angle.
- The angle at the centre of a circle is twice the angle at the circumference.
- The angle in a semicircle is a right angle.
- Angles in the same segment are equal.
- Opposite angles of a cyclic quadrilateral sum to 180°.

5 Probability

This lesson will remind you how to calculate probabilities of combined events.

 Did you know that...?

The Italian **Jerome Cardan** (1501–1576) wrote the first book on probability. *Liber de ludo aleae* was written in the 1560s but not published until 1663. Besides the discussion of probability, the book has as a section on effective ways of cheating.

Today's meaning of 'probability' is almost the opposite of the meaning of the word 'probity' from which it stems. Before the 17th century, evidence in court was given by people with probity or integrity. The idea of empirical or scientific evidence barely existed.

Today, probability is the measure of the weight of empirical evidence in science, arrived at from inductive or statistical inference.

Exercise 5

Mutually exclusive outcomes are outcomes which cannot happen at the same time.

For example, when one counter is chosen at random from a bag of coloured counters, the outcome 'red' cannot happen at the same time as the outcome 'green', so they are mutually exclusive.

For mutually exclusive events, the probability of **A** or **B** occurring is P(**A**) + P(**B**).

Two events are **independent** if one event happening does not affect the probability of the other event happening.

For example, a fair three-sided spinner is spun and a fair coin is tossed at the same time. The outcomes from spinning the spinner do not affect the outcomes from tossing the coin, so the events are independent.

For independent events, the probability of **A** and **B** occurring is P(**A**) × P(**B**).

Probability tree diagrams are useful for solving probability problems, especially when the outcome of the first event changes the probability of the second event.

Example

Amy and Beth are going to take a driving test.

The probability Amy will pass the test is 0.7.
The probability Beth will pass the test is 0.8.

The probability tree diagram shows this information.

Work out the probability that:

a Amy and Beth will both pass the test;

P(**Amy, pass** and **Beth, pass**) = P(**Amy, pass**) × P(**Beth, pass**)
= 0.7 × 0.8 = 0.56

b only Amy will pass the test;

P(**Amy, pass** and **Beth, not pass**) = P(**Amy, pass**) × P(**Beth, not pass**)
= 0.7 × 0.2 = 0.14

c neither Amy nor Beth will pass the test.

P(**Amy, not pass** and **Beth, not pass**) = P(**Amy, not pass**) × P(**Beth, not pass**)
= 0.3 × 0.2 = 0.06

① *2008 level 7*

Here are the rules of a game.

> Each person chooses heads or tails at random, then a coin is thrown.
>
> People who choose the side shown by the coin are left in the game.
>
> The rest are out of the game.

A group of 1000 people is going to play this game.
How many people might you expect to be left in the game after 5 throws?

(2) *2003 level 7*

A headteacher wants to choose a pupil from Year 7, 8 or 9 to appear on television.
The headteacher gives each pupil one ticket, then selects the winning ticket at random.

The table shows information about the ticket used.

	Colour of the ticket	Numbers used
Year 7	red	1 to 80
Year 8	blue	1 to 75
Year 9	yellow	1 to 90

a What is the probability that the winning ticket will be blue?

b What is the probability that the winning ticket will show number 39?

c The headteacher selects the winning ticket at random.
She says: 'The winning ticket number is 39'.
What is the probability that this winning ticket is blue?

(3) *2008 level 8*

Dario has five cards showing different shapes.

He is going to mix them up, then take out one card at random.
Then he is going to take out a second card without replacing the first card.

a What is the probability that he will take out the square first and then the circle?

b What is the probability that he will take out the square and the circle, in either order?

(4) *2000 level 8*

John makes two clay pots. Each pot is fired independently.
The probability that a pot cracks while being fired is 0.03.

a Calculate the probability that both of John's pots crack while being fired.
Show your working.

b Calculate the probability that only one of John's pots cracks while being fired.
Show your working.

c John has enough clay for 80 pots. He receives an order for 75 pots.
Does he have enough clay to make 75 pots without cracks? Explain your answer.

(5) *2003 level 8*

A girl plays the same computer game lots of times.
The computer scores each game using 1 for win, 0 for lose.
After each game, the computer calculates her overall mean score.

The graph shows the results for the first 20 games.

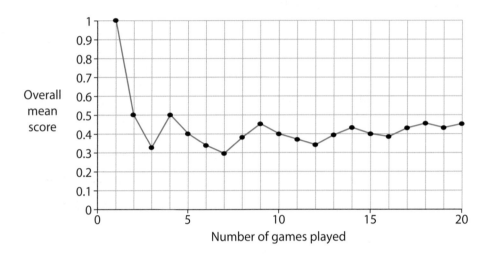

a   For each of the first 3 games, write **W** if she won or **L** if she lost.

b   What percentage of the 20 games did the girl win?

c   The graph below shows the girl's results for the first 100 games.

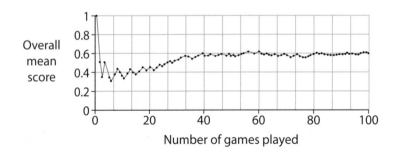

She is going to play the game again.
Estimate the probability that she will win.

d   Suppose for the 101st to 120th games, the girl were to lose each game.
What would the graph look like up to the 120th game?
Sketch a graph to show your answer.

6 *GCSE 1387 June 2006*

Simon plays one game of tennis and one game of snooker.

The probability that Simon will win at tennis is $\frac{3}{4}$.

The probability that Simon will win at snooker is $\frac{1}{3}$.

a Copy and complete the tree diagram.

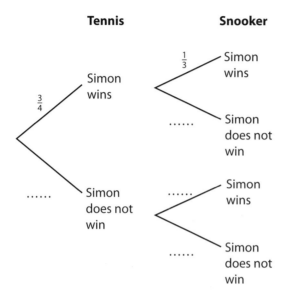

b Work out the probability that Simon wins both games.

c Work out the probability that Simon wins only one game.

7 *1999 level 8*

On a road there are two sets of traffic lights. The traffic lights work independently. For each set of traffic lights, the probability that a driver will have to stop is 0.7.

a A woman is going to drive along the road. What is the probability that:

  i she will have to stop at both sets of traffic lights?

  ii she will have to stop at only one of the two sets of traffic lights?

  Show your working.

b In one year, a man drives 200 times along the road.
Calculate an estimate of the number of times he drives through both sets of traffic lights without stopping.
Show your working.

Extension problem

 8 *1995 Exceptional performance*

Pupils at a school invented a game called Wordo. They tried it out with a large sample. They found that the probability of winning Wordo was 0.6.

The pupils invented another word game, Lango. The same sample played Lango. The pupils drew this tree diagram to show the probabilities of winning:

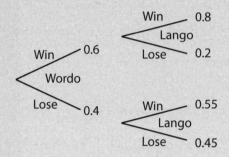

a What was the probability of someone from the sample winning Lango?

b What was the probability of someone from the sample winning only one of the two word games?

c The pupils also invented a dice game. They tried it out with the same sample of people who had already played Wordo and Lango.

The probability of winning the dice game was 0.9. This was found to be independent of the probabilities for Wordo and Lango. Calculate the probability of someone from the sample winning two out of these three games.

⊙ Points to remember

- ⊙ Mutually exclusive outcomes cannot occur at the same time. If events are mutually exclusive, the probability of **A** or **B** occurring is P(**A**) + P(**B**).

- ⊙ Two events are independent if the outcomes of one event do not affect the outcomes of the other. For independent events, the probability of **A** and **B** occurring is P(**A**) × P(**B**).

- ⊙ Tree diagrams are used to calculate probabilities. They are particularly useful when events are not equally likely or when they are not independent.

Revision unit 2

This unit will help you to:

- revise your work during the year so far;
- answer questions similar to those in tests and examinations;
- help you to decide whether you are achieving National Curriculum level 8.

1 Indices and standard form

This lesson will remind you how to work with indices and use standard form.

Exercise 1

To **multiply** two numbers in index form, add the indices, so $a^m \times a^n = a^{m+n}$.

To **divide** two numbers in index form, subtract the indices, so $a^m \div a^n = a^{m-n}$.

To **raise the power of a number to a power**, multiply the indices, so $(a^m)^n = a^{m \times n}$.

These index laws hold for positive and negative integer and fractional powers.

A number in **standard form** has the form $A \times 10^n$, where A is a number between 1 and 10 and n is an integer. You can write an approximate value of a number in standard form by rounding A to 1 significant figure: for example, $3.75 \times 10^7 \approx 4 \times 10^7$.

Example 1

Write 425 in standard form. $425 = 4.25 \times 100 = 4.25 \times 10^2$ in standard form

Example 2

Write 8.75×10^{-4} as an ordinary number. $8.75 \div 10^4 = 0.000\,875$

Example 3

Estimate the value of $(8.97 \times 10^{11}) \div (1.987 \times 10^7)$.

Write each decimal correct to 1 significant figure, so an estimated value is:

$(9 \times 10^{11}) \div (2 \times 10^7) = 4.5 \times 10^4$

You need **R7.2 Resource sheet 1.1** for question 10.

1 *2008 level 7*

    a Explain why $\sqrt{89}$ must be between 9 and 10.

    b $\sqrt{389}$ is also between two consecutive whole numbers. What are the two numbers?

2 *2008 level 8*

    a Ed writes:

$$\frac{1}{2} \text{ of } 10^3 = 5^3$$

    Show why Ed is **wrong**.

    b Sasha writes:

$$\frac{1}{2} \text{ of } 6 \times 10^8 = 3 \times 10^4$$

    Show why Sasha is **wrong**.

    c Work out $\frac{1}{2}$ of 1.65×10^6. Give your answer in standard form.

3 *2002 level 8*

The star nearest the Earth (other than the Sun) is Proxima Centauri.
Proxima Centauri is 4.22 light-years away.
(One light-year is 9.46×10^{12} kilometres.)

Suppose a spaceship could travel at 40 000 km per hour.

    a Write what each of the following calculations represents.

    The first one is done for you.

      i $4.22 \times 9.46 \times 10^{12}$

        Number of km from Earth to Proxima Centauri

      ii $\dfrac{4.22 \times 9.46 \times 10^{12}}{40\,000}$

      iii $\dfrac{4.22 \times 9.46 \times 10^{12}}{40\,000 \times 24 \times 365.25}$

    b Work out $\dfrac{4.22 \times 9.46 \times 10^{12}}{40\,000 \times 24 \times 365.25}$.

    Give your answer to the nearest thousand.

(4) *2006 level 8*

a Look at this number.

$$8.679 \times 10^4$$

Round it to the nearest thousand. Give your answer in standard form.

b Now look at this number.

$$8.679 \times 10^{-4}$$

Round it to the nearest thousandth. Give your answer in standard form.

(5) *1995 level 8*

Sir Isaac Newton (1642–1727) was a mathematician, physicist and astronomer.
In his work on the gravitational force between two bodies he found that he needed to multiply their masses together.

a Work out the value of the mass of the Earth multiplied by the mass of the Moon.
Give your answer in standard form.

> Mass of Earth $= 5.98 \times 10^{24}$ kg
>
> Mass of Moon $= 7.35 \times 10^{22}$ kg

Newton also found that he needed to work out the square of the distance between the two bodies.

b Work out the square of the distance between the Earth and the Moon.
Give your answer in standard form.

> Distance between Earth and Moon $= 3.89 \times 10^5$ km

Newton's formula to calculate the gravitational force (F) between two bodies is
$F = \dfrac{Gm_1 m_2}{R_2}$ where G is the gravitational constant, m_1 and m_2 are the masses of the
two bodies, and R is the distance between them.

c Work out the gravitational force (F) between the Sun and the Earth using the formula
$F = \dfrac{Gm_1 m_2}{R_2}$ with the information in the box below. Give your answer in standard form.

> $m_1 m_2 = 1.19 \times 10^{55}$ kg^2
>
> $R_2 = 2.25 \times 10^{16}$ km^2
>
> $G = 6.67 \times 10^{-20}$

6 *GCSE 1387 November 2006*

When you are h feet above sea level, you can see d miles to the horizon, where

$$d = \sqrt{\frac{3h}{2}}$$

Calculate the value of d when $h = 8.4 \times 10^3$.
Give your answer in standard form correct to 3 significant figures.

7 *GCSE 1387 November 2007*

In 2003 the population of Great Britain was 6.0×10^7.

In 2003 the population of India was 9.9×10^8.

a Work out the difference between the population of India and the population of Great Britain in 2003. Give your answer in standard form.

b In 1933 the population of Great Britain was 4.5×10^7.

Calculate the percentage increase in the population of Great Britain from 1933 to 2003.
Give your answer correct to one decimal place.

8 **a** Jupiter is 4.84×10^8 miles from the Sun.
It orbits the Sun at an average speed of 2.92×10^4 miles per hour.

Assuming that its orbit is a circle, find in years the time it takes to circle the Sun.

b The Earth is 93 million miles from the Sun.
It orbits the Sun once a year.

Assuming that its orbit is a circle, what is the Earth's average speed round the Sun in miles per second?

9 *2007 level 8*

The diagram shows the Earth and two other planets.

Planet P is 6.9×10^7 km from Earth.

Planet Q is 9.2×10^7 km from Earth.

How far is Planet P from Planet Q?
Give your answer in standard form.

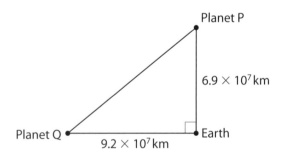

Extension problem

10 *1996 Exceptional performance*

You need a copy of the table of powers on **Resource sheet 1.1**. The table shows the powers of 2 up to 4096. Some entries have been filled in to show how these numbers can also be expressed as powers of 4, 8, 16, and so on.

a Complete the column of powers of 4. Write the indices as fractions.

b There is one missing entry in the table where the index should be $\frac{1}{2}$. Fill in this entry.

c Complete the row for the number 4096. Write the indices as fractions.

d The indices for the row for 4096 form a number pattern.
Rewrite all these indices below the table so that this number pattern is shown clearly.

 Points to remember

⊙ $\sqrt[n]{a}$ or $a^{1/n}$ means the nth root of a.

⊙ $a^m \times a^n = a^{m+n}$, $a^m \div a^n = a^{m-n}$ and $(a^m)^n = a^{m \times n}$,
for positive or negative integer or fractional values of m and n.

⊙ A number in standard form is of the form $A \times 10^n$, where $1 \leqslant A < 10$ and n is an integer.

⊙ Standard form is a useful way of writing very large or very small numbers.

⊙ Answers to calculations involving numbers in standard form are usually given to 3 significant figures.

2 Equations and inequalities

This lesson will remind you how to solve linear and quadratic equations and linear inequalities.

Exercise 2

Example 1

Solve the linear equation $5(3x + 9) - 2(x - 4) = 24x + 20$.

multiply out the brackets	$15x + 45 - 2x + 8 = 24x + 20$
collect like terms	$13x + 53 = 24x + 20$
bring all unknowns to one side	$53 - 20 = 24x - 13x$
simplify	$33 = 11x$
divide by 11	$x = 3$

Example 2

Represent all the points satisfying the inequalities:

$y \geqslant 3x - 2$, $y \geqslant 5 - x$ and $y < 6$

Draw $y = 3x - 2$ and $y = 5 - x$ as continuous lines.
Draw $y = 6$ as a dotted line.
Shade the unwanted regions.

All the points satisfying the system of inequalities
$y \geqslant 3x - 2$, $y \geqslant 5 - x$ and $y < 6$ are in the **unshaded** region.

There are five integer solutions:

(0, 5), (1, 4), (1, 5), (2, 4), (2, 5)

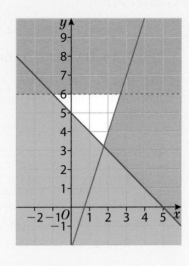

Example 3

Use factorisation to solve the equation
$x^2 - 13x + 42 = 0$.

Find a factor pair of 42 with a sum of -13:
-6 and -7.

$(x - 7)(x - 6) = 0$

So $x = \mathbf{7}$ or $x = \mathbf{6}$

Example 4

Use the quadratic formula to solve the equation
$x^2 - 9x + 10 = 0$.

The formula is: $x = \dfrac{-b \pm \sqrt{b^2 - 4ac}}{2a}$

Substitute $a = 1$, $b = -9$ and $c = 10$.

So $x = \dfrac{9 \pm \sqrt{41}}{2}$, which gives

$x = \mathbf{7.70}$ or $x = \mathbf{1.30}$ (to 3 s.f.).

You need some squared paper for question 4 and graph paper for question 7.

1 Solve these linear equations.

    a $2(3x - 4) - 7(8x - 3) = 63$ **b** $5(4x + 2) - 2(3x - 4) = 20x$

    c $\dfrac{2x}{3} + \dfrac{3x}{4} = 17$ **d** $\dfrac{6}{x} + \dfrac{4}{x} = 1$

2 **a** Jasmine and Rob live 180 miles apart by road.
      They set off by car to meet each other at the same time.
      Jasmine travels at an average speed of 50 mph.
      Rob travels at an average speed of 40 mph.
      After how many hours will Jasmine and Rob meet?

    b Ali and Kyle each leave home to cycle towards each other.
      Their route is 16 miles long.
      Ali travels at an average speed that is 6 mph faster than Kyle's average speed.
      They meet after half an hour.
      What was Kyle's average speed?

3 *2005 level 8*

In this question, a and b are numbers where $a = b + 2$.

The sum of a and b is equal to the product of a and b.

Show that a and b are not integers.

4 *GCSE 1387 June 2003*

a $-2 < x \leqslant 1$, x is an integer.

Write down all the possible values of x.

b $-2 < x \leqslant 1$, $y > -2$, $y < x + 1$,

x and y are integers.

Copy the grid on the right on squared paper.

On your grid, mark with a cross (✗) each of the six points which satisfies all three of these inequalities.

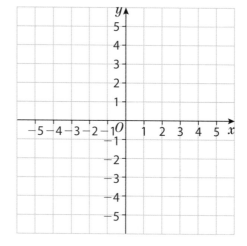

5 An outdoor centre is booking transport for 92 people.

A large bus seats 18 passengers and costs £300.
A small bus seats 10 passengers and costs £225.

The total number of buses must not exceed 6.

Let x be the number of large buses.
Let y the number of smaller buses.

a Set up four inequalities to represent the information.

b Draw a graph to show the region which satisfies these inequalities.

c Which of your solutions minimises the cost?

6 Use the method of factorisation to solve these quadratic equations.
Check your answers by substituting each value for x back into the original equation.

a $x^2 - 7x + 12 = 0$

b $x^2 + 2x - 15 = 0$

c $x^2 - x - 12 = 0$

7 *GCSE 1387 November 2007*

 a Copy this grid on graph paper.

 On the grid, draw the graph of
 $y = 2x^2 - 4x$ for values of x
 from -2 to 3.

 b **i** On the same axes, draw the
 straight line $y = 2.5$.

 ii Write down the values of x
 for which $2x^2 - 4x = 2.5$.

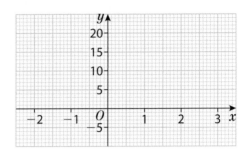

8 *GCSE 2540 June 2008*

 a Show that the equation $\dfrac{5}{x + 2} = \dfrac{4 - 3x}{x - 1}$
 can be rearranged to give $3x^2 + 7x - 13 = 0$.

 b Solve $3x^2 + 7x - 13 = 0$.
 Give your solutions correct to 2 decimal places.

9 *GCSE June 2005*

 The diagram shows a 6-sided shape.
 All the corners are right angles.

 All measurements are given in centimetres.

 The area of the shape is 25 cm^2.

 a Show that $6x^2 + 17x - 39 = 0$.

 b **i** Solve the equation $6x^2 + 17x - 39 = 0$.

 ii Hence work out the length of the
 longest side of the shape.

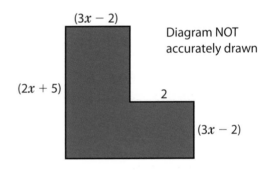

Diagram NOT
accurately drawn

Extension problems

10 *GCSE 2540 November 2008*

Solve the simultaneous equations

$x^2 + y^2 = 5$
$y = 3x + 1$

11 *GCSE 1387 November 2004*

Solve

$$\frac{2}{x + 1} + \frac{3}{x - 1} = \frac{5}{x^2 - 1}$$

3 Functions and graphs

This lesson will remind you how to recognise quadratic, cubic, reciprocal, exponential and trigonometric graphs and the transformations of functions.

Exercise 3

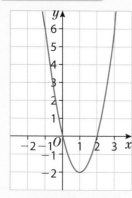

quadratic graph
$y = 2x^2 - 4x$

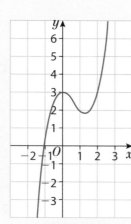

cubic graph
$y = x^3 - 2x^2 + 3$

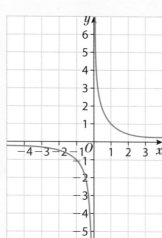

reciprocal graph
$y = \dfrac{1}{x}$

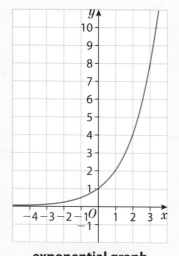

exponential graph
$y = 2^x$

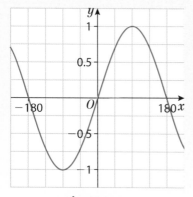

sine curve
$y = \sin x$

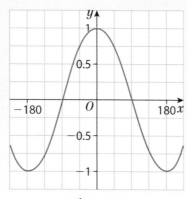

cosine curve
$y = \cos x$

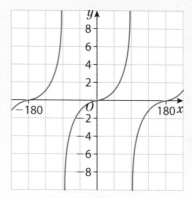

tangent curve
$y = \tan x$

1. **a** What is the maximum number of times a quadratic graph can cut the x-axis?

   b Write the equation of a graph that does not cut the x-axis.

   c What are the coordinates of the points where the function $f(x) = x^2 + x - 12$ cuts the x-axis?

   d Explain how your answer to part **c** helps you solve the equation $x^2 + x - 12 = 0$.

2. *1998 level 8*

   The shaded region is bounded by the curve $y = x^2$ and the line $y = 2$.

   Write the two inequalities from the list which together fully describe the shaded region.

$y < x^2$	$x < 0$	$y < 2$	$y < 0$
$y > x^2$	$x > 0$	$y > 2$	$y > 0$

   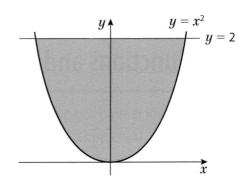

3. *GCSE 1387 November 2006*

   A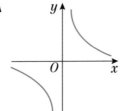

   B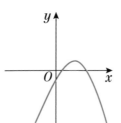

   C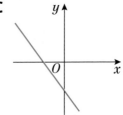

   D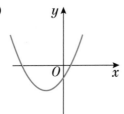

   E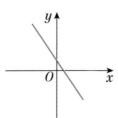

   F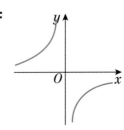

   G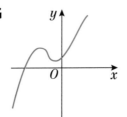

   H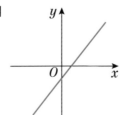

   I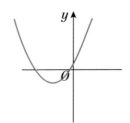

   Write down the letter of the graph which could have the equation:

   a $y = 1 - 3x$

   b $y = \dfrac{1}{x}$

   c $y = 2x^2 + 7x + 3$

(4) Match each function to one of the graphs **A** to **F**.

a $f(x) = 3^x + 2$

b $f(x) = \dfrac{1}{2x}$

c $f(x) = 3x^2 - 4$

d $f(x) = x^3 - 4x^2 + 5$

e $f(x) = \sin 2x$

f $f(x) = 2\cos x$

A
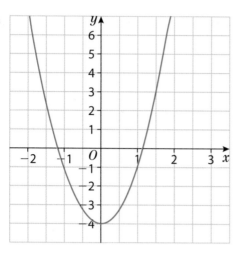

B
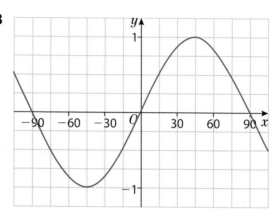

C
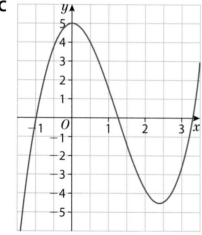

D
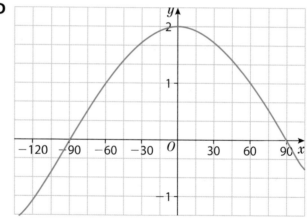

E
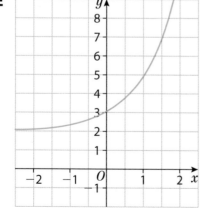

F
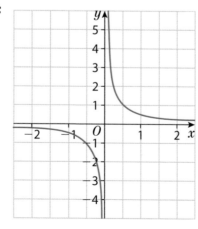

5 In each question, g(x) is a transformation of f(x). Describe the transformation.

    a   f(x) = 4x + 3   **b**   f(x) = x^2 + 1   **c**   f(x) = 2^x

         g(x) = 4x + 9   g(x) = $-x^2$ $-$ 1   g(x) = 2^{-x}

    d   f(x) = sin x **e**   f(x) = sin x **f**   f(x) = x^2

         g(x) = sin 6x g(x) = 10sin x g(x) = x^2 + 4x + 4

Extension problem

 GCSE June 2004

A sketch of the curve $y = \sin x$ for
$0° \leqslant x \leqslant 360°$ is shown opposite.

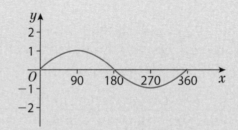

a   Using the sketch above, or otherwise, find the equation of each of the curves below.

   i 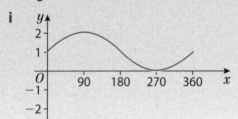   **ii**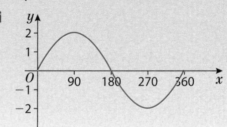

b   Describe fully the sequence of two transformations that maps the graph of $y = \sin x$
onto the graph of $y = 3\sin 2x$.

◉ Points to remember

⊙ A polynomial equation is of the form $y = ax^n + bx^{n-1} + cx^{n-2} + \ldots$,
where n is a positive integer.

⊙ A reciprocal equation is of the form $y = \dfrac{a}{bx}$.

⊙ An exponential equation is of the form $y = a^x$.

⊙ A trigonometric equation is of the form
$y = a \sin bx$, $y = a \cos bx$ or $y = a \tan bx$.

⊙ A function f(x) can be transformed as follows:

  – f(x) + a is a translation of a units in the y-direction;

  – f(x + a) is a translation of $-a$ units in the x-direction;

  – af(x) is a stretch with scale factor a in the y-direction;

  – f(ax) is a stretch with scale factor $\dfrac{1}{a}$ in the x-direction;

  – $-$f(x) is a reflection in the x-axis;

  – f($-x$) is a reflection in the y-axis.

4 Pythagoras' theorem and trigonometry

This lesson will remind you how to find lengths and angles in right-angled triangles using Pythagoras' theorem and the trigonometric ratios.

Exercise 4

The longest side of a right-angled triangle, opposite the right angle, is the **hypotenuse**. In the diagram, c is the hypotenuse.

Pythagoras' theorem shows that, in any right-angled triangle, the square of the longest side is the sum of the squares of the other two sides, or:

$a^2 + b^2 = c^2$

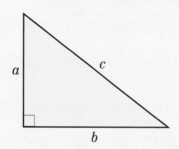

You can use **trigonometric ratios** to work out the lengths of sides and the sizes of angles in right-angled triangles.

$$\sin x = \frac{\text{opposite}}{\text{hypotenuse}}$$

$$\cos x = \frac{\text{adjacent}}{\text{hypotenuse}}$$

$$\tan x = \frac{\text{opposite}}{\text{adjacent}}$$

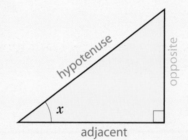

Example 1

The diagram shows a rectangular field with the corners labelled A, B, C and D.

Calculate the length of the diagonal of the field.

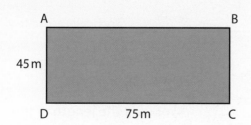

As the field is rectangular all the corners are right angles and the diagonals are of the same length.

In triangle ABC, use Pythagoras' theorem to find the length of AC:

$AC^2 = AB^2 + BC^2$
$AC^2 = 75^2 + 45^2$
$AC^2 = 5625 + 2025$
$AC^2 = 7650$
$AC = 87.5\,\text{m}$ (to 3 s.f.)

Example 2

In the diagram of the field in Example 1, calculate angle BAC.

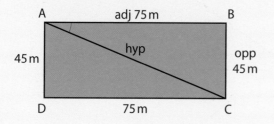

Triangle ABC has a right angle at B.
AC is the hypotenuse.
BC is the side opposite to angle BAC.
AB is the side adjacent to angle BAC.

As the opposite and adjacent sides are known, use the tangent formula.

$$\tan(\text{angle BAC}) = \frac{\text{opposite}}{\text{adjacent}} = \frac{45}{75} = 0.6$$

angle BAC $= \tan^{-1} 0.6$

angle BAC $= 31.0°$ (to 3 s.f.)

---

(1) *1999 level 8*

A table top is in the shape of a trapezium.

Calculate the area of the table top. Show your working.

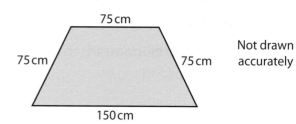

Not drawn accurately

(2) *GCSE 2540 June 2008*

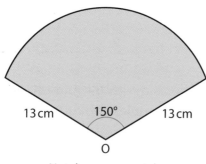

Not drawn accurately

The diagram shows a sector of a circle, centre O.

The radius of the circle is 13 cm.
The angle of the sector is 150°.

Calculate the area of the sector. Give your answer correct to 3 significant figures.

(3) *GCSE 2540 June 2008*

OAB is a sector of a circle, centre O.

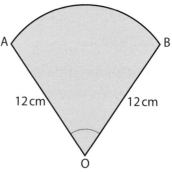

Not drawn accurately

Angle AOB is 60°.
OA = OB = 12 cm

Work out the length of the arc AB. Give your answer in terms of π.

4 *2003 level 8*

Two right-angled triangles are joined together to make a larger triangle ACD.

a Show that the perimeter of triangle ACD is 78 cm.

b Show that triangle ACD is also a right-angled triangle.

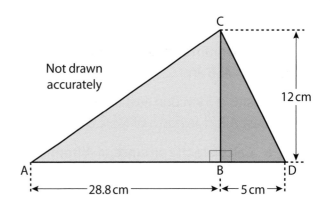

Not drawn accurately

12 cm

28.8 cm   5 cm

5 *2007 level 8*

I have a square piece of card.

I cut a triangle from each corner so that the remaining card is in the shape of a regular octagon.

The perimeter of the regular octagon is 32 cm. Work out length y.

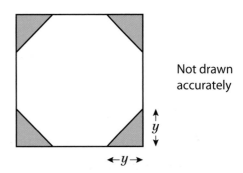

Not drawn accurately

y

y

6 *GCSE 1384 June 1996*

In the diagram, XY is a vertical tower on level ground. A and B are points due west of Y. The distance AB is 30 metres.

The angle of elevation of X from A is 30°. The angle of elevation of X from B is 50°.

Calculate the height, in metres, of the tower XY. Give your answer correct to 2 decimal places.

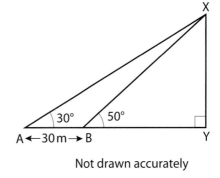

X

30°   50°

A ←30 m→ B   Y

Not drawn accurately

7 *GCSE 1388 January 2003*

Ambletown, Bowtown and Comptown are three towns.

Ambletown is 9.6 km due west of Bowtown. Bowtown is 7.4 km due south of Comptown.

Calculate the bearing of Ambletown from Comptown. Give your answer correct to 1 decimal place.

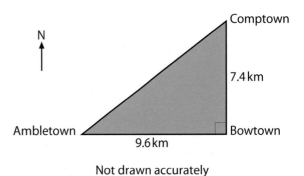

N

Comptown

7.4 km

Ambletown   Bowtown
        9.6 km

Not drawn accurately

(8) *GCSE 1385 June 1999*

The diagram shows the positions of three telephone masts A, B and C.

Mast C is 5 km due east of Mast B.
Mast A is due north of Mast B and 8 km from Mast C.

a Calculate the distance of A from B.
  Give your answer correct to 3 significant figures.

b i Calculate the size of the angle marked x.
   Give your angle correct to 1 decimal place.

 ii Calculate the bearing of A from C.
    Give your answer correct to 1 decimal place.

 iii Calculate the bearing of C from A.
     Give your bearing correct to 1 decimal place.

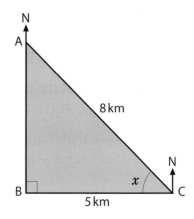

Not drawn accurately

(9) *1998 level 8*

a Cape Point is 7.5 km east and 4.8 km north of Arton.

  Calculate the direct distance from Arton to Cape Point.

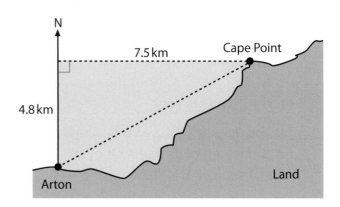

Not drawn accurately

b Bargate is 6 km east and 4 km north of Cape Point.

  Steve wants to sail directly from Cape Point to Bargate.

  On what bearing should he sail? Show your working.

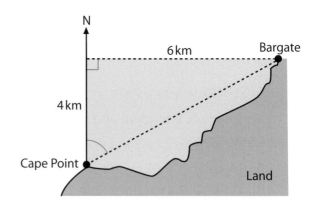

Not drawn accurately

c Anna sails from Cape Point on a bearing of 048°.
  She stops when she is due north of Bargate.
  How far north of Bargate is Anna? Show your working.

GCSE 1387 November 2004

The diagram represents a cuboid ABCDEFGH.

AB = 5 cm

BC = 7 cm

AE = 3 cm

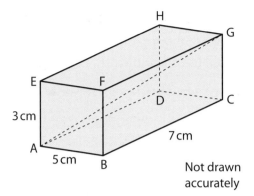

Not drawn accurately

a Calculate the length of AG.

Give your answer correct to 3 significant figures.

b Calculate the size of the angle between AG and the face ABCD.

Give your answer correct to 1 decimal place.

 Points to remember

⊙ If you know two sides of a right-angled triangle:

– use Pythagoras' theorem to work out the length of the third side;

– use trigonometric ratios to find angles.

⊙ If you know one non-right angle and one side of a right-angled triangle:

– use trigonometric ratios to find the lengths of the other sides.

⊙ Use the formula for the area of a circle to find areas of sectors of circles.

5 Graphs, charts and statistics

This lesson will remind you how to interpret graphs, compare distributions and calculate statistics.

Exercise 5

Histograms

A **histogram** represents continuous data so there are no gaps between the bars.

There is a scale on the horizontal axis.

In a histogram, the area of each bar is proportional to the **frequency**.

When a histogram has class intervals with varying widths, the vertical scale is used to plot **frequency density**, where:

$$\text{frequency density} = \frac{\text{frequency}}{\text{class width}}$$

Example 1

The table gives information about the time it takes 50 people who work in the same office to travel to work.

Construct a histogram to show the data.

Time (minutes)	Frequency
$0 < x \leqslant 5$	1
$5 < x \leqslant 10$	4
$10 < x \leqslant 15$	6
$15 < x \leqslant 20$	12
$20 < x \leqslant 25$	16
$25 < x \leqslant 30$	4
$30 < x \leqslant 35$	5
$35 < x \leqslant 40$	2

The data is grouped continuous data.

This data can be represented as a histogram.

As the groups are the same width, use frequency on the vertical axis rather than frequency density.

The horizontal axis is marked with a scale.

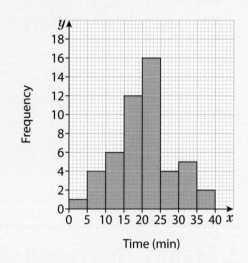

Time (min)

Cumulative frequency

Cumulative frequency is the running total.
It is found by adding all the frequencies up to a certain point in the data.

- ☺ The **median** is the value that is halfway through the data.

- ☺ The **lower quartile** is the value that is a quarter of the way through the data.

- ☺ The **upper quartile** is the value that is three-quarters of the way through the data.

- ☺ The **interquartile range** is a measure of how spread out values are over the middle 50% of data.

  interquartile range = upper quartile − lower quartile

A data set can be organised in a **cumulative frequency table** and plotted to form a **cumulative frequency graph**.

Cumulative frequency curves can be used to **estimate** the median, the lower and upper quartiles and the interquartile range for a large data set.

For a large data set with n values, read off the cumulative frequency axis at:

⊙ $\frac{n}{2}$ for the median;

⊙ $\frac{n}{4}$ for the lower quartile;

⊙ $\frac{3n}{4}$ for the upper quartile.

Use the estimates for the upper and lower quartiles to estimate the interquartile range.

Example 2

This **cumulative frequency graph** shows the amount of time that 50 students spent doing a maths homework.

Estimate the median, upper and lower quartiles, and the interquartile range.

The maximum value for the cumulative frequency is 50.

$\frac{3}{4} \times 50 = 37.5$

Start at 37.5 to read off the upper quartile. The upper quartile is approximately 24.25 minutes.

$\frac{1}{2} \times 50 = 25$

Start at 25 to read off the median. The median is approximately 20.25 minutes.

$\frac{1}{4} \times 50 = 12.5$

Start at 12.5 to read off the lower quartile. The lower quartile is approximately 16 minutes.

An estimate for the interquartile range is

$24.25 - 16 = 8.25$ minutes.

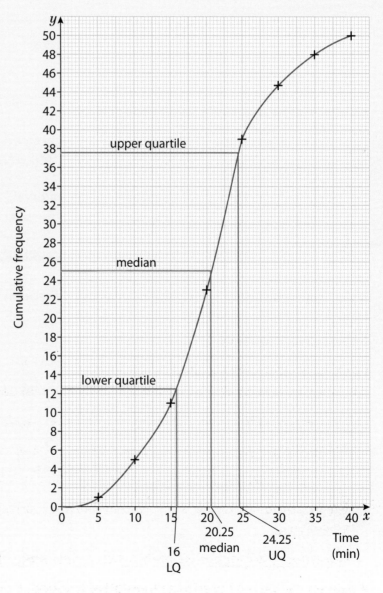

Box plots

Box plots (sometimes called box-and-whisker diagrams) are diagrams that show the spread of data. The median, lower and upper quartiles along with the minimum and maximum values are used to draw a box plot.

They should always be drawn to scale.

Box plots are particularly useful for comparing distributions, when they should be drawn with one above the other using a common scale.

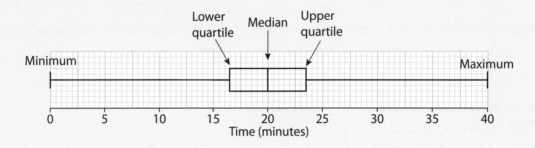

Estimating the mean of a set of grouped data

To calculate an **estimate of the mean** of a set of grouped data, assume that the mean of the data values in each class interval is the **midpoint** of the class interval. Work out:

$$\frac{\text{the sum of (midpoint of class interval} \times \text{frequency)}}{\text{the sum of the frequencies}}$$

For example, this table shows the amount of time spent by 50 pupils on a maths homework.

Time (minutes)	Midpoint of interval	Frequency	Midpoint × frequency
$0 < x \leqslant 5$	2.5	1	2.5
$5 < x \leqslant 10$	7.5	4	30
$10 < x \leqslant 15$	12.5	6	75
$15 < x \leqslant 20$	17.5	12	210
$20 < x \leqslant 25$	22.5	16	360
$25 < x \leqslant 30$	27.5	4	110
$30 < x \leqslant 35$	32.5	5	162.5
$35 < x \leqslant 40$	37.5	2	75
		Total = 50	Total = 1025

The estimated mean time is 1025 ÷ 50 = 20.5 minutes.

You need some graph paper.

1 *2002 level 7*

The percentage charts show information about the wing length of adult blackbirds, measured to the nearest millimetre.

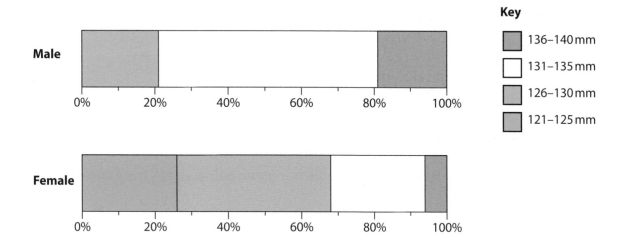

Key

- 136–140 mm
- 131–135 mm
- 126–130 mm
- 121–125 mm

For each statement, write **true**, **false** or **not enough information to say** and explain your answer.

a The smallest male's wing length is larger than the smallest female's wing length.

b The biggest male's wing length is larger than the biggest female's wing length.

2 *2007 level 8*

On a street, there are 100 houses.

   60 are terraced houses.

   30 are semi-detached.

   The rest are detached.

The table shows the mean number of bedrooms in each type of house.

Type of house	Mean number of bedrooms
Terraced	2.5
Semi-detached	3.3
Detached	4.1

What is the mean number of bedrooms per house on this street?

3 *2005 level 8*

Here is information about a data set.

> There are 100 values in the set.
>
> The median is 90.
>
> The mean is 95.

I increase the highest value in the data set by 200.
Now what are the median and the mean of the data set?

4 *1999 level 8*

Thirty pupils took a maths test. The frequency graph below shows the pupils' results.

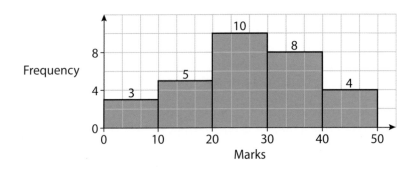

a Draw a cumulative frequency graph of the pupils' results.

b The 30 pupils also took a science test.

The cumulative frequency graph on the right shows their results.

Draw a frequency graph to show their science results.

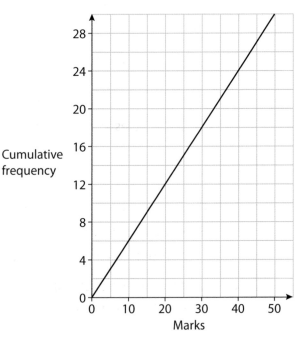

5 *2006 level 8*

The mean of a set of numbers is zero.

For each statement, state whether it **must be true**, **could be true** or **cannot be true**.

a All the numbers in the set are zero.

b The sum of the numbers in the set is zero.

c There are as many positive numbers as negative numbers in the set.

6 *2003 level 8*

Tom did a survey of the age distribution of people at a theme park. He asked 160 people. The cumulative frequency graph shows his results.

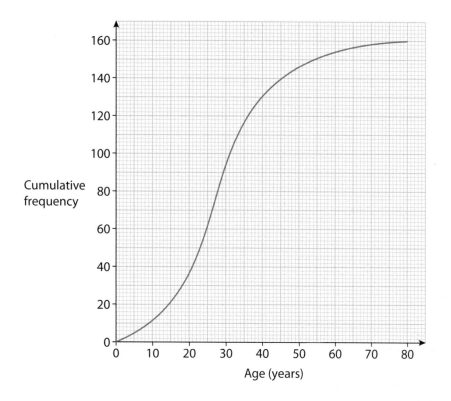

a Use the graph to estimate the median age of people at the theme park.

b Use the graph to estimate the interquartile range of the age of people at the theme park.

c Tom did a similar survey at a flower show. He found that:

the median age was 47 years;

the interquartile range was 29 years.

Compare the age distribution of the people at the flower show with that of the people at the theme park.

2000 level 8

A teacher asked 50 pupils in Year 9 how much time they spent on homework last night. Here are the results.

Time spent on homework (minutes)	Frequency
$0 \leqslant$ time $\leqslant 30$	6
$30 <$ time $\leqslant 60$	14
$60 <$ time $\leqslant 90$	21
$90 <$ time $\leqslant 120$	9
Total	**50**

a Show that an estimate of the mean time spent on homework is 64.8 minutes.

b The teacher used the data to draw a cumulative frequency diagram.

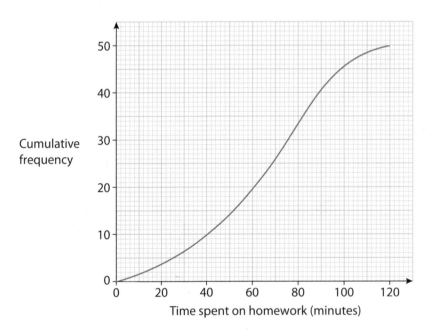

Use the diagram to estimate the median time pupils spent on their homework.

c Use the diagram to estimate how many pupils spent more than 100 minutes on their homework.

8 *GCSE 1387 November 2006*

The table shows information about the ages of 240 people at a club.

Age (*t* years)	Frequency
$15 \leqslant t < 20$	95
$20 \leqslant t < 25$	90
$25 \leqslant t < 30$	35
$30 \leqslant t < 35$	15
$35 \leqslant t < 40$	5

a Copy and complete the cumulative frequency table.

Age (*t* years)	Cumulative frequency
$15 \leqslant t < 20$	
$15 \leqslant t < 25$	
$15 \leqslant t < 30$	
$15 \leqslant t < 35$	
$15 \leqslant t < 40$	

b Copy this grid on graph paper.

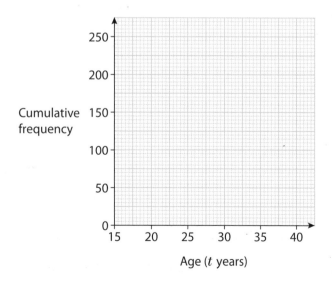

Draw the cumulative frequency graph for your table.

c Use your graph to find an estimate for the median age of the people.

Extension problem

 9 *1999 Exceptional performance*

The graph shows the rate at which cars left a car park from 5 pm to 6 pm.

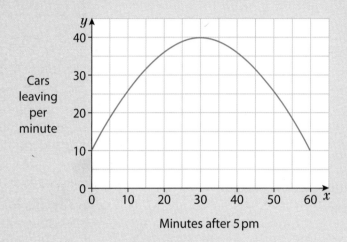

Minutes after 5 pm

The lowest rate was 10 cars per minute at 5 pm and 6 pm.
The highest rate was 40 cars per minute at 5:30 pm.

$y = ax^2 + bx + c$ is the relationship between y, the number of cars leaving per minute, and x, the number of minutes after 5 pm.

a Explain how you can work out from the graph that the value of c is 10.

b Use the graph to form equations to work out the values of a and b in the equation $y = ax^2 + bx + c$. Show your working.

c The table below uses the same data for cars leaving the car park.
It shows the number of cars leaving the car park during the periods specified.

Number n of minutes after 5 pm	$0 \leqslant n < 5$	$5 \leqslant n < 10$	$10 \leqslant n < 20$	$20 \leqslant n < 50$	$50 \leqslant n < 60$
Number of cars leaving	74	115	248	1174	189

d On graph paper, draw the histogram to show the information in the table.
Write down the frequency density for each rectangle of the histogram.

Points to remember

⊙ A cumulative frequency graph can be used to find the median and the interquartile range.

⊙ Graphs and statistics can be used to compare distributions.

Answers to
How well are you doing?

N7.1 Powers and roots

1 a $a = 4, b = 3$ b $c = 7$

2 a 100   b 6

3 a $0.8n$ b $n^2, \sqrt{n}$ and $\dfrac{1}{n}$
    c $0.8n, \sqrt{n}$ and $\dfrac{1}{n}$ d $n^2, 0.8n$

4 a 8   b $2\sqrt{2}$
    c $5\sqrt{2}$ d $\dfrac{\sqrt{2}}{2} + 1$

5 a Using Pythagoras, the two shorter sides of the rectangle are each:
$$\sqrt{3^2 + 3^2} = \sqrt{18} = 3\sqrt{2}$$
Using Pythagoras, the two longer sides are each:
$$\sqrt{4^2 + 4^2} = \sqrt{32} = 4\sqrt{2}$$
The perimeter is twice the shorter side plus twice the longer side, or:
$$6\sqrt{2} + 8\sqrt{2} = 14\sqrt{2}$$

    b Using Pythagoras, the two shorter sides of the rectangle are each:
$$\sqrt{2^2 + 4^2} = \sqrt{20} = 2\sqrt{5}$$
Using Pythagoras, the two longer sides are each:
$$\sqrt{3^2 + 6^2} = \sqrt{45} = 3\sqrt{5}$$
The perimeter is twice the shorter side plus twice the longer side, or:
$$4\sqrt{5} + 6\sqrt{5} = 10\sqrt{5}$$

    c Length of one side of the square is $\sqrt{29}$, so the square of one side is 29.

29 expressed as the sum of two integer squares is
$$25 + 4 = 5^2 + 2^2$$
So a possible square is:

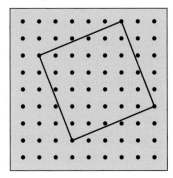

d Assume that the trapezium is isosceles. The perimeter is the sum of the two parallel sides, plus the sum of the two sloping sides, which are equal in length.

Assume that the sum of the two parallel sides is 6, and that the shorter side is 1 and the longer side is 5.

Assume that the sum of the two sloping sides is $4\sqrt{2}$, so one side is $2\sqrt{2}$. The square of $2\sqrt{2}$ is 8, and 8 is $2^2 + 2^2$.

So a possible trapezium is:

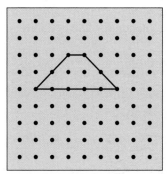

A7.1 Linear graphs and inequalities

1 Length of line is
$$\sqrt{(14 + 10)^2 + (10 - 3)^2} = \sqrt{24^2 + 7^2} = 25$$

2 Midpoint is
$$\left(\dfrac{4 - 6}{2}, \dfrac{5 + 3}{2}\right) \text{ or } (-1, 4)$$

3 a Any equation of the form $y = \frac{1}{2}x + c$
    b Any equation of the form $y = mx + 1$
    c $y = -2x + 26$

4 $3x + 7y = 18$ (i)
    $x + 2y = 5$ (ii)

    Rearrange (i) $x = 5 - 2y$ (iii)
    Substitute in (ii) $3(5 - 2y) + 7y = 18$
                      $15 - 6y + 7y = 18$
                             $y = 3$
    Substitute in (iii) $x = 5 - (2 \times 3)$
                      $x = -1$

5 a $-1, 0, 1, 2, 3$
    b   i $x \geqslant 3.5$ ii 4

6 The **unshaded** region is the required region.

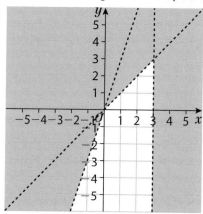

N7.2 Decimals and accuracy

1 a 9.43×10^{12} km **b** 7.3554×10^{13} km

2 a India **b** Gambia

c Population per km² in UK is
$$\frac{6.0 \times 10^7}{2.4 \times 10^5} = 2.5 \times 10^2 = 250$$
Population per km² in USA is
$$\frac{2.8 \times 10^8}{9.3 \times 10^6} = \frac{2.8 \times 10^2}{9.3} = 30 \text{ to 2 s.f.}$$
So, on average, there are $250 - 30 = 220$ more people per km² in the UK than in the USA.

3 $\frac{600}{3 \times 10} = 20$

4 a length **b** area

c area **d** volume

5 1146.7 cm³ = 1150 cm³ (to 3 s.f.)

6 a 100.5 m **b** 10.515 seconds

c 9.557 774 608 m/s **d** 9.453 681 71 m/s

7 a Width of canal is AB.

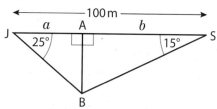

$AB = a \tan 25° = (100 - a) \tan 15°$
So $a(\tan 25° + \tan 15°) = 100 \tan 15°$
$$a = \frac{100 \tan 15°}{\tan 25°} + \tan 15° = 36.492\ldots\text{m}$$
$AB = 17$ m to the nearest m

b The width of the canal is greatest when JS is the maximum (i.e. 101 m) and the angles are the maximum (i.e. 27° and 17°).
$$a = \frac{101 \tan 17°}{\tan 27° + \tan 17°} = 37.876\ldots\text{m}$$
$AB = a \tan 27° = 19$ m to the nearest m

S7.1 Enquiry 1

1 50 girls are one tenth of the total number of girls. One tenth of the number of girls in Year 8 is 5.

2 a The total number of pupils is 1500.
The number in the Year 7 sample should be
$\frac{350}{1500} \times 100 = 23$ to the nearest whole number.
The other years are calculated similarly.

Year 7: 23, Year 8: 22, Year 9: 19,
Year 10: 19, Year 11: 17

b random sample

3 a

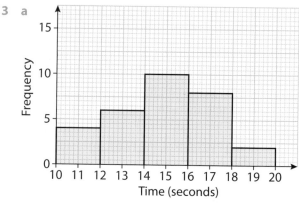

b The histogram shows that there were a few very fast pupils and a few very slow ones.

4 a

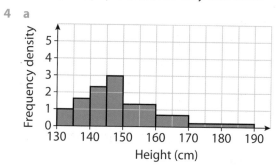

b The histogram shows that most people had heights less than 150 cm; only a very few were taller than this.

5 a 1280 **b** 1420

G7.1 Measures and mensuration

1 a Area A $= \frac{1}{8}\pi r^2 = \frac{1}{8}\pi \times 5^2 = 9.82$ cm (to 2 d.p.)
Area B $= \frac{1}{5}\pi r^2 = \frac{1}{5}\pi \times 4^2 = 10.05$ cm (to 2 d.p.)
So Area B is larger.

b $C = \pi D$
Perimeter A $= \frac{1}{8}\pi D + 2r$
$= \frac{1}{8}\pi \times 10 + 2 \times 5 = 13.93$ cm (to 2 d.p.)
Perimeter B $= \frac{1}{5}\pi D + 2r$
$= \frac{1}{5}\pi \times 8 + 2 \times 4 = 13.03$ cm (to 2 d.p.)
So Perimeter A is larger.

c Area of semicircle $= \frac{1}{2}\pi r^2$
$= \frac{1}{2}\pi \times 4^2 = 8\pi$
Area of circle $= \pi r^2 = 8\pi$
$r^2 = 8$
$r = 2.83$ cm (to 2 d.p.)

2 Volume of cylinder $= \pi r^2 h = 4.5$ cm^3
$\pi \times 2.5^2 \times h = 4.5$
$h = 0.23$ cm (to 2 d.p.)

3 a 1.01×10^5 N/m^2 b $16.7 : 1$
c 5.79×10^{10} km$^3 = 6 \times 10^{10}$ km^3 (to 1 s.f.)

4 a Volume of prism is
area of cross-section $\times$ height
Area of cross-section is
$(2x \times 4x) - (2x \times x) = 8x^2 - 2x^2 = 6x^2$
Height $= 3x$
Volume of prism $= 6x^2 \times 3x = 18x^3$
b $90°$
c Volume of prism $= 8x^3 \sin a$
$8x^3 \sin a = 500$
$x^3 = 125$
$x = 5$ cm

5 a 1150 cm^3 (to 3 s.f.)   b $V = \frac{1}{3}\pi h a^2$

6 Area of windscreen $= 132 \times 72 = 9504$ cm^2
Area cleaned is
$\frac{160}{360} \times \pi \times 60^2 - \frac{160}{360} \times \pi \times 20^2$
$= \frac{4}{9}\pi(60^2 - 20^2) = 4468.04$ cm^2
Percentage cleaned is
$\frac{4468.04}{9504} \times 100 = 47.0\%$ (to 1 d.p.)

A7.2 Expressions and formulae

1 a The first way.
b 1320 kg

2 a $(y + 3)^2 = y^2 + 6y + 9$
b $y^2 + 7y + 10$
c $y^2 - 12y + 36$
d $6y^2 - y - 40$

3 b $y + 15$ c $2y$
d $y + 3a$

4 a a b $a - b$
c $\frac{a^2 - b^2}{a - b} = \frac{(a - b)(a + b)}{a - b} = a + b$

5 $x^2 + 7x + 6 = (x + 1)(x + 6)$ or $(x + 6)(x + 1)$
$x^2 + 7x + 10 = (x + 2)(x + 5)$ or $(x + 5)(x + 2)$
$x^2 + 7x + 12 = (x + 3)(x + 4)$ or $(x + 4)(x + 3)$

6 $n + n + 1 + n + 2 + n + 3 = 4n + 6$
$(n + 3)(n + 2) - (n + 1)n = 4n + 6$

G7.2 Trigonometry 1

1 a 17.2 cm (to 1 d.p.)   b $35.0°$ (to 1 d.p.)
2 a 10.9 cm (to 1 d.p.)   b $24.6°$ (to 1 d.p.)
3 $x = 11.3$ cm, $y = 32.1$ cm (to 1 d.p.)
4 9.12 cm (to 3 s.f.)
5 $13.5°$ (to 1 d.p.)
6 $AB^2 = 10^2 + 10^2 = 14.4$ cm
$AB = BC = CA = 14.4$ cm
Perimeter $= 3 \times 14.4$ cm $= 42.4$ cm (to 1 d.p.)

N7.3 Proportional reasoning

1 a In 1997 the company employed 10% of
$4400 = 440$ more people.
b 4000×1.1^2
c 1995 n people
1996 $n \times \frac{80}{100} = 0.8n$
1997 $0.8n \times \frac{110}{100} = 0.88n$

2 a D   b C   c B
3 a $F = \frac{36}{x^2}$ b 9   c 0.75
4 85% of original price $= £38.25$
Original price $= \frac{38.25}{85} \times 100 = £45$
5 $£348.48$
6 a $\frac{m}{42} = \frac{40}{60}$
$m = \frac{40}{60} \times 42 = 28$ cm
b $C = \frac{1}{2}\pi h(a^2 + ab + b^2)$
$= \frac{1}{2}\pi \times 42(60^2 + 60 \times 36 + 36^2)$
$= 21\pi(3600 + 2160 + 1296)$
$= 21\pi \times 7056 = 465\,508.63$
1 litre $= 1000$cm^3
so $C = 466$ litres (to nearest litre)
c Ratio of widths is $40 : 60 = 2 : 3$
Ratio of capacities is
$\frac{1}{2}\pi.2(4 + 4 + 4) : \frac{1}{2}\pi.3(9 + 9 + 9) = 8 : 27$

G7.3 Geometrical reasoning

1 a i $65°$
ii Angle at centre $= 2 \times$ angle at circumference
b $125°$
2 a $\triangle OAB$ is isosceles, so $\angle ABO = \angle BAO = x$
$\triangle OCB$ is isosceles, so $\angle CBO = \angle BCO = y$
b $\angle ABC = x + y$
$\angle COB = 180° - 2y$
$\angle BOA = 180° - 2x$
$\angle COB + \angle BOA = 180°$
$= 180° - 2y + 180° - 2x$
so $x + y = 90°$

3 a 126°   b 27°   c 63°

4 a ∠BCA = ∠DAC (alternate angles)
    ∠CBD = ∠ADB (alternate angles)
    ∠BXC = ∠DXA (vertically opposite)
    So △BCX is congruent to △DAX (AAA).

  b ∠ABX = ∠CDX (alternate angles)
    ∠BAX = ∠DCX (alternate angles)
    ∠BXA = ∠DXC (vertically opposite)
    So △ABX is congruent to △CDX (AAA).

5 a BC = DC (sides of square)
    ∠FDC = ∠FCD = ∠ECB = ∠EBC = 60°
    (equilateral triangles)
    So △BEC is congruent to △DCF (ASA).

  b BE = DF (congruent triangles)
    ∠FDC = ∠CBE (congruent triangles)
    ∠CDB = ∠CBD (angles in an isos. triangle)
    So ∠FDB = ∠EBD
    If BE = DF and ∠FDB = ∠EBD, then the
    trapezium DBEF is an isosceles trapezium.
    So the diagonals are equal and ED = BF.
    In the parallelogram BEGF,
    BF = EG (properties of a parallelogram)
    So ED = EG.

6 a 8 cm   b 96 cm³

S7.2 Probability 1

1 a 0.51   b 0.34

2 P(white on 1st pick) $= \dfrac{n-6}{n}$

  P(white on 2nd pick) $= \dfrac{n-7}{n-1}$

  P(white on 1st and 2nd pick) $= \dfrac{n-6}{n} \times \dfrac{n-7}{n-1} = \dfrac{1}{2}$
  $(n-6)(n-7) = \frac{1}{2}n(n-1)$
  $2(n^2 - 13n + 42) = n^2 - n$
  $2n^2 - n^2 - 26n + n + 84 = 0$
  $n^2 - 25n + 84 = 0$

3 a 0.88   b 0.08
  c 0.93, 0.43   d 0.0049
  e 0.1849

4 a 0.000 625   b 0.048 75
  c 120

5 a Outcomes from counter 1 affect probabilities
    for counter 2.

  b Counter 1   Counter 2

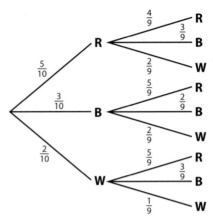

  c 93

6 a $\dfrac{2}{9} \times \dfrac{1}{8} = \dfrac{1}{36}$

  b $\dfrac{3}{9} \times \dfrac{2}{8} \times \dfrac{1}{7} = \dfrac{1}{84}$ (one line)
    There are 8 possible lines.
    P(straight line) $= 8 \times \dfrac{1}{84} = \dfrac{8}{84}$ or $\dfrac{2}{21}$

  c $\dfrac{4}{9} \times \dfrac{3}{8} \times \dfrac{2}{7} \times \dfrac{1}{6} = \dfrac{1}{126}$ (one square)
    There are 6 possible squares.
    P(square) $= 6 \times \dfrac{1}{126} = \dfrac{6}{126}$ or $\dfrac{1}{21}$

A7.3 Solving equations

1   $\dfrac{5(2y-3)}{3y} = 3$
    $5(2y-3) = 9y$
    $10y - 15 = 9y$
    $y = 15$

2   $(x-25)^2 = x^2 - 25$
    $x^2 - 50x + 625 = x^2 - 25$
    $50x = 650$
    $x = 13$

3 a $(x+2)(x+4)$
  b $x = -2$ or $x = -4$

4 a $x(3x+4) + 3x(2x-7) = 85$,
    so $9x^2 - 17x - 85 = 0$
  b i $x = 4.16$ or $x = -2.27$ (to 3 s.f.)
     ii 4.16 cm

5 $x = 1.8, y = 4.7$ (to 1 d.p.)
  $x = -2.6, y = -4.3$ (to 1 d.p.)

6 $x = 1.83, y = 4.65$ (to 2 d.p.)
  $x = -2.63, y = -4.25$ (to 2 d.p.)

7 a The two pairs of numbers are $-2, 3$ and $2, -3$.
  b Pupils' number pairs

G7.4 Transformations and vectors

1 a $\begin{pmatrix} 6 \\ 2 \end{pmatrix}$ b 6.32 units (to 2 d.p.)

2 a (4, 6) b $\begin{pmatrix} -3 \\ -4 \end{pmatrix}$ c 5 units

3 a $2(2\mathbf{c} + \mathbf{a})$

   b $\overrightarrow{OQ} = 3(2\mathbf{c} + \mathbf{a})$
   so OPQ is a straight line

4 a i $\overrightarrow{BC} = \mathbf{a}$ ii $\overrightarrow{BM} = \frac{1}{2}\mathbf{a}$

   iii $\overrightarrow{OM} = \frac{1}{2}(2\mathbf{b} + \mathbf{a})$

   b $\overrightarrow{AM} = \mathbf{b} - \frac{1}{2}\mathbf{a}$ and $\overrightarrow{AX} = 2\mathbf{b} - \mathbf{a}$
   so AMX is a straight line

5 a $\mathbf{a} + \mathbf{b}$

   b $\overrightarrow{DX} = \overrightarrow{DC} + \overrightarrow{CX} = 2\mathbf{a}$
   so $\overrightarrow{DX}$ is parallel to $\overrightarrow{AB}$

6 a i $\overrightarrow{PR} = 5\mathbf{p}$ ii $\overrightarrow{QS} = 2\mathbf{q}$

   iii $\overrightarrow{PQ} = 4\mathbf{p} - \mathbf{q}$

   b $3\mathbf{p} - 2\mathbf{q}$

S7.3 Enquiry 2

1 a False, as the median was about 44.5.

   b True, as the LQ is about 33.5, the UQ is about
   56.5 so the IQR = 56.5 − 33.5 = 23.

   c False, as the graph for paper 2 is always lower.

2 a Median for group A is 26, and for group B is 29.

   b Group A, as the distance between 24 and 29 is
   greater than that between 27 and 31.

   c For example:

   The two groups could have collected the
   samples at different times of year.

   Group A could have picked from one side of the
   tree and group B from the other side.

   One group could have picked from the tree, the
   other from the ground.

   Group B may have collected first and taken
   most of the larger ones.

3 a Q3

   b Q3 is July to September which includes school
   summer holidays.

   c 2700, 2700

   d The trend increased slightly and then began to
   decrease.

4 a

Time t (minutes)	Frequency density	Frequency
$17 \leqslant t < 22$	16.0	80
$22 \leqslant t < 27$	28.0	140
$27 \leqslant t < 32$	12.4	62
$32 \leqslant t < 52$	1.1	22

b

Time t (minutes)	Frequency destiny	Frequency	Midpoint × frequency
$17 \leqslant t < 22$	16.0	80	1560
$22 \leqslant t < 27$	28.0	140	3430
$27 \leqslant t < 32$	12.4	62	1829
$32 \leqslant t < 52$	1.1	22	924

Estimated total of times
= 1560 + 3430 + 1829 + 924 = 7743
Number of people = 304
Estimated mean $= \frac{7743}{304}$
$= 25.5$ minutes (to 1 d.p.)

c 80 people did better than 22 minutes.
84 did worse than 27 minutes.
So the middle person of the 304 must be in
$22 \leqslant t < 27$ because 140 people are in that
interval.

d The median value is the $\frac{1}{2}(n+1)$th value where
n is the number of people.
So $\frac{304 + 1}{2} = 152.5$
The median value lies between the 152nd and
153rd values, which fall in the $22 \leqslant t < 27$
group. There are 80 values in the first group so
we are looking for the 72nd and 73rd values in
the $22 \leqslant t < 27$ group.
If the 140 values in $22 \leqslant t < 27$ are evenly
spaced, then
152nd value: $((27 - 22) \times \frac{72}{140}) + 22$
$= 24.57$ (to 2 d.p.)
153rd value: $((27 - 22) \times \frac{73}{140}) + 22$
$= 24.61$ (to 2 d.p.)
The 152.5th value will lie between these two
values so
$\frac{1}{2}(24.57 + 24.61) = 24.6$ minutes (to 1 d.p.)

e The distributions are not symmetrical.

f The sample is not typical.

G7.5 Trigonometry 2

1 a   63.4° (to 1 d.p.)   b   70.5° (to 1 d.p.)

2 5.89 cm (to 3 s.f.)

3 76.3° (to 1 d.p.)

4 a   estimated angles are 114°, 246°

   b   estimated angles are 41°, 319°

5 a $\dfrac{a}{\sin A} = \dfrac{b}{\sin B}$

$$\frac{x}{\frac{5}{6}} = \frac{x-1}{\sin 30°}$$

$$\frac{6x}{5} = \frac{x-1}{\frac{1}{2}}$$

$$\frac{1}{2} \times 6x = 5(x-1)$$

$$3x = 5x - 5$$

$$2x = 5$$

$$x = 2.5$$

   b $\sin A = \dfrac{a \sin B}{b}$ $\sin A \leqslant \dfrac{4}{5}$

$$\frac{a \sin B}{b} \leqslant \frac{4}{5}$$

$$\frac{\frac{1}{2}x}{x-1} \leqslant \frac{4}{5}$$

$$\frac{1}{2}x \leqslant \frac{4}{5}(x-1)$$

$$5x \leqslant 8(x-1)$$

$$5x \leqslant 8x - 8$$

$$3x \geqslant 8$$

$$x \geqslant 2.67 \text{ (to 2 d.p.)}$$

6 a $\angle AOC = 126°$, $\angle OCA = 27°$, $\angle CAD = 63°$

   b   Area of a triangle $= \frac{1}{2}ab \sin C$

$$= \frac{1}{2} \times 18 \times 3 \times \sin 63° = 24.1 \text{ cm}^2 \text{ (to 3 s.f.)}$$

   c $a^2 = b^2 + c^2 - 2bc \cos A$

$$= 18^2 + 3^2 - 2 \times 18 \times 3 \cos 63°$$

$$= 333 - 49.0 = 284$$

$$c = 16.9 \text{ cm (to 3 s.f.)}$$

   d $\dfrac{a}{\sin A} = \dfrac{b}{\sin B}$

$$\frac{x}{\sin 27°} = \frac{16.9}{\sin 126°}$$

$$x = \frac{16.9 \sin 27°}{\sin 126°}$$

$$x = 9.48 \text{ cm (to 3 s.f.)}$$

7 a $a^2 = b^2 + c^2 - 2bc \cos A$

$$= 650^2 + 480^2 - 2 \times 650 \times 480 \cos 78°$$

$$= 652\,900 - 129\,736.90$$

$$= 523\,163.10$$

$$a = 723.3 \text{ m}$$

$$b + c = 650 + 480 = 1130 \text{ m}$$

$$1130 - 723.3 = 406.7 \text{ m} = 407 \text{ m (to 3 s.f.)}$$

   b $\dfrac{a}{\sin A} = \dfrac{b}{\sin B}$

$$\sin A = \frac{a \sin B}{b} = \frac{480 \sin 78°}{723.3}$$

$$A = 40.5°$$

$$90° - 40.5° = 49.5°$$

A bearing between 049° and 050°

   c $\sin C = \dfrac{c \sin B}{b} = \dfrac{650 \sin 78°}{723.3}$

$$C = 61.5°$$

$$90° + 61.5° = 151.5°$$

A bearing between 151° and 152°

S7.4 Probability 2

1 a   Because you will get a fractional number of blue counters.

   b

Blue	Red	Green	Yellow
1	6	9	4

2 a   P(North, East, North)

= P(North) × P(East) × P(North)

$$= \frac{1}{4} \times \frac{1}{4} \times \frac{1}{4} = \frac{1}{64}$$

   b $\dfrac{3}{64}$

3 a   99

   b   Pupils' answers, for example, births, deaths, migration, hunting, change to habitat

4 a   Total of 50 points = 5 × 10 points

P(10 points) = 0.23

P(10 points 5 times) $= 0.23^5 = 0.00064$

   b   Total of 49 points

= 1 × 9 points and 4 × 10 points

P(9) = 0.17, P(10) = 0.23

P(9 points and 10 points 4 times)

$= 0.17 \times 0.23^4 \times 5$ ways of getting 49 points:

     (9, 10, 10, 10, 10)

     (10, 9, 10, 10, 10)

     (10, 10, 9, 10, 10)

     (10, 10, 10, 9, 10)

     (10, 10, 10, 10, 9)

So P(49) $= 5 \times (0.17 \times 0.23^4)$

$$= 0.00238$$

   c   P(4 or fewer) = P(4 or 3 or 2 or 1)

= 0.07 + 0.05 + 0.02 + 0.02 = 0.16

P(4 or fewer 5 times)

$= 0.16^5 = 0.00010$

d P(18 or more) = P(18, 19 or 20)

P(18) is the sum of

P(8 and 10) and P(10 and 8) and P(9 and 9)

P(19) is the sum of

P(9 and 10) and P(10 and 9)

P(20) is P(10 and 10)

So P(18 or more) is

(0.14 × 0.23) + (0.23 × 0.14) + (0.17 × 0.17) +

(0.17 × 0.23) + (0.23 × 0.17) + (0.23 × 0.23)

= 0.224

5 a P(END) = P(E) × P(N) × P(D)

$= \frac{12}{100} \times \frac{6}{99} \times \frac{4}{98} = \frac{4}{13\,475}$

b P(END) + P(EDN) + P(NED) + P(NDE) + P(DEN)

+ P(DNE)

$= 6 \times \frac{4}{13\,475} = \frac{24}{13\,475}$

c

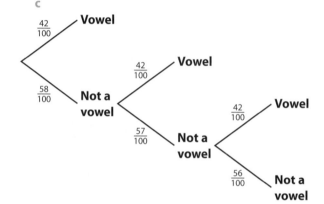

Not vowel + Not vowel and Vowel = 2 points

So P(2 points) $= \frac{58}{100} \times \frac{57}{99} \times \frac{42}{98}$

$= \frac{551}{3850} = 0.143$

d P(2 or fewer)

= P(2) + P(1) + P(0)

= P(NV + NV + V) + P(NV + V) + P(V)

$= \frac{551}{3850} + \frac{58}{100} \times \frac{42}{99} + \frac{42}{100}$

$= \frac{4673}{5775} = 0.809$

A7.4 Exploring graphs

1 a (3, 4) and (3, −4)   **b** 5

c (3.5, 3.5) or (−3.5, −3.5) (to 1 d.p.)

2 $a = 50, b = 50, k = 4$

3 a Graph D   **b** Graph C

c Graph B   **d** Graph A

e Graph E

4 a A (0, 16), B (4, 0), C (−4, 0)

b B_1 (4, 24)

c $y = x^2 + 8$

5 $p = 1.25, q = 4$

6 a 10

b $y = \frac{8a^3}{x^2 + 4a^2}$ $a = 2, y = 1.5$

$1.5 = \frac{8(2^3)}{x^2 + 4(2^2)}$

$1.5(x^2 + 16) = 64$

$x^2 + 16 = 42.67$

$x^2 = 26.67$

$x = \pm 5.16$ (to 3 s.f.)

c $y = \frac{2a}{5}$

$\frac{8a^3}{x^2 + 4a^2} = \frac{2a}{5}$

$40a^3 = 2a(x^2 + 4a)$

$2ax^2 + 8a^3 = 40a^3$

$2ax^2 = 32a^3$

$x^2 = 16a^2$

$x = \pm 4a$

N7.4 Using and applying maths

1 a Area $= \frac{1}{2}(\sqrt{6} - \sqrt{2})(\sqrt{6} + \sqrt{2})$

$= \frac{1}{2}(6 - \sqrt{2} + \sqrt{2} - 2) = 2$ units

b $QR^2 = (\sqrt{6} + \sqrt{2})^2 + (\sqrt{6} - \sqrt{2})^2$

$= 6 + 2\sqrt{12} + 2 + 6 - 2\sqrt{12} + 2 = 16$,

so QR = 4 units

2 3 packs of buns and 5 packs of burgers

3 Let odd numbers be $2a + 1$ and $2b + 1$.

Sum of squares $= (2a + 1)^2 + (2b + 1)^2$

$= 4a^2 + 4a + 4b^2 + 4b + 2$

$= 4(a^2 + a + b^2 + b) + 2$

So sum of squares divided by 4 will have remainder 2.

4 a Sum $= n + n + 1 + n + 2 + n + 3 = 2(2n + 3)$

b Product $= n(n + 3)$

c $n(n + 3) = 2(2n + 3)$ gives $n = -2$ or $n = 3$

d −2, −1, 0, 1 and 3, 4, 5, 6

5 If $n = 6, 6n - 1 = 35$, which is not a prime.

6 a **i** r^2 **ii** $\frac{1}{2}pq$ **iii** $(p + q)^2$

b $4 \times \frac{1}{2}pq + r^2 = 2pq + r^2$

c $2pq + r^2 = (p + q)^2$ gives $r^2 = p^2 + q^2$

7 a **i** $4(a + b + c - 6)$

ii $2(ac + ab + bc - 4a - 4b - 4c + 12)$

iii $(a - 2)(b - 2)(c - 2)$

b $8 + 12(a - 2) + 6(a - 2)^2 + (a - 2)^3$

$= 8 + 12a - 24 + 6(a^2 - 4a + 4) +$

$(a - 2)(a^2 - 4a + 4)$

$= 12a - 16 + 6a^2 - 24a + 24 + a^3 - 4a^2 +$

$4a - 2a^2 + 8a - 8$

$= a^3$

Index

2D shapes 45, 72, 115, 125, 264, 267, 281
3D shapes 45, 72, 77–8, 81, 83, 109, 115–16, 118, 125, 171, 227, 264, 267, 281

acceleration 44
accuracy 32–50, 91, 122, 148, 198, 304, 306
acute-angled triangle 277
adjacent 119, 122, 265, 385–6
algebra 6, 18, 29, 97, 99, 104, 106, 113, 176, 201, 212–16, 308, 330, 338, 341, 343, 345, 346–7, 356, 358
algorithm 6
Al-Khwarizmi 6
alternate segment theorem 160
amplitude 322–4
angle of depression 121–4
angle of elevation 121–4, 387
approximation 32–5, 37–8, 48, 54, 89, 90, 94, 112, 252, 337, 358, 373
aquariums 178–9
Arabic 6
arc 72–5, 82, 85, 93, 104, 110, 386
Archimedes 42, 77, 81, 338
architecture 164, 221
arguments 338, 345
assumptions 34, 292, 298, 307, 336–7
astronomy 36, 210, 222, 264, 278, 311, 319, 375
Augustus 127
average 35, 43, 48–9, 51, 65, 68–9, 141, 201, 212, 241, 251, 258, 343, 376, 378
axes 16, 22, 57–8, 274, 317–20, 322–3, 380

Babylonia 208
bearing 121, 124, 222–4, 226, 230, 284, 288, 387–8
Bhaskara II 210
Big Bang 36, 134
binostat 301
bisector 167, 328–30
box plots 240, 252–4, 261–2, 392
Boyle's Law 199
bracket key 33

brackets 7, 97, 99–103, 105, 113, 353–4, 356, 377
Brahmagupta 210

calculations 1, 6, 10, 32, 34–5, 40, 48, 108, 145, 227, 278, 366, 374, 377
calculator display 34, 49
capacity 147
capture-recapture method 289–92
card games 298
Cardan, Jerome 367
Cardano, Girolamo 180
Cartesian 16
census 54, 240, 251, 289
chance 52, 54, 186–7, 189, 289, 296, 300, 303
charts 389, 393
checking procedures 306
chords 75, 150–4, 157, 159, 160, 164, 168, 170, 177, 288, 362, 367
circle theorems 150, 153, 156, 160
circles 8–9, 72, 75–7, 90, 93, 155, 164, 168, 176, 199, 329, 362, 364, 389
circular arc 72, 93
circumference 40, 43, 45, 47, 72, 75, 77, 79, 81–2, 110, 117, 146, 152–7, 159–64, 170, 333, 363–4, 367
class interval 56–7, 59–62, 64, 250–1, 254–5, 257, 389, 392
class width 56, 59–60, 62–4, 254–7, 389
coefficient 206, 312
collecting data 55
combinations 27, 184, 220, 236, 274
combined events 180, 184, 193–4, 196–7, 289, 296, 303, 367
combined outcomes 181–2
common factors 97, 99
compass 74, 110, 118, 150
compound interest 127–30, 145, 147
computers 26, 31, 149, 198–9, 202, 213–14, 220, 227, 241, 264, 274, 309, 312, 315–17, 319, 322, 325, 328, 337, 370
concentric circles 8

conclusions 30, 70, 148–9, 178, 198, 238, 306–7, 337

conditional probability 189, 193

cones 72, 74, 77–83, 91, 93, 96, 110–11, 125, 173, 175, 177, 340, 359

congruency 168

congruent shapes 165, 168

congruent triangles 150, 164, 166–9, 171, 176

conjecture 107, 109, 326–7

constant of proportionality 131, 134–5, 139, 142

constants 275, 324

constructions 150, 171

contexts 198, 289, 303, 306, 336, 338

continuous data 51, 55–6, 59, 254, 318, 378, 389–90

conversion 77

coordinate grid 16, 23

coordinates 1, 12–14, 16, 21, 23, 28, 89, 99, 232, 236, 321, 325, 329–30, 333–4, 359, 382

cosine 119, 122, 264–5, 271–2, 278–9, 281–2, 285–6, 319–21, 381

cosmology 36

costs 16–17, 23–6, 127–30, 138–9, 147, 336–7, 348, 379

Coxeter, Harold Scott MacDonald 362

cross-section 30, 78, 80, 88, 95, 113, 117, 179

cubes 4–6, 79, 135–8, 172–3, 211, 267, 338, 340, 347, 358

cube root 4–6, 173

cubic equation 309, 311

cubic functions 308, 381

cuboid 31, 43, 45, 47, 78, 104, 116–17, 129, 174, 179, 205, 211, 266, 347, 389

cultures 221, 341

cumulative frequency 240, 245–51, 254, 261, 390–1, 394–8

cumulative frequency tables 240, 245, 261

cyclic quadrilateral 156–64, 363, 367

cylinders 39, 45, 72, 77–83, 85, 88, 91, 93–4, 104, 110–11, 118, 172, 174–5, 178, 211, 340, 359

da Vinci, Leonardo 221

Dantzig, George B 26

decimal multipliers 127, 130, 348, 352

decimal places 2, 5, 12, 40, 43–4, 105, 203, 320, 380, 387

decimals 5, 32–50, 206

deltahedra 341

deltahedron 339

denominators 7–10, 97–9, 115, 122, 125, 200–2

Descartes, René 1, 3, 16

designs 179

diameter 14–15, 35, 39–40, 43, 47, 73, 75, 79–83, 88, 111–12, 118, 141, 146, 152–3, 155–6, 163, 176, 179, 364

dice 186, 191, 194–5, 295–300, 372

dimensions 18, 30–2, 45–8, 83, 115, 129, 147, 286

direct proportion 131– 8, 142–4, 337, 358

discrete data 51, 56, 59, 247

displacement 222–4, 226, 228, 230

distribution 31, 59–60, 240, 251–2, 254–5, 261, 263, 301–2, 389, 392, 395, 398

Doctrine of Fluxions 131

dodecahedron 338

Earth 38, 48, 94, 112, 134, 141, 374–6

economics 24, 26, 51, 180

Elements, The 150

elimination method 354

ellipse 89–90

Emerson, William 131

engineering 271

enlargements 171

equations 216, 377

equidistant 15, 267, 328–30

equilateral triangles 87, 105, 109, 117, 126, 152, 177

estimates 35, 217, 248, 287, 290, 337, 391

Euclid 150, 208

Euler, Leonhard 3

evidence 251, 254, 367

evolution 134

examinations 348, 373

experiment 51, 54, 91, 182–3, 199, 302

experimental probability 180, 197, 298

exponent 318

exponential functions 308, 316, 318, 333, 381, 384

factorisation 97, 102–3, 113–14, 203–7, 212–3, 216, 309, 353, 355–6, 378–9, 381

Fermat, Pierre de 180

Fibonacci, Leonardo 341–2

first significant figure 32, 35

five-figure summary 240, 243–4, 252, 261

formulae 72, 84, 97–114, 268, 356, 358

Foster, Sir Norman 164

fractions 4–5, 7–8, 79, 87, 97, 99, 127, 200–1, 206, 348–9, 373, 377

fractional indices 3

fractional powers 1, 4, 6, 10

Franklin, Benjamin 91
frequency density 62, 64, 69, 254–7, 263, 389–90, 398
frequency diagram 56, 59, 396
frieze patterns 221
frustum 72, 78, 84, 91, 93
function notation 324
functions 272, 274, 308, 311, 314, 316, 324, 333, 356, 381

Galton, Sir Francis 242, 301
generalisation 104
geometric problems 231–2, 235
geometrical reasoning 150–77, 362
Geometrie, La 3
geometry 77, 150, 221, 362
Gherardo 6
glide reflection 220–1
gradient 14–15, 131–2, 310, 329, 357, 361
graph plotter 31, 103, 202, 213–14, 309, 312, 315, 317, 319, 322, 325, 328
graphical representation 61
graphics calculator 22, 31, 103, 202, 213–14, 274, 309, 312, 315, 317, 319, 322, 325, 328, 353
gravity 44, 375
Great Trigonometric Survey 119
Greeks 6, 42
grouped data 250, 392
grouped frequency 56–7, 60–1, 69, 245–7, 249, 251

Hamilton, Sir William 227
Harriot, Thomas 311
hectares 25, 46
hemisphere 79
Hérigone 319
Heron 104–5, 268
Heron's formula 104–5, 268
hexagons 105, 167, 174, 237, 339, 366
Hipparchus 319
Hisab al-jabr 6
histograms 51, 56, 58–64, 68–9, 240, 254–7, 261, 263, 389–90, 398
hypotenuse 8, 82, 101, 116, 118–19, 165, 168, 171, 207, 265, 271, 385–6

icosahedron 338
ICT 148, 198, 202–3, 213–15, 306, 336
independent events 180–3, 186, 191, 193, 195, 199, 368, 372

index form 1, 3, 373
index laws 1, 4, 6, 373
indices 1, 3, 39, 97, 99, 373, 377
industry 24, 26
inequalities 12–29, 377–9, 381–2
integers 1, 3, 5, 7–8, 11, 18–19, 22, 29, 36, 39, 87, 106, 109, 114, 202, 204, 206, 311, 314, 341–3, 346, 355, 373, 377–9, 384
intercept 14–15
Internet 51, 147, 221, 341, 344
interpretation 30, 51, 61, 68, 148, 178, 198, 240, 254, 261, 306, 336, 389
interquartile range 242–4, 248–9, 261–2, 390–1, 395, 398
intersection 18, 155, 212, 214–5, 330, 364
inverse functions 119
inverse proportion 127, 138, 141–2, 145
investigation 107, 109
investment 129–30
irrational numbers 1, 5–6
isometry 221
isosceles triangle 13, 77, 106, 118, 151–4, 157, 161–2, 167, 169, 226, 234, 363, 365

Kantorovich, Leonid 24
kinetic energy 137
kite 105, 120, 237, 352

language 70
Laplace, Pierre 289
Latin 3, 6, 208, 222, 319
limitations 148, 198, 306
line of symmetry 119
line segment 12–13, 225
linear equations 14, 16, 21, 200–1, 213–16, 353, 356, 377–8, 381
linear expressions 100–1, 103, 208
linear function 325–7
linear graphs 12–29, 312
linear programming 24, 26
loci 308, 328
locus 328–30
lower bound 39, 41–4, 49
lower quartile 243–4, 248–50, 390–1
lowest common denominator 200–1

M81 Galaxy 38
magic number 106–7

magic square 106–7

magnets 140, 146, 315

magnitude 222–31, 235–6

mass 94, 133, 375

mathematical modelling 26

mean 12, 54, 65, 67, 241–2, 250–1, 257, 263, 291, 370, 392–6

measurements 32, 39, 41–2, 45, 48, 50–1, 205, 216, 380

measures 18, 41–2, 46, 50, 83–4, 211, 242, 250, 331

median 13, 241–4, 248–50, 252, 254, 256, 258, 261–3, 390–2, 394–8

mensuration 72–96

Mere, Chevalier de 296

method of elimination 16, 18, 355

method of substitution 18

methods 18, 26, 30, 51, 68, 148, 178, 198, 289, 292, 306, 336

midpoints 12–15, 28, 65, 118, 151, 153, 167, 169–70, 232–3, 235–7, 243, 250–1, 265, 267, 286, 329, 362, 392

Miller, JCP 340

Mises, Richard von 292

modal class 250

mode 241

Moon 278, 375

Moscow Papyrus 84

moving averages 65–7, 240, 257–62

mutually exclusive outcomes 181, 183–4, 186, 193–4, 293–4, 367, 372

myriad 42

negative integers 1, 3, 373, 377

negative numbers 19, 21

negative powers 1, 10, 39

Neumann, John von 26

Newton, Sir Isaac 1, 375

newtons 133, 140, 230

Nobel Prize 24, 26

nonagon 106

non-linear equations 200, 214–16

non-routine problems 198, 338, 345

non-zero digit 32, 35

nth root 4, 6, 377

number generator 52, 54

number line 19–21

numerals 6

numerator 7, 9, 97–9, 201

obtuse 278, 279

octagon 9, 101, 136, 360, 366, 387

octahedron 338–40

operations 24, 148, 198, 306, 336, 381

optimisation 24

orbit 376

oscillation frequency 144

outcomes 181–6, 188–93, 199, 293–4, 296, 367–8, 372

Pappus of Alexandria 338

papyrus 84

parallel lines 15, 361

parallelogram 14, 104, 170, 177, 228, 234–7, 270, 280

Pascal, Blaise 180, 296, 300, 302

patterns 59, 61, 107, 109, 148, 198–1, 220–1, 260, 306, 336

Pearson, Karl 61

pendulum 44, 74, 143

pentagon 119, 133, 339

percentage 43, 67, 74, 87, 96, 127, 129–30, 132, 145, 149, 256, 348–9, 352, 370, 376, 393

perimeter 8, 11, 13, 18, 30, 41, 45, 72–5, 89–90, 93, 104, 109, 126, 133, 136, 174, 268, 387

periodic 271, 275, 319, 321–2, 324

perpendicular 14–15, 28, 30, 78–9, 82, 104–5, 110–11, 118, 150–1, 153, 157, 160, 164, 167, 170, 206, 265, 278, 285, 287, 325, 328–30, 357, 361–2

perspectives 148, 198, 306, 336

Peterson, Carl George Johannes 289

physicists 375

planets 222, 278, 376

planning data 55

Plato 338

Platonic solid 338–9

polygonal faces 78

polygons 106, 109, 168, 171, 175, 270, 338–9

polyhedra 338, 341

polynomial functions 308, 311, 313–14, 325–7, 333, 384

population 34, 43, 48, 51–4, 242, 250–1, 254–5, 289–92, 303–4, 376

position vector 232, 233, 235

positive integers 7, 206, 311, 314, 342, 384

positive numbers 10, 19, 21, 395

power key 33

powers 1–3, 39, 42, 97, 99, 311, 373, 377

predictions 240, 251, 257, 260–1

presentation 70, 221, 238

primary data 51

prime number 346

prism 78, 80, 95, 105, 117, 173, 179, 207, 266, 284

probabilities 180–2, 184, 186–93, 197–9, 289, 292–6, 301–3, 367, 372

problem solving 92, 231, 330

profit 25, 66, 127, 129–30, 336

profits 130, 337

properties of angles 168

properties of shapes 92, 168

proportion 52, 76, 87–8, 130–1, 134–5, 138, 141–2, 145, 290, 352

proportional reasoning 92, 127–47

proposition 150

protractor 110, 223, 229, 231

Ptolemy, Claudius 278

pyramids 72, 78, 80–2, 84, 93, 117–18, 126, 134, 174, 265–7, 282–3, 285–6

Pyramids of Giza 171

Pythagoras' theorem 12, 77, 101, 105, 115–16, 118, 125, 264–5, 267, 278, 286, 321, 328, 385, 389

quadrants 72, 74, 77, 274–5, 311–314, 316, 319, 321

quadratics
    curve 135, 138
    equations 200, 202–13, 216, 308, 311, 356, 377, 379, 381
    expression 102–3, 205, 207
    formula 210, 378
    function 325–7
    functions 308, 381
    graph 203, 381–2
    graphs 309

quadrilateral 105, 156–64, 168–70, 224, 226, 233, 269, 277, 280–1, 363

qualitative data 51

quantitative data 51

quaternion multiplication 227

quincunx 301–2

radii 72, 79–80, 150–1, 153–4, 157

random 52–4, 181–99, 241, 291, 294–6, 298, 303, 305, 367–9

random sample 52–4, 198

ratio 38, 76, 79, 81, 94, 115, 119, 122, 125, 131, 134, 137, 147, 171, 175, 187–9, 234–5, 265, 267, 348–50, 352, 367

rational numbers 1, 5

rationalising 6–10

real numbers 5

real-life problems 26–7

reciprocal functions 207, 308, 314, 316, 333, 381, 384

Recorde, Robert 6

rectangle 8, 13, 18, 38, 45–7, 62, 64, 81, 113, 121, 140, 146, 170, 207, 234, 254, 257, 265, 283, 349, 398

rectangular grid 12, 28

reflection 165, 220–1, 325, 327, 334, 384

regular triangles 168

relationships 127, 145, 148, 198, 306, 336

relative frequency 180, 189, 197

relativity theory 45

replacement 292, 298, 305

representations 148, 198, 306, 336

representative stratified sample 52

research 221, 337, 344

resultant 220, 228, 230, 236

rhombicuboctahedron 340

rhombus 169, 224, 230, 234

right-angled triangle 8, 12, 82, 101, 115–19, 122, 124–5, 207, 225, 264–5, 267, 275, 278, 385, 387, 389

Romans 127, 278

root keys 33

roots 202

rosette patterns 221

rotations 221, 227

rounding 33, 35, 37, 373

routine problems 345

Rudolff, Christoff 3

rule 104

sampling 51–4, 68, 240, 290–2

Sandreckoner, The 42

satellites 264

scalar 220, 225, 227, 232, 235–6

scale factor 90, 171–3, 325, 327, 384

Scarne, John 298

science 180, 271, 367, 394

scientific calculator 116, 120, 123, 241, 265, 269, 272, 276, 279, 282, 307, 309, 312, 315, 317, 319, 325, 328

scientists 91, 180, 198–9, 289–92

seasonality 257, 260

second significant figure 32

secondary data 51

sector 72–5, 77, 82, 85, 93, 104, 110, 386, 389

segments 72, 75, 77

seismology 264

selective sampling 52, 54

semicircles 73, 75–7, 93, 101, 153, 156, 160, 164, 363, 367

simplify 6–7, 24, 95, 97, 99, 101, 113, 156, 201, 205, 324–5, 352, 377

simultaneous equations 12, 16, 18, 28–9, 200, 212–15, 217, 329, 354–5, 360, 380

simultaneous linear equations 16–17, 212, 214, 216

sine 119, 122, 264, 268–9, 271–2, 275–8, 281, 285–6, 319–21, 381

Sitka spruce 35

solids 171–2, 175, 338–41

spheres 38, 72, 74, 77–83, 91, 93, 111–12, 118, 175, 315, 340

spreadsheet 31, 149, 198–9, 337

square number 7, 191, 355

square root 3–6, 115, 142–4, 173, 205, 208, 212, 345

standard form 32, 36–9, 46, 48, 86, 91, 94, 373–7

statistical enquiry 55, 57, 60, 240, 251, 254

statistical inference 367

statisticians 61, 252, 292

statistics 61, 240, 243, 250, 252, 255, 261, 389, 398

straight line graphs 356

strategies 92, 187, 189, 289, 300, 303

stratified sample 53–4, 68

subtracting vectors 228

Sun 35, 38, 134, 278, 374–6

surds 1, 6–10, 209, 225–6

surface area 38, 72, 81–3, 93, 104, 129, 172–5, 177, 179, 205, 207, 211, 358

survey 51–3, 240, 291, 350, 395

symbols 106, 361

symmetry 220, 221, 360, 362

systematic sampling 52–4

tangents 15, 119, 122, 150–3, 155, 157–64, 168, 177, 264, 271–2, 288, 310, 320, 362, 367, 381, 386

technology 26

tessellation 339

tests 41, 348, 373

tetrahedron 137, 285, 287, 338, 340

theodolite 119

theorem 1, 77, 101, 105, 115–16, 118, 125, 158, 161, 221, 264, 265, 267, 278, 286, 321, 328, 362, 385, 389

theoretical probability 189, 302

time series data 51, 68, 260

time series graph 65, 67, 257–9

tools 30, 148, 178, 198, 306, 336

transformations 220–3, 274, 308, 324, 327, 333, 381, 384

translations 220–1, 223, 235–7, 273, 384

trapezium 11, 20, 73, 104, 205–6, 209, 229, 234, 331, 386

tree diagram 181–3, 185, 187–9, 191–3, 197, 199, 292–3, 296, 305, 368, 371–2

trend 59, 61, 65–7, 240, 257–62, 298

trial and improvement 203

triangle law 228–9, 232

trigonometric functions 264, 271, 273, 275, 286, 308, 319, 321, 333

trigonometric graphs 271, 275, 324, 381

trigonometric problems 282

trigonometric ratios 115, 119, 122, 124–5, 264, 272, 385, 389

trigonometry 77, 106, 115–26, 264–88, 319, 385

Tukey, John 252

two-dimensional geometrical problems 220, 236

ultrasound 264

unitary method 127, 130, 134, 348, 352

Universe 36, 42, 134

upper bound 39, 41–3, 49

upper quartile 243–4, 248–50, 390–1

variables 12, 16, 19, 21, 27–8, 92, 107, 109, 132, 134, 136, 212, 214, 330, 332

vector notation 220, 222, 236

vectors 220–37

velocity 137

vertex 13, 78, 85, 265, 270, 325, 338–40

vertices 9, 75, 85, 156, 171, 268, 339, 341

vinculum 3

wallpaper patterns 221

wartime 24

weight 17, 30, 34, 133, 141, 179, 367

whole number 29, 40, 52, 346, 374

Yang Hui 106, 300